CONSUMER AND CAREER MATHEMATICS

SECOND EDITION

L. Carey Bolster

H. Douglas Woodburn

Joella H. Gipson

Scott, Foresman and Company
Editorial Offices: Glenview, Illinois

Regional Offices: Palo Alto, California •
Tucker, Georgia • Glenview, Illinois •
Oakland, New Jersey • Dallas, Texas

Authors

L. Carey Bolster
Supervisor of Mathematics
Baltimore County Public Schools
Towson, Maryland

H. Douglas Woodburn
Chairman of the Mathematics Department
Perry Hall Middle School
Baltimore County, Maryland

Joella H. Gipson
Professor, College of Education
Wayne State University
Detroit, Michigan

Readers/Consultants

Marita H. Eng
Mathematics Department Chairman
Sandalwood Junior-Senior High School
Jacksonville, Florida

Robert Y. Hamada
Instructional Specialist, Mathematics
Los Angeles Unified School District
Los Angeles, California

Linda Borry Hausmann
Manager of Instructional Systems
EduSystems, Inc.
Minneapolis, Minnesota

William C. Messersmith, Jr.
Teacher/Coordinator of Data Processing Services
Rich Township High School
Richton Park, Illinois

Sidney Sharron
Supervisor, Instructional Media and Resources Branch
Los Angeles Unified School District
Los Angeles, California

ISBN: 0-673-13286-2

Acknowledgements

For permission to reproduce indicated information on the
following pages, acknowledgment is made to:

4–5, 1980 Census Forms, Courtesy Bureau of the Census.

66, 88, 90, 92, 94–95, 97, and *108,* Deposit slip, check,
check register, bank statements, and promissory note,
Reprinted by permission of Glenview State Bank, Glenview,
Illinois.

120, Piano, Courtesy Andrews-Edwards Music Service,
Wilmette, Illinois

135, Puzzle, from MATHEMATICS: PROBLEM SOLVING
THROUGH RECREATIONAL MATHEMATICS by Bonnie
Averbach and Orin Chein. W.M. Freeman and Company.
Copyright © 1980. Reprinted by permission.

224–225, Violin and accessories, Courtesy Fritz Reuter and
Sons, Chicago.

232, Table, adapted from "Averages for Selected Metropolitan
Areas for All Major Lenders," from Federal Home Loan
Bank Board *News.* Courtesy Federal Home Loan Bank Board.

258, 260, 264, and *266,* Form W–2, "Who Must File"
instructions, and Form 1040A, Courtesy Internal Revenue Service.

293, Table, Courtesy Social Security Administration.

300–301, United States Savings Bonds, Courtesy United States
Department of the Treasury.

302, Certificate of deposit, Reprinted by permission of
Glenview State Bank, Glenview, Illinois.

309, Puzzle, from MATHEMATICAL PUZZLES AND PASTIMES
by Aaron Bakst. Copyright © 1965 by Van Nostrand Reinhold
Company. Reprinted by permission of the publisher.

346–347, Stained glass, Courtesy Stained Glass & More,
Northfield, Illinois.

347, Needlepoint, Courtesy Needlepoint & More, Northfield,
Illinois. Designs, Courtesy Dede Needleworks, San Francisco.

402–405, Tables for wage-bracket method of withholding,
Courtesy Internal Revenue Service.

406–409, 1980 Tax Tables and Schedules, Courtesy Internal
Revenue Service.

Photographs

Unless otherwise credited, all photographs are the property of
Scott, Foresman and Company.

19, Stacy Pick/Lensman; *42,* Focus on Sports; *52,* Jon
Brenneis/FPG; *138–139,* Used with permission; *178–179,*
E. Simonsen/H. Armstrong Roberts; *192–193, 215,* and *237,*
Cameramann International; *247,* Michael Philip Manheim/
Photo Researchers.

Original Art

15, Susan Atlas Kelley; *26–27,* Garrett Reese; *33* and *253,*
John Youssi; *42, 44, 49, 111,* and *173,* Jack Wallen; *50–51,*
65, 127, 189, and *375,* Sandy Rabinowitz; *135,* Pat Dypold;
233, Dick Martin; *332,* Johanna Yount Baldwin; *344,* Bobbye
Cochran.

Unit 1 Mathematics Skills

Chapter 1
Whole Numbers, Decimals, and Fractions

Rounding Whole Numbers and Decimals 4

Adding and Subtracting Whole Numbers and Decimals 6

Multiplying Whole Numbers 8

Multiplying Decimals 10

Dividing Whole Numbers and Decimals 12

Comparing and Renaming Fractions and Mixed Numbers 14

BREAK TIME 15

Multiplying and Dividing Fractions and Mixed Numbers 16

Adding and Subtracting Fractions and Mixed Numbers 18

CALCULATOR APPLICATIONS Fractions as Decimals 20

Chapter 1 Review 21

Chapter 1 Test 22

Chapter 2
Equations, Proportions, and Percent

Addition and Subtraction Equations 24

Multiplication and Division Equations 26

Two-Step Equations 28

Ratio and Proportion 30

Writing Percents, Decimals, and Fractions 32

Using Percent 34

BREAK TIME 37

CALCULATOR APPLICATIONS Percent and Discounts 38

Chapter 2 Review 39

Chapter 2 Test 40

Chapter 3
Measurement and Statistics

Metric Units of Length 42

Area and Volume 44

BREAK TIME 45

Metric Units of Capacity and Mass 46

Renaming Metric Units of Measure 48

Temperature 50

Time 52

Bar Graphs and Line Graphs 54

Circle Graphs 56

Mean, Median, and Mode 58

CALCULATOR APPLICATIONS Finding Means 60

Chapter 3 Review 61

Chapter 3 Test 62

End-of-Unit Materials

Unit 1 Test 63

BREAK TIME/MENTAL MATH 65

Unit 2 Income, Banking, and Credit

Chapter 4
Income

Hourly Rate and Overtime
Rate 68

Hourly Rate Plus Tips 70

BREAK TIME 71

Straight Commission 72

Career Bookkeeper 74

Graduated Commission 76

CALCULATOR APPLICATIONS
Selling-Cost Percent 77

Net Pay 78

Jobs in Classified Ads 82

Skills Tune-Up 84

Chapter 4 Review 85

Chapter 4 Test 86

Chapter 5
Personal Banking

Deposit Slips 88

Checks and Check Stubs 90

Check Registers 92

Reconciling a Bank
Statement 94

CALCULATOR APPLICATIONS
Checking Accounts 97

Career Personal Banking
Representative 98

BREAK TIME 99

Compound Interest 100

Compound Interest
Tables 102

BREAK TIME 103

Skills Tune-Up 104

Chapter 5 Review 105

Chapter 5 Test 106

Chapter 6
Consumer Credit

Promissory Notes 108

Credit Card Finance
Charges 110

BREAK TIME 111

Career Credit
Counselor 112

CALCULATOR APPLICATIONS
Charge Accounts 114

Minimum Payments on
Charge Accounts 115

Level-Payment Loans 116

Installment Buying 118

Comparing Credit Plans 120

Skills Tune-Up 122

Chapter 6 Review 123

Chapter 6 Test 124

End-of-Unit Materials

Unit 2 Test 125

BREAK TIME/MENTAL MATH 127

COMPUTER APPLICATIONS
Charge Accounts 128

Unit 3 Transportation

Chapter 7
Buying a Car

New Car Sticker Price *132*

Making an Offer for a
Car *134*

BREAK TIME *135*

Finding Total Cost of a
Car *136*

Shopping for a Car *138*

Financing a Car *140*

CALCULATOR APPLICATIONS
Annual Percentage
Rates *143*

Career Automobile
Salesperson *144*

Skills Tune-Up *146*

Chapter 7 Review *147*

Chapter 7 Test *148*

Chapter 8
Automobile Operating Expenses

Finding Gasoline Costs *150*

Depreciation *152*

Selling Price Based on
Depreciation *154*

CALCULATOR APPLICATIONS
Fuel Economy *155*

Career Automobile
Mechanic *156*

BREAK TIME *159*

Automobile Liability
Insurance *160*

Automobile Collision and
Comprehensive
Insurance *162*

Annual Expenses *164*

Alternatives to Owning a
Car *166*

Skills Tune-Up *168*

Chapter 8 Review *169*

Chapter 8 Test *170*

Chapter 9
Travel

Reading a Distance
Chart *172*

Finding Distance and Travel
Time *174*

Expenses on the Road *176*

BREAK TIME *177*

Air Travel *178*

Renting a Car *180*

CALCULATOR APPLICATIONS
Car-Rental Costs *181*

Career Travel Agent *182*

Skills Tune-Up *184*

Chapter 9 Review *185*

Chapter 9 Test *186*

End-of-Unit Materials

Unit 3 Test *187*

BREAK TIME/MENTAL MATH *189*

COMPUTER APPLICATIONS
Auto Financing *190*

Unit 4 Housing

Chapter 10
Renting and Decorating a Home

Amount to Spend for Rent 194

Selecting a Place to Rent 196

Career Meter Reader 198

CALCULATOR APPLICATIONS Electricity Costs 200

BREAK TIME 201

Career Interior Designer 202

Installing Floor Tiles 204

Painting an Apartment 206

Ordering Wallpaper 208

Personal Property Insurance 210

Skills Tune-Up 212

Chapter 10 Review 213

Chapter 10 Test 214

Chapter 11
Buying a Home

Amount to Borrow for a Home 216

Down Payment and Monthly Payment 218

Interest on a Mortgage Loan 220

Principal and Interest in a Monthly Payment 222

CALCULATOR APPLICATIONS Amortization Tables 223

Homeowner's Insurance 224

Real Estate Taxes 226

Closing Costs 228

Career Real Estate Agent 230

BREAK TIME 233

Skills Tune-Up 234

Chapter 11 Review 235

Chapter 11 Test 236

Chapter 12
Building a Home

Career Surveyor 238

Cost of Building a House 240

BREAK TIME 242

CALCULATOR APPLICATIONS Building Costs 243

Cost of Installing a Driveway 244

Career Bricklayer 246

Skills Tune-Up 248

Chapter 12 Review 249

Chapter 12 Test 250

End-of-Unit Materials

Unit 4 Test 251

BREAK TIME/MENTAL MATH 253

COMPUTER APPLICATIONS Amortization Tables 254

Unit 5 Taxes, Insurance, and Investments

Chapter 13
Income Tax

Who Must File a Tax
Return 258

Adjusted Gross Income and
Tax Credit 260

BREAK TIME 262

Tax Liability 263

Tax Refund or Balance
Due 264

Completing Form
1040A 266

Career Tax Consultant 268

CALCULATOR APPLICATIONS
Tax Penalty Charges 271

State Income Tax 272

Skills Tune-Up 274

Chapter 13 Review 275

Chapter 13 Test 276

Chapter 14
Health, Life, and
Retirement Insurance

Health Insurance 278

Term Life Insurance 280

Straight Life, Limited Payment
Life, and Endowment
Insurance 282

Career Insurance
Agent 286

CALCULATOR APPLICATIONS
Insurance Premiums 288

BREAK TIME 289

Choosing Insurance and
Savings Plans 290

Social Security Retirement
Benefits 292

Skills Tune-Up 296

Chapter 14 Review 297

Chapter 14 Test 298

Chapter 15
Investments

United States Savings
Bonds 300

Certificates of Deposit 302

CALCULATOR APPLICATIONS
Compound Interest 305

Common Stock 306

BREAK TIME 309

Career Investment
Counselor 310

Skills Tune-Up 312

Chapter 15 Review 313

Chapter 15 Test 314

End-of-Unit Materials

Unit 5 Test 315

BREAK TIME/MENTAL MATH 317

COMPUTER APPLICATIONS
Payroll Deductions 318

Unit 6 Purchasing and Budgeting

Chapter 16
Buying Food

Career Nutritionist *322*

Calorie Usage *324*

Grocery Shopping *326*

CALCULATOR APPLICATIONS
Food Costs *329*

Comparing Meat Prices *330*

Comparing Meal Costs *332*

BREAK TIME *333*

Skills Tune-Up *334*

Chapter 16 Review *335*

Chapter 16 Test *336*

Chapter 17
Buying, Making, and Renting Goods

Catalog Buying *338*

CALCULATOR APPLICATIONS
Completing Order
Forms *341*

Sewing Costs *342*

Seasonal Sales *344*

BREAK TIME *345*

Buying Craft Supplies *346*

Buying Building
Materials *348*

Career Rental Clerk *350*

Skills Tune-Up *352*

Chapter 17 Review *353*

Chapter 17 Test *354*

Chapter 18
Budgeting

Analyzing Spending
Habits *356*

BREAK TIME *359*

Budgeting Variable
Expenses *360*

Making a Budget *362*

CALCULATOR APPLICATIONS
Percent of Increase *365*

Adjusting a Budget *366*

Career Economist *368*

Skills Tune-Up *370*

Chapter 18 Review *371*

Chapter 18 Test *372*

End-of-Unit Materials

Unit 6 Test *373*

BREAK TIME/MENTAL MATH *375*

COMPUTER APPLICATIONS
Cash Registers *376*

End-of-Book Materials

Skills File *379*

Computer Literacy *394*

Tables *400*

Careers Chart *410*

Glossary *414*

Selected Answers *418*

Index *452*

CONSUMER AND CAREER MATHEMATICS

SECOND EDITION

Unit 1 Mathematics Skills

Chapter 1 Whole Numbers, Decimals, and Fractions

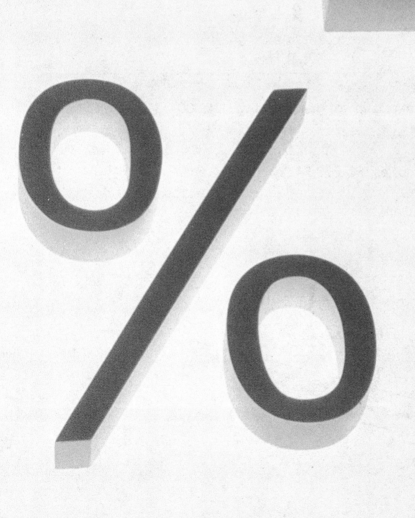

Rounding Whole Numbers and Decimals

When rounding a number, look at the digit to the right of the place to which you are rounding. If the digit is 5 or greater, round up. If the digit is less than 5, round down.

Problem A

According to the United States Census, the population of Hampstead, Maryland, in 1980 was 24,862. What was the population rounded to the nearest thousand?

Round 24,862 to the nearest thousand.

Solution

Look at the digit to the right of the thousands place. It is greater than 5, so round up.

24,862

Thousands place ⎯⎯⎯ 8 is greater than 5.
Round up to 25,000.

To the nearest thousand, the population of Hampstead was 25,000.

Problem B

The population density of Hampstead was 70.342 people per square kilometer. What was the density to the nearest tenth?

Round 70.342 to the nearest tenth.

Solution

Look at the digit to the right of the tenths place. It is less than 5, so round down.

70.**34**2

Tenths place ⎯⎯⎯ 4 is less than 5.
Round down to 70.3.

To the nearest tenth, the density of Hampstead was 70.3 people per square kilometer.

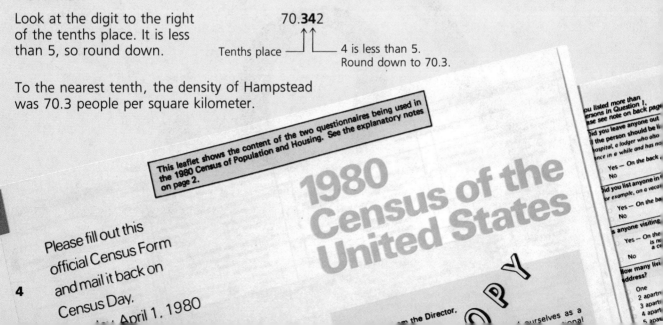

This leaflet shows the content of the two questionnaires being used in the 1980 Census of Population and Housing. See the explanatory notes on page 2.

1980 Census of the United States

Please fill out this official Census Form and mail it back on Census Day, April 1, 1980

4

Exercises

Set A
Round each number to the nearest thousand, nearest hundred, and nearest ten.

1. 1536
2. 2321
3. 4872
4. 855
5. 927
6. 5013
7. 6005
8. 80,089
9. 7002
10. 16,010

Set B
Round each number to the nearest whole number, nearest tenth, and nearest hundredth.

11. 12.684
12. 5.27
13. 13.882
14. 17.5039
15. 47.973
16. 126.1293
17. 320.709
18. 97.005
19. 100.084
20. 10.002

Related Problems

21. In 1980, Maryland had a population of about 4,216,446. What was the population to the nearest million?

22. In 1980, the population density of Maryland was 151.378 people per square kilometer. What was the density to the nearest tenth of a square kilometer?

Typical monthly electric bills (for 1980, 500 kilowatt-hours) for homes in four Maryland cities are listed below. Round each amount to the nearest ten cents and to the nearest dollar.

	City	Typical bill	Nearest ten cents	Nearest dollar
23.	Elkton	$28.06		
24.	Greenbelt	$29.62		
25.	Rockville	$30.15		
26.	Frederick	$27.12		

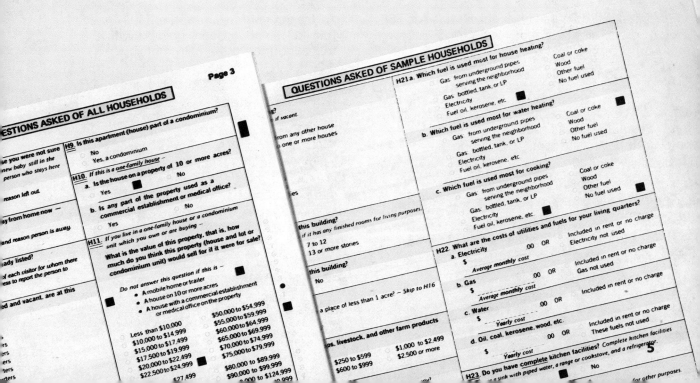

5

Adding and Subtracting Whole Numbers and Decimals

When adding or subtracting decimals, write the numbers so that the decimal points align.

Problem A

Jim and Robin Rada bought a table for $88, a chair for $185, and a lamp for $43. How much money did they spend?

Find $88 + $185 + $43.

Solution

Estimate. Round each number to the same place and add.

		Find the actual sum.
88 ⟶	90	88
185 ⟶	190	185
43 ⟶	+ 40	+ 43
	320	316

Jim and Robin spent $316.

Problem B

To make picture frames, the Radas needed four pieces of wooden molding with the following measures: 2.36 meters, 4.8 meters, 1.52 meters, and 1.4 meters. How much molding did they need in all?

Find 2.36 + 4.8 + 1.52 + 1.4.

Solution

Estimate. Round each number to the same place and add.

		Find the actual sum.	
2.36 ⟶	2	2.36	
4.8 ⟶	5	4.8	Align the
1.52 ⟶	2	1.52	decimal
1.4 ⟶	+ 1	+ 1.4	points.
	10	10.08	

The Radas needed 10.08 meters of molding.

Problem C

A frostless refrigerator costs $949, and a regular refrigerator costs $425. How much less does the regular refrigerator cost?

Find $949 − $425.

Solution

Estimate the difference.

```
949 ⟶   900
425 ⟶ − 400
          500
```

Find the actual difference.

```
  949
− 425
  524
```

The regular refrigerator costs $524 less.

Problem D

A bolt of fabric contained 8 meters of fabric. Robin bought 6.8 meters. How much fabric was left on the bolt?

Find 8 − 6.8.

Solution

Estimate the difference.

```
8   ⟶   8
6.8 ⟶ − 7
          1
```

Find the actual difference.

```
  8.0
− 6.8
  1.2
```

Sometimes you need to write extra zeros.

There was 1.2 meters of fabric left.

Exercises

Estimate each sum or difference. Then find each actual sum or difference.

Set A

1. 42 + 28 + 39
2. 23 + 46 + 267
3. 74 + 12 + 18
4. 86 + 58 + 17
5. 62 + 129 + 243
6. 81 + 56 + 25 + 34
7. 93 + 8 + 17 + 18
8. 267 + 194 + 301
9. 356 + 217 + 592
10. 101 + 463 + 786

Set B

11. 4.7 + 40.25
12. 63.91 + 12.28
13. 1.82 + 3.47 + 1.9
14. 1.31 + 0.35 + 2.5
15. 2.34 + 6.79 + 5.28 + 4.05
16. 1.04 + 3.71 + 8.65 + 7.249
17. 0.57 + 0.93 + 0.15 + 1.08

Set C

18. 31 − 19
19. 82 − 38
20. 67 − 42
21. 91 − 7
22. 806 − 489
23. 983 − 779

Set D

24. 47.3 − 21.2
25. 95.85 − 8.16
26. 73.51 − 41.6
27. 40.933 − 36.2
28. 53.9 − 8
29. 27.31 − 18
30. 18 − 5.6
31. 27 − 12.45
32. 83.73 − 17.008
33. 45.6 − 14.986

Related Problems

34. Estimate the total cost of these items: tacks—$0.89; hammer—$2.95; varnish—$3.49; wire—$0.59.

35. How much change would Jim receive if he paid for the items in problem 34 with a $20 bill?

Multiplying Whole Numbers

When multiplying whole numbers that end in zeros, multiply the nonzero digits. Then count the zeros in both factors and write that number of zeros in your answer.

Problem A

Phil Miller planted 300 acres of corn. He expects a yield of 90 bushels per acre. What is his expected total yield?

Find 90×300.

Solution

$90 \times 3\mathbf{00} = 27,\mathbf{000}$

Phil's expected total yield is 27,000 bushels of corn.

Problem B

Phil plants 94 pounds of wheat per acre. How much wheat will he need for 190 acres?

Find 94×190.

Solution

Estimate. Round each factor so that only the first digit is not zero. Then multiply.

$$94 \times 190$$
$$\downarrow \qquad \downarrow$$
$$90 \times 200 = 18,000$$

Find the actual product.

$$
\begin{array}{r}
190 \\
\times \quad 94 \\
\hline
760 \leftarrow 4 \times 190 \\
17100 \leftarrow 90 \times 190 \\
\hline
17860
\end{array}
$$

Phil will need 17,860 pounds of wheat.

Exercises

Set A Find each product.

1. 50 × 90
2. 700 × 60
3. 7 × 2000
4. 4000 × 3000
5. 600 × 800
6. 9 × 700
7. 9000 × 600
8. 60 × 500
9. 800 × 50
10. 60 × 300
11. 90 × 20
12. 5000 × 4
13. 90 × 900
14. 50 × 200
15. 300 × 8
16. 40 × 9000

Set B Estimate. Then find each product.

17. 53 × 28
18. 89 × 81
19. 54 × 19
20. 84 × 28
21. 184 × 74
22. 64 × 570
23. 58 × 304
24. 903 × 90
25. 237 × 456
26. 381 × 952
27. 214 × 301
28. 502 × 805
29. 1203 × 45
30. 4216 × 37
31. 94 × 7621
32. 79 × 6101
33. 8004 × 195
34. 496 × 4099
35. 506 × 4204
36. 9007 × 705

Mixed Practice Find each product.

37. 320 × 1000
38. 25 × 38
39. 512 × 691
40. 2200 × 30
41. 68 × 439
42. 91 × 704
43. 410 × 600
44. 9000 × 8
45. 8100 × 6000
46. 930 × 500
47. 467 × 13
48. 67 × 79
49. 48 × 65
50. 100 × 1400
51. 802 × 43
52. 698 × 724
53. 110 × 600
54. 210 × 40
55. 34 × 97
56. 5100 × 300
57. 40 × 400
58. 59 × 319
59. 520 × 700
60. 785 × 82

Related Problems

61. Phil's neighbor expects to get 33 bushels of soybeans per acre from his 153-acre field. Estimate the total soybean production from the field.

62. Phil uses 32 pounds of oats to plant one acre. Will 500 pounds of oats be enough to plant 15 acres?

63. Phil plants 14 pounds of corn per acre. How much corn will he need to plant his 300-acre field?

64. Last year Phil harvested 32 bushels of wheat per acre. What was the total amount of wheat harvested from his 190-acre field?

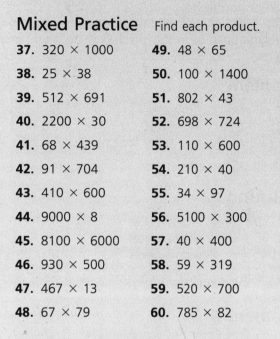

Multiplying Decimals

When multiplying decimals, multiply as with whole numbers. Then add the number of decimal places in the factors to find the number of decimal places in the product. You might have to write extra zeros.

Problem A

Patsy Bowen's dishwasher uses about 0.9 kilowatt-hour of electricity per load. At $0.05 per kilowatt-hour, what is the cost of the electricity for one dishwasher load?

Find $0.05 × 0.9.

Solution

```
    0.9  ←—— 1 decimal place
 ×  0.05 ←—— 2 decimal places
  0.045  ←—— 3 decimal places
```

The electric cost for one dishwasher load is about $0.045.

Problem B

At $0.048 per kilowatt-hour, what is the cost per week to operate a refrigerator that uses about 42.5 kilowatt-hours of electricity a week?

Find $0.048 × 42.5.

Solution

Estimate. Round each factor to get a number with one nonzero digit. Then multiply.

$$0.048 × 42.5$$
$$0.05 × 40 = 2$$

Find the actual product.

```
    42.5  ←—— 1 decimal place
 ×  0.048 ←—— 3 decimal places
    3400
   17000
  2.0400  ←—— 4 decimal places
```

The cost per week to operate the refrigerator is about $2.04.

Exercises

Set A Find each product.

1. 0.4 × 0.2
2. 0.3 × 0.1
3. 0.08 × 0.8
4. 0.7 × 0.03
5. 0.09 × 0.04
6. 0.6 × 0.06
7. 0.008 × 0.7
8. 0.005 × 5
9. 0.005 × 500
10. 6 × 0.03
11. 9 × 0.009
12. 0.005 × 2
13. 5000 × 0.8
14. 0.09 × 0.08
15. 0.4 × 0.05
16. 0.001 × 0.01
17. 0.03 × 5000
18. 600 × 0.05
19. 900 × 0.006
20. 0.09 × 700

Set B Estimate. Then find each product.

21. 0.56 × 320
22. 2.7 × 0.043
23. 0.79 × 0.052
24. 86 × 0.42
25. 38.7 × 0.62
26. 4.5 × 11.6
27. 9.58 × 0.014
28. 9.4 × 47.8
29. 8.808 × 2.1
30. 0.3204 × 75
31. 0.45 × 1121
32. 2.9 × 1.989
33. 0.946 × 0.187
34. 0.609 × 1.97
35. 83.1 × 0.288
36. 587 × 4.62
37. 4.001 × 89.9
38. 55.04 × 0.0436
39. 5.603 × 3.21
40. 61.91 × 0.873

Mixed Practice Find each product.

41. 0.04 × 0.8
42. 2.59 × 35
43. 17 × 0.83
44. 12.34 × 5.7
45. 0.12 × 0.02
46. 4.8 × 6.3
47. 120 × 0.03
48. 0.158 × 44.2
49. 0.413 × 5.5
50. 1500 × 0.4
51. 0.88 × 1409
52. 0.5 × 0.007
53. 0.601 × 80.7
54. 11 × 0.003
55. 0.014 × 50
56. 13 × 0.03

Related Problems

57. At $0.049 per kilowatt-hour, what is the electric cost per year to operate a frostless refrigerator that uses about 1690 kilowatt-hours a year?

58. At $0.049 per kilowatt-hour, what is the electric cost per year to operate a standard electric water heater that uses about 6340 kilowatt-hours a year?

59. At $0.049 per kilowatt-hour, what is the electric cost per year to operate a "miser" electric water heater that uses about 5890 kilowatt-hours a year?

60. For one year, how much less is the electric cost for a miser water heater than for a standard water heater?

Dividing Whole Numbers and Decimals

When rounding a quotient, divide until there is one more decimal place than required. Write extra zeros in the dividend if necessary.

When dividing by a decimal, make the divisor a whole number by "moving" the decimal point. Then "move" the decimal point in the dividend the same direction and the same number of places.

Problem A

The Masemore Construction Company owns property with 1375 feet of frontage along Willow View Road. How many lots 65 feet wide will fit along the road? How many feet of frontage will be left over?

Find 1375 ÷ 65.

Solution

```
      21 R10
65)1375
    130  ←── 2 × 65
    ───
     75
     65  ←── 1 × 65
     ──
     10
```

Use estimation to decide if the answer is reasonable. Round the quotient and the divisor and multiply.

21 × 65
↓   ↓
20 × 70 = 1400

Since 1400 is close to 1375, the estimate indicates that the answer, 21 R10, is reasonable.

Twenty-one 65-foot lots will fit along the road. There will be 10 feet of frontage left over.

Problem B

Marlin Masemore plans to divide a 22.8-acre plot of land into 18 lots. To the nearest hundredth of an acre, how large will each lot be?

Find 22.8 ÷ 18.

Solution

```
       1.266 ≈ 1.27
18)22.800
   18
   ──
    4 8
    3 6
    ───
    1 20
    1 08
    ────
      120
      108
      ───
       12
```

Remember that ≈ means "is approximately equal to."

Continue dividing to the thousandths place. Then round to the nearest hundredth.

Use estimation to decide if the answer is reasonable. Round the quotient and the divisor and multiply.

1.27 × 18
 ↓   ↓
 1   × 20 = 20

The answer is reasonable.

To the nearest hundredth of an acre, each lot will be 1.27 acres.

Problem C

Marlin bought a 2.1-acre plot of land for $975. To the nearest dollar, what was the price per acre?

Find $975 ÷ 2.1.

Solution

$$
\begin{array}{r}
46\,4.2 \approx 464 \\
2.1\overline{)975.0\,0} \\
84 \\
\overline{135} \\
126 \\
\overline{9\,0} \\
8\,4 \\
\overline{6\,0} \\
4\,2 \\
\overline{1\,8}
\end{array}
$$

Continue dividing to the tenths place. Then round to the nearest whole number.

Use estimation to decide if the answer is reasonable.

$$
\begin{array}{ccc}
464 & \times & 2.1 \\
\downarrow & & \downarrow \\
500 & \times & 2 = 1000
\end{array}
$$

The answer is reasonable.

To the nearest dollar, the price per acre was $464.

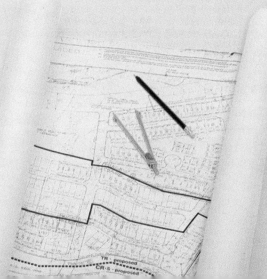

Exercises

Set A Find each quotient. Estimate to decide if the answer is reasonable.

1. 3152 ÷ 8
2. 2128 ÷ 7
3. 830 ÷ 23
4. 963 ÷ 49
5. 3875 ÷ 78
6. 2359 ÷ 61
7. 39,565 ÷ 84
8. 209,915 ÷ 32
9. 95,140 ÷ 543
10. 182,216 ÷ 902

Set B Find each quotient to the nearest hundredth. Estimate to decide if the answer is reasonable.

11. 268.7 ÷ 9
12. 1834 ÷ 6
13. 41.52 ÷ 19
14. 5.42 ÷ 12
15. 15.6 ÷ 79
16. 79.9 ÷ 39
17. 118.62 ÷ 56
18. 21.6 ÷ 14
19. 1168 ÷ 242
20. 42.89 ÷ 381

Set C Find each quotient to the nearest whole number. Estimate to decide if the answer is reasonable.

21. 71.52 ÷ 9.32
22. 58.9 ÷ 8.4
23. 11.53 ÷ 2.66
24. 4.4 ÷ 1.83
25. 19 ÷ 3.56
26. 0.08 ÷ 0.04
27. 9.3 ÷ 3.1
28. 604 ÷ 97.1
29. 0.635 ÷ 0.07
30. 8.3 ÷ 0.23

Related Problems

31. Marlin wants to put 14 lots along a plot of land with 1250 feet of road frontage. To the nearest tenth of a foot, how wide will each lot be?

32. A 77.5-acre farm sold for $65,000. Find the price per acre, to the nearest dollar.

Comparing and Renaming Fractions and Mixed Numbers

> Multiplying or dividing both the numerator and the denominator of a fraction by the same number does not change the value of the fraction.
>
> A fraction is in lowest terms if the only number that will divide both the numerator and the denominator is 1.

Problem A

Mrs. Gourley's Home Ec class plans to make rye bread. The recipe for *Grandma's Rye Bread* calls for $5\frac{2}{3}$ cups of flour. The recipe for *Old-Fashioned Rye Bread* calls for $5\frac{3}{4}$ cups of flour. Which recipe uses less flour?

Compare $5\frac{2}{3}$ and $5\frac{3}{4}$.

Solution

Since $5\frac{2}{3}$ and $5\frac{3}{4}$ have the same whole number, consider only the fractions, $\frac{2}{3}$ and $\frac{3}{4}$.

List the multiples of 4 until you have a multiple of 3.

4 8 **12**   12 is a common multiple of 4 and 3.

Write each fraction with a denominator of 12.

$$\frac{2}{3} = \frac{2 \times 4}{3 \times 4} = \frac{8}{12}$$

$$\frac{3}{4} = \frac{3 \times 3}{4 \times 3} = \frac{9}{12}$$

Compare $\frac{8}{12}$ and $\frac{9}{12}$.

$$\frac{8}{12} < \frac{9}{12}$$
$$\downarrow \quad \downarrow$$
$$\frac{2}{3} < \frac{3}{4}$$

Remember, $>$ means "is greater than," and $<$ means "is less than." $8 < 9$, so $\frac{8}{12} < \frac{9}{12}$.

$$5\frac{2}{3} < 5\frac{3}{4}$$

The recipe for *Grandma's Rye Bread* uses less flour.

Problem B

Sheila bought $\frac{24}{36}$ of a yard (24 inches) of elastic for a skirt.

Rename $\frac{24}{36}$ in lowest terms.

Solution

$$\frac{24}{36} = \frac{24 \div 6}{36 \div 6} = \frac{4}{6}$$

$$\frac{4}{6} = \frac{4 \div 2}{6 \div 2} = \frac{2}{3}$$

$$\frac{24}{36} = \frac{2}{3}$$

$\frac{2}{3}$ is in lowest terms because the only number that divides both 2 and 3 is 1.

In lowest terms, $\frac{24}{36}$ is $\frac{2}{3}$.

Problem C

Rick bought $2\frac{3}{4}$ yards of fabric for pillows.

Rename $2\frac{3}{4}$ as a fraction.

Solution

$$2\frac{3}{4} = \frac{4 \times 2 + 3}{4} = \frac{11}{4}$$

$$2\frac{3}{4} = \frac{11}{4}$$

Multiply 2 by 4 to find the number of fourths in 2. Then add 3.

As a fraction, $2\frac{3}{4}$ is $\frac{11}{4}$.

Problem D

Jamie measured $\frac{5}{4}$ cups of milk for biscuits.
Rename $\frac{5}{4}$ as a mixed number.

Solution

$\frac{5}{4}$ means

$5 \div 4.$

$$4\overline{)5}^{1\frac{1}{4}}$$
$$\underline{4}$$
$$1$$

Divide the numerator by the denominator. Then express the remainder as a fraction.

As a mixed number, $\frac{5}{4}$ is $1\frac{1}{4}$.

Exercises

Set A
Compare these fractions or mixed numbers. Replace ● with $<$, $>$, or $=$.

1. $\frac{3}{4}$ ● $\frac{9}{16}$
4. $\frac{5}{6}$ ● $\frac{8}{9}$
7. $2\frac{4}{9}$ ● $2\frac{5}{12}$

2. $\frac{4}{7}$ ● $\frac{1}{2}$
5. $\frac{3}{4}$ ● $\frac{3}{5}$
8. $8\frac{1}{3}$ ● $9\frac{1}{6}$

3. $\frac{1}{3}$ ● $\frac{2}{5}$
6. $\frac{1}{2}$ ● $\frac{8}{16}$
9. $1\frac{5}{6}$ ● $1\frac{5}{8}$

Set B
Rename in lowest terms.

10. $\frac{8}{10}$
12. $\frac{24}{40}$
14. $\frac{75}{100}$
16. $\frac{22}{66}$

11. $\frac{18}{24}$
13. $\frac{10}{25}$
15. $\frac{42}{56}$
17. $\frac{24}{72}$

Set C
Rename as a fraction.

18. $2\frac{4}{5}$
20. 4
22. $2\frac{5}{16}$
24. $3\frac{5}{6}$

19. $9\frac{2}{3}$
21. $4\frac{5}{12}$
23. $6\frac{7}{8}$
25. $7\frac{1}{10}$

Set D
Rename as a mixed number.

26. $\frac{28}{5}$
28. $\frac{24}{7}$
30. $\frac{42}{12}$
32. $\frac{34}{6}$

27. $\frac{14}{3}$
29. $\frac{72}{8}$
31. $\frac{24}{10}$
33. $\frac{48}{16}$

Related Problems

34. A recipe for salad dressing calls for $\frac{5}{8}$ cup of oil and $\frac{3}{4}$ cup of vinegar. Does the recipe use more oil or more vinegar?

35. Dan has $\frac{2}{3}$ cup of oil. His recipe calls for $\frac{7}{8}$ cup. Does he have enough oil?

Break Time

In the division below, replace each symbol with a different digit. Identical symbols represent the same digit.

Multiplying and Dividing Fractions and Mixed Numbers

> When multiplying fractions, first multiply the numerators. Then multiply the denominators.
>
> To divide fractions and mixed numbers, multiply the dividend by the reciprocal of the divisor.

Problem A

The wheels on John Sauble's car are $\frac{5}{8}$ as wide as the wheels on his pickup truck. The truck wheels are $\frac{2}{3}$ of a foot wide. How wide are the car wheels?

Find $\frac{5}{8} \times \frac{2}{3}$.

Solution

$\frac{5}{8} \times \frac{2}{3}$

$\frac{5 \times 2}{8 \times 3}$	Multiply numerators. Multiply denominators.
$\frac{10}{24}$	
$\frac{5}{12}$	Express the answer in lowest terms.

You can use this shortcut.

$\frac{5}{\underset{4}{8}} \times \frac{\overset{1}{2}}{3}$	Divide a numerator and a denominator by the same number, 2.
$\frac{5}{12}$	Then multiply.

The car wheels are $\frac{5}{12}$ of a foot wide.

Problem B

The fuel tank of John's semitrailer truck holds $3\frac{1}{3}$ times as much as the fuel tank of his car. The car fuel tank holds $14\frac{1}{2}$ gallons. How much does the truck fuel tank hold?

Find $3\frac{1}{3} \times 14\frac{1}{2}$.

Solution

Estimate. Round each factor to the nearest whole number. If the fraction is $\frac{1}{2}$ or greater, round up. If the fraction is less than $\frac{1}{2}$, round down.

$$3\frac{1}{3} \times 14\frac{1}{2}$$
$$\downarrow \qquad \downarrow$$
$$3 \times 15 = 45$$

Find the actual product.

$3\frac{1}{3} \times 14\frac{1}{2}$

$\frac{10}{3} \times \frac{29}{2}$	Rename the mixed numbers as fractions.
$\frac{\overset{5}{10}}{3} \times \frac{29}{\underset{1}{2}}$	Divide a numerator and a denominator by the same number, 2. Then multiply.
$\frac{145}{3}$	
$48\frac{1}{3}$	Rename the answer as a mixed number.

The truck fuel tank holds $48\frac{1}{3}$ gallons.

Problem C

John drove his pickup truck 170 miles in $3\frac{3}{4}$ hours. What was his average speed?

Find $170 \div 3\frac{3}{4}$.

Solution

$170 \div 3\frac{3}{4}$

$\frac{170}{1} \div \frac{15}{4}$	Rename the whole or mixed numbers as fractions.
$\frac{170}{1} \times \frac{4}{15}$	Multiply the dividend by the reciprocal of the divisor. Remember, $\frac{15}{4}$ and $\frac{4}{15}$ are reciprocals because $\frac{15}{4} \times \frac{4}{15} = 1$.
$\overset{34}{\underset{3}{\frac{170}{1} \times \frac{4}{15}}}$	Simplify.
$\frac{136}{3}$	Multiply.
$45\frac{1}{3}$	Express the answer as a mixed number.

Use estimation to decide if the answer is reasonable. Round the quotient and the divisor and multiply.

$45\frac{1}{3} \times 3\frac{3}{4}$
$\quad\downarrow \qquad \downarrow$
$\ 45\ \times\ 4\ =\ 180$

Since 180 is close to 170, the estimate indicates that the answer, $45\frac{1}{3}$ is reasonable.

John's average speed was $45\frac{1}{3}$ miles per hour.

Exercises

Set A   Find each product.

1. $\frac{1}{2} \times \frac{5}{6}$ 3. $\frac{3}{5} \times \frac{5}{6}$ 5. $\frac{1}{5} \times 4$

2. $\frac{1}{4} \times \frac{2}{3}$ 4. $\frac{7}{10} \times \frac{15}{28}$ 6. $\frac{7}{8} \times 6$

Set B   Estimate. Then find each product.

7. $3\frac{1}{2} \times 1\frac{1}{5}$ 10. $2\frac{11}{12} \times 6$

8. $2\frac{3}{16} \times 1\frac{3}{5}$ 11. $4 \times 8\frac{7}{8}$

9. $4\frac{1}{3} \times 3\frac{3}{5}$ 12. $1\frac{5}{6} \times 5\frac{1}{3}$

Set C   Find each quotient. Estimate to decide if the answer is reasonable.

13. $2\frac{2}{3} \div 3\frac{1}{5}$ 16. $6\frac{3}{8} \div 2\frac{1}{8}$

14. $3\frac{1}{8} \div 1\frac{1}{4}$ 17. $4\frac{1}{3} \div 1\frac{1}{6}$

15. $4\frac{1}{5} \div 2\frac{1}{3}$ 18. $8\frac{5}{6} \div 2\frac{2}{3}$

Mixed Practice   Multiply or divide.

19. $1\frac{2}{3} \div \frac{7}{9}$ 24. $\frac{1}{2} \times 4\frac{1}{2} \times 3\frac{1}{3}$

20. $5\frac{1}{3} \times \frac{1}{2}$ 25. $3\frac{1}{3} \div \frac{5}{6}$

21. $12\frac{3}{8} \div 8\frac{1}{4}$ 26. $\frac{5}{6} \div 2\frac{1}{2}$

22. $3 \div 1\frac{1}{3}$ 27. $\frac{1}{2} \times \frac{2}{3} \times \frac{5}{8}$

23. $2\frac{5}{8} \times \frac{5}{6}$ 28. $2\frac{1}{2} \div 3\frac{1}{8}$

Related Problems

29. At 50 miles per hour, how far can John drive in $7\frac{1}{2}$ hours?

30. John's semitrailer truck travels $8\frac{1}{3}$ miles per gallon of fuel. How much fuel will be used during a 3200-mile trip?

Adding and Subtracting Fractions and Mixed Numbers

When adding or subtracting fractions and mixed numbers, write the fractions with a common denominator.

Problem A

Melinda Tanaka bought stock when the selling price was $8\frac{3}{4}$ ($8\frac{3}{4}$ dollars) per share. During the next quarter (three months), the value of a share rose $3\frac{7}{8}$ ($3\frac{7}{8}$ dollars). What was the new selling price of the stock?

Find $8\frac{3}{4} + 3\frac{7}{8}$.

Solution

Estimate. Round to the nearest whole number.

$$8\frac{3}{4} \longrightarrow 9$$
$$3\frac{7}{8} \longrightarrow \underline{+\ 4}$$
$$13$$

Find the actual sum.

$$8\frac{3}{4} = 8\frac{6}{8}$$
$$\underline{+\ 3\frac{7}{8} = 3\frac{7}{8}}$$
$$11\frac{13}{8}$$

Write the fractions with a common denominator. Then add the numerators and use the common denominator. Add the whole numbers.

$$11\frac{13}{8} = 11 + 1\frac{5}{8} = 12\frac{5}{8} \qquad \text{Simplify the answer.}$$

The new selling price of the stock was $12\frac{5}{8}$ ($12\frac{5}{8}$ dollars).

Problem B

The high and low prices for a given quarter were $15\frac{1}{4}$ ($15\frac{1}{4}$ dollars) and $12\frac{3}{8}$ ($12\frac{3}{8}$ dollars). Find the difference between the high and the low prices.

Find $15\frac{1}{4} - 12\frac{3}{8}$.

Solution

Estimate. Round to the nearest whole number.

$$15\frac{1}{4} \longrightarrow 15$$
$$12\frac{3}{8} \longrightarrow \underline{-\ 12}$$
$$3$$

Find the actual difference.

$$15\frac{1}{4} = 15\frac{2}{8} = 14\frac{10}{8}$$
$$\underline{-\ 12\frac{3}{8} = 12\frac{3}{8} = 12\ \frac{3}{8}}$$
$$2\frac{7}{8}$$

Write the fractions with a common denominator. Since $\frac{3}{8}$ cannot be subtracted from $\frac{2}{8}$, rename $15\frac{2}{8}$ as $14\frac{10}{8}$. Then subtract.

The difference between the high and the low prices was $2\frac{7}{8}$ ($2\frac{7}{8}$ dollars).

Exercises

Set A Find each sum.

1. $\frac{1}{8} + \frac{1}{3}$ 6. $\frac{1}{12} + \frac{2}{3}$

2. $\frac{5}{6} + \frac{1}{4}$ 7. $\frac{1}{4} + \frac{5}{9}$

3. $\frac{3}{7} + \frac{1}{2}$ 8. $\frac{3}{7} + \frac{1}{3}$

4. $\frac{3}{4} + \frac{4}{5}$ 9. $\frac{1}{2} + \frac{5}{8} + \frac{5}{6}$

5. $\frac{9}{16} + \frac{5}{8}$ 10. $\frac{2}{3} + \frac{1}{2} + \frac{3}{5}$

Estimate. Then find each sum.

11. $2\frac{1}{3} + 4\frac{5}{6}$ 17. $12\frac{3}{8} + \frac{2}{3}$

12. $7\frac{3}{5} + 9\frac{1}{10}$ 18. $3\frac{5}{7} + \frac{1}{2}$

13. $1\frac{3}{4} + 1\frac{1}{10}$ 19. $8\frac{1}{16} + 2\frac{7}{8}$

14. $2\frac{6}{7} + 3\frac{1}{3}$ 20. $4\frac{4}{5} + 5\frac{2}{3}$

15. $6\frac{2}{3} + 4\frac{1}{4}$ 21. $2\frac{1}{4} + 1\frac{1}{5} + 4\frac{1}{2}$

16. $4\frac{7}{8} + 1\frac{4}{5}$ 22. $10\frac{2}{3} + 3\frac{7}{8} + 4\frac{1}{6}$

Set B Find each difference.

23. $\frac{5}{8} - \frac{1}{2}$ 28. $\frac{1}{3} - \frac{1}{4}$

24. $\frac{3}{5} - \frac{1}{2}$ 29. $\frac{3}{8} - \frac{1}{3}$

25. $\frac{11}{12} - \frac{2}{3}$ 30. $\frac{1}{2} - \frac{2}{7}$

26. $\frac{3}{4} - \frac{2}{5}$ 31. $4 - \frac{3}{5}$

27. $\frac{7}{8} - \frac{5}{6}$ 32. $10 - \frac{5}{16}$

Estimate. Then find each difference.

33. $6\frac{1}{8} - 2\frac{7}{8}$ 39. $15\frac{1}{2} - 1\frac{11}{16}$

34. $27\frac{1}{3} - 18$ 40. $17\frac{5}{6} - 9\frac{2}{3}$

35. $16 - 4\frac{3}{8}$ 41. $12\frac{3}{5} - 4\frac{3}{4}$

36. $11 - 2\frac{5}{12}$ 42. $16\frac{2}{9} - 2\frac{5}{6}$

37. $12\frac{1}{3} - 7\frac{1}{9}$ 43. $10\frac{1}{3} - 4\frac{7}{8}$

38. $14\frac{5}{8} - 5\frac{3}{4}$ 44. $11\frac{1}{4} - 3\frac{5}{6}$

Related Problems

45. Melinda bought another stock for $7\frac{1}{8}$. During the next quarter, it rose $4\frac{1}{2}$. Then, during the following quarter, it rose $4\frac{3}{4}$. What was the price of the stock at the end of the two quarters?

46. At the beginning of the fourth quarter, the price of a stock was $16\frac{3}{8}$. During the quarter, the price fell $2\frac{7}{8}$. What was the price at the end of the quarter?

19

CALCULATOR APPLICATIONS

Stock quotations in newspapers list figures for stocks in fractional form. For instance, a price of $43\frac{3}{8}$ means $43\frac{3}{8}$ dollars. When used in computation, the figures are often written as decimals.

Write $43\frac{3}{8}$ as a decimal to the nearest thousandth.

First, use your calculator to find the decimal for $\frac{3}{8}$ to the nearest thousandth.

$$\frac{3}{8} = 3 \div 8 = 0.375$$

Then, use 0.375 for $\frac{3}{8}$ to rewrite $43\frac{3}{8}$.

$$43\frac{3}{8} = 43 + \frac{3}{8}$$
$$= 43 + 0.375$$
$$= 43.375$$

As a decimal to the nearest thousandth, $43\frac{3}{8}$ is 43.375.

Write each fraction or mixed number as a decimal to the nearest thousandth.

1. $\frac{5}{6}$	9. $\frac{15}{52}$	17. $2\frac{4}{5}$	25. $17\frac{3}{11}$
2. $\frac{7}{9}$	10. $\frac{13}{16}$	18. $10\frac{7}{8}$	26. $20\frac{33}{111}$
3. $\frac{11}{13}$	11. $\frac{75}{70}$	19. $14\frac{5}{12}$	27. $53\frac{4}{9}$
4. $\frac{20}{21}$	12. $\frac{36}{17}$	20. $27\frac{11}{16}$	28. $12\frac{4}{99}$
5. $\frac{5}{8}$	13. $\frac{97}{37}$	21. $31\frac{1}{15}$	29. $15\frac{33}{99}$
6. $\frac{23}{40}$	14. $\frac{111}{24}$	22. $40\frac{1}{18}$	30. $8\frac{17}{99}$
7. $\frac{7}{18}$	15. $\frac{114}{15}$	23. $2\frac{2}{11}$	31. $6\frac{35}{99}$
8. $\frac{37}{60}$	16. $\frac{250}{100}$	24. $3\frac{5}{9}$	32. $4\frac{98}{99}$

Chapter 1 Review

Rounding whole numbers and decimals, pages 4–5

1. Round 7481 to the nearest thousand, nearest hundred, and nearest ten.

2. Round 23.716 to the nearest whole number, nearest tenth, and nearest hundredth.

Adding and subtracting whole numbers and decimals, pages 6–7

3. $26 + 52 + 63$

4. $2.1 + 0.36 + 5.82$

5. $91 - 57$

6. $65.2 - 23.74$

Multiplying whole numbers, pages 8–9

7. 30×700

8. 576×42

Multiplying decimals, pages 10–11

9. 50×0.07

10. 5.23×6.7

Dividing whole numbers and decimals, pages 12–13

11. $9312 \div 16$

12. Find the quotient to the nearest hundredth for $43.6 \div 7$.

13. Find the quotient to the nearest whole number for $84.1 \div 0.24$.

Comparing and renaming fractions and mixed numbers, pages 14–15

14. Compare. Replace ● with $<$, $>$, or $=$.
$4\frac{2}{3}$ ● $4\frac{3}{5}$

15. Rename $\frac{12}{18}$ in lowest terms.

16. Rename $4\frac{7}{8}$ as a fraction.

17. Rename $\frac{28}{3}$ as a mixed number.

Multiplying and dividing fractions and mixed numbers, pages 16–17

18. $\frac{1}{3} \times \frac{5}{7}$

19. $1\frac{1}{6} \times 2\frac{2}{3}$

20. $\frac{3}{4} \div \frac{1}{6}$

21. $3\frac{1}{2} \div 1\frac{1}{4}$

Adding and subtracting fractions and mixed numbers, pages 18–19

22. $\frac{3}{4} + \frac{1}{5}$

23. $2\frac{1}{3} + 3\frac{7}{8}$

24. $\frac{7}{8} - \frac{2}{5}$

25. $5\frac{2}{3} - 2\frac{1}{9}$

Chapter 1 Test

1. Round 3172 to the nearest thousand, nearest hundred, and nearest ten.

2. Round 58.236 to the nearest whole number, nearest tenth, and nearest hundredth.

3. $32 + 74 + 25$

4. $8.12 + 3.27 + 5.64$

5. $83 - 26$

6. $57.36 - 24.71$

7. 20×800

8. 324×67

9. 0.7×0.04

10. 4.62×32

11. $3728 \div 6$

12. Find the quotient to the nearest hundredth for $56.2 \div 9$.

13. Find the quotient to the nearest whole number for $15.55 \div 0.32$.

14. Compare. Replace ● with $<$, $>$, or $=$.
    $2\frac{11}{12}$ ● $2\frac{3}{4}$

15. Rename $\frac{18}{27}$ in lowest terms.

16. Rename $6\frac{2}{3}$ as a fraction.

17. Rename $\frac{35}{4}$ as a mixed number.

18. $\frac{1}{2} \times \frac{3}{8}$

19. $1\frac{3}{4} \times 3\frac{1}{3}$

20. $\frac{5}{6} \div \frac{4}{5}$

21. $4\frac{2}{3} \div 3\frac{1}{2}$

22. $\frac{2}{3} + \frac{1}{4}$

23. $2\frac{2}{5} + 1\frac{1}{3}$

24. $\frac{5}{6} - \frac{2}{3}$

25. $4\frac{7}{8} - 1\frac{1}{2}$

Chapter 2 Equations, Proportions, and Percent

Addition and Subtraction Equations

To solve an addition equation, subtract the same number from both sides. To solve a subtraction equation, add the same number to both sides.

Problem A

Bud ordered some prints of a photograph. The total bill was $5.25, including postage. If the prints cost $4.65, how much was postage?

Solve. $p + 4.65 = 5.25$

Solution

$$p + 4.65 = 5.25$$ 4.65 is added to p.

$$p + 4.65 - 4.65 = 5.25 - 4.65$$ To undo the addition, subtract 4.65 from both sides of the equation.

$$p = 0.60$$

Check: $p + 4.65 = 5.25$ Substitute 0.60 for p
$0.60 + 4.65 \stackrel{?}{=} 5.25$ in the original equation.
$5.25 = 5.25$

The postage was $0.60.

Problem B

Bud ordered film from a mail-order company and paid $0.37 a roll less than the retail price. If he paid $1.76 per roll, what was the retail price?

Solve. $r - 0.37 = 1.76$

Solution

$$r - 0.37 = 1.76$$ 0.37 is subtracted from r.

$$r - 0.37 + 0.37 = 1.76 + 0.37$$ To undo the subtraction, add 0.37 to both sides of the equation.

$$r = 2.13$$

Check: $r - 0.37 = 1.76$ Substitute 2.13 for r in
$2.13 - 0.37 \stackrel{?}{=} 1.76$ the original equation.
$1.76 = 1.76$

The retail price was $2.13.

Exercises

Set A   Solve and check.

1. $a + 6 = 21$

2. $d + 28 = 37$

3. $f + 1.87 = 3.4$

4. $x + 3.3 = 4$

5. $9.2 = c + 2.9$

6. $4 = b + 3.01$

7. $8 = 3.9 + y$

8. $4.7 = 2.7 + w$

9. $m + 83 = 104$

10. $r + 21 = 76.5$

11. $t + 8.4 = 17.3$

12. $x + 0.4 = 1.8$

13. $2.7 + m = 8.7$

14. $4.32 = r + 1.9$

Set B   Solve and check.

15. $g - 13 = 10$

16. $m - 2 = 4$

17. $h - 0.25 = 1.13$

18. $a - 0.03 = 1.8$

19. $7 = n - 17$

20. $17 = r - 8$

21. $0.09 = k - 0.7$

22. $x - 0.8 = 1.3$

23. $100 = m - 47$

24. $3.4 = y - 8.1$

25. $t - 31 = 4.8$

26. $a - 8 = 7.4$

27. $0.92 = x - 7.1$

28. $0.4 = m - 3$

Mixed Practice   Solve and check.

29. $45 = 18 + t$

30. $d - 39 = 85$

31. $14 + m = 26$

32. $30 = a + 4.3$

33. $t - 0.32 = 0.61$

34. $r + 2.08 = 3$

35. $4.6 = s - 1$

36. $22 = v + 18$

37. $w - 45.19 = 6$

38. $7.5 = 4.11 + x$

39. $6 = y - 47$

40. $z + 100 = 499$

41. $p - 83 = 8$

42. $4.9 = a - 33.7$

43. $3.3 + b = 6.06$

44. $s + 10.6 = 30$

45. $3.9 = z - 5.15$

46. $d - 2.7 = 7.4$

47. $98.6 + g = 132$

48. $18.3 = 3.8 + x$

Related Problems

Write an equation for each problem. Then solve and check.

49. By using a coupon, Peg saved $1.25 when she ordered prints. If she paid $11.85, what was the regular price?

50. Yana bought a camera case for $14.75 plus tax. If his total bill was $15.49, how much was the tax?

Multiplication and Division Equations

To solve a multiplication equation, divide both sides by the same number.
To solve a division equation, multiply both sides by the same number.

Problem A

How many games were bowled if $82.45 was paid at a special rate of $0.85 per game?

Solve. $0.85g = 82.45$

Solution

$0.85g = 82.45$ $0.85g$ means $0.85 \times g$.

$$\frac{0.85g}{0.85} = \frac{82.45}{0.85}$$ To undo the multiplication, divide both sides of the equation by 0.85.

$$g = 97$$

Check: $\quad 0.85g = 82.45$
$$0.85(97) \overset{?}{=} 82.45$$
$$82.45 = 82.45$$

97 games were bowled.

Problem B

A team's average was 86.2 pins per game in 15 games. What was the total number of pins?

Solve. $\frac{p}{15} = 86.2$

Solution

$\frac{p}{15} = 86.2$ $\frac{p}{15}$ means $p \div 15$.

$\frac{p}{15}(15) = 86.2(15)$ To undo the division, multiply both sides of the equation by 15.

$$p = 1293$$

Check: $\quad \frac{p}{15} = 86.2$
$$\frac{1293}{15} \overset{?}{=} 86.2$$
$$86.2 = 86.2$$

The total number of pins was 1293.

Problem C

There are 8 students in the beginning bowling class and 9 students in the advanced class. Each student rented shoes, and the total charge for shoe rental was $12.75. What was the rental charge for each pair of shoes?

Solve. $8c + 9c = 12.75$

Solution

$8c + 9c = 12.75$ Combine like terms. $8c$ and $9c$ are like terms because 8 and 9 are both multiplied by c.
$8c + 9c = (8 + 9)c = 17c$

$17c = 12.75$

$$\frac{17c}{17} = \frac{12.75}{17}$$ To undo the multiplication, divide both sides by 17.

$$c = 0.75$$

Check: $\qquad 8c + 9c = 12.75$
$$8(0.75) + 9(0.75) \overset{?}{=} 12.75$$
$$6 + 6.75 \overset{?}{=} 12.75$$
$$12.75 = 12.75$$

The rental charge for each pair of shoes was $0.75.

Exercises

Set A Solve and check.

1. $3a = 141$
2. $1.2b = 8.4$
3. $153 = 9c$
4. $0.8x = 72$
5. $3.15 = 3.5x$

Set B Solve and check.

6. $\dfrac{d}{5} = 0.08$
7. $\dfrac{f}{0.2} = 3$
8. $0.45 = \dfrac{g}{0.7}$
9. $\dfrac{r}{0.8} = 19$
10. $0.04 = \dfrac{h}{25}$

Set C Solve and check.

11. $7a + 8a = 45$
12. $10c - 2c = 32$
13. $99 = 5t + 6t$
14. $0.2d + 2.2d = 48$
15. $84 = 15x - 8x$

Mixed Practice
Solve and check.

16. $0.5r = 17.5$
17. $\dfrac{f}{0.16} = 0.6$
18. $17c + 28c = 45$
19. $47y = 0$
20. $2b + 2b + 3b = 56$
21. $0.09z = 8.1$
22. $\dfrac{x}{5.07} = 1.1$
23. $1.08 = 0.27s$
24. $12a + a = 26$
25. $318x - 167x = 0$
26. $\dfrac{d}{0.5} = 0.8$
27. $3.5 = 0.07x$
28. $105 = 16q - q$
29. $\dfrac{k}{4.018} = 0$
30. $0.22 = \dfrac{m}{1.7}$

Related Problems

Write an equation for each problem.
Then solve and check.

31. The cost of bowling one game is $0.85. How many games could Tim bowl for $7.65?

32. The women's league had 2 sessions. In the first session, 108 games were bowled. In the second, 159 games were bowled. If a total of $253.65 was collected, what was the cost of each game?

33. In Sandy's league, there are 5 people on every team. Each team bowls 3 games a week. The league bowls a total of 135 games per week. How many teams are in the league?

Two-Step Equations

Problem A

Before he retired, Bill Oberle purchased a 4-unit apartment building as an investment. From the rent he collects each month, Bill pays out $600 for expenses. How much rent must he charge for each of the 4 apartments if he wants to make $500 profit each month? The amount of rent is the same for each of the apartments.

Solve. $4r - 600 = 500$

Solution

$$4r - 600 = 500$$

r is multiplied by 4 and 600 is subtracted from $4r$.

$$4r - 600 + 600 = 500 + 600$$

To undo the subtraction, add 600 to both sides.

$$4r = 1100$$

$$\frac{4r}{4} = \frac{1100}{4}$$

To undo the multiplication, divide both sides by 4.

$$r = 275$$

Check:
$$4r - 600 = 500$$
$$4(275) - 600 \overset{?}{=} 500$$
$$1100 - 600 \overset{?}{=} 500$$
$$500 = 500$$

Bill must charge $275 rent for each apartment.

Problem B

Ruth Santos and her son own an apartment building together. They split the rental income equally. Ruth's monthly income is $980. She earns $450 per month at a part-time job. The rest of her monthly income is her share of the rental income. What is the total rental income?

Solve. $\frac{x}{2} + 450 = 980$

Solution

$\frac{x}{2} + 450 = 980$ x is divided by 2 and 450 is added to $\frac{x}{2}$.

$\frac{x}{2} + 450 - 450 = 980 - 450$ To undo the addition, subtract 450 from both sides.

$\frac{x}{2} = 530$

$\frac{x}{2}(2) = 530(2)$ To undo the division, multiply both sides by 2.

$x = 1060$

Check: $\frac{x}{2} + 450 = 980$

$\frac{1060}{2} + 450 \stackrel{?}{=} 980$

$530 + 450 \stackrel{?}{=} 980$

$980 = 980$

The total rental income is $1060.

Exercises

Set A   Solve and check.

1. $5a + 3 = 8$
2. $3s - 14 = 16$
3. $7n + 2 = 65$
4. $11 = 6 + 2r$
5. $0 = 2b - 7$
6. $12x + 32 = 89$
7. $45 = 13m - 20$
8. $29 = 4a + 16$
9. $105n - 6 = 99$
10. $79x + 45 = 282$

Set B   Solve and check.

11. $\frac{m}{2} + 3 = 6$
12. $\frac{a}{3} - 7 = 5$
13. $\frac{t}{7} + 9 = 10$
14. $24 = 11 + \frac{c}{4}$
15. $0 = \frac{n}{4} - 9$
16. $\frac{a}{10} + 12 = 18$
17. $\frac{b}{6} - 21 = 3$
18. $4 = \frac{x}{6} - 4$
19. $\frac{x}{9} + 49 = 58$
20. $38 = \frac{a}{2} - 6$

Mixed Practice   Solve and check.

21. $20 = 5z - 20$
22. $12 + 2c = 12$
23. $\frac{x}{2} + 6 = 15$
24. $2.9 + \frac{d}{5} = 3.5$
25. $1.2 + 6m = 2.4$
26. $0.9n - 4.7 = 1.6$
27. $0.1x - 0.1 = 0.1$
28. $40 = 32 + \frac{y}{9}$
29. $1 = \frac{b}{0.1} - 39$
30. $43 = 7 + 3w$

Related Problems

Write an equation for each problem. Then solve and check.

31. Larry Houser owns a building with 3 apartments. He pays out $450 in monthly expenses. How much rent does Larry charge for each apartment if his monthly profit is $315? He charges the same amount of rent for each apartment.

32. Kay and her sister share an apartment. They each pay half of the rent, but Kay pays $25 extra per month for the use of a garage. Kay pays $175 per month. What is the monthly rent for the apartment?

Ratio and Proportion

Equal ratios form a proportion. Two ratios are equal if their cross-products are equal. If the cross-products are not equal, the ratios are not equal.

Problem A

To create a new billboard, a designer first made a sketch on which the picture was 11.5 centimeters wide. Using a scale of 0.5 to 12, the designer computed the actual width of the picture on the billboard to be 276 centimeters. Did the designer compute the actual width correctly?

Tell whether these ratios are equal. $\frac{0.5}{12} \overset{?}{=} \frac{11.5}{276}$ ← Width of sketch
← Actual width

Solution

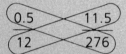

$0.5 \times 276 \quad 12 \times 11.5$

Multiply 0.5×276 and 12×11.5 to find cross-products.

$138 = 138$

$\frac{0.5}{12} = \frac{11.5}{276}$

The cross-products are equal, so the ratios are equal.

The designer computed the actual width correctly.

30

Problem B

A painted billboard is built so that the ratio of height to width is 0.5 to 2. If the board is 4 meters high, how wide is it?

Solve. $\dfrac{0.5}{2} = \dfrac{4}{w}$ $\longleftarrow$ Height
$\longleftarrow$ Width

Solution

$$\frac{0.5}{2} = \frac{4}{w}$$

$0.5 \times w = 2 \times 4$ Find the cross-products.

$0.5w = 8$

$\dfrac{0.5w}{0.5} = \dfrac{8}{0.5}$ To undo the multiplication, divide both sides by 0.5.

$w = 16$

Check: $\dfrac{0.5}{2} = \dfrac{4}{w}$ Substitute 16 for w in the original proportion.

$\dfrac{0.5}{2} \overset{?}{=} \dfrac{4}{16}$

$0.5 \times 16 \overset{?}{=} 2 \times 4$ Find the cross-products.

$8 = 8$ The cross-products are equal, so the ratios are equal, and $w = 16$.

The billboard is 16 meters wide.

Exercises

Set A   Find the cross-products. Tell whether the ratios are equal.

1. $\dfrac{7}{28}$ $\dfrac{3}{12}$ 4. $\dfrac{30}{8}$ $\dfrac{70}{21}$

2. $\dfrac{20}{100}$ $\dfrac{7}{35}$ 5. $\dfrac{24}{64}$ $\dfrac{3}{8}$

3. $\dfrac{5}{6}$ $\dfrac{37}{42}$ 6. $\dfrac{20}{35}$ $\dfrac{12}{21}$

7. $\dfrac{11}{12}$ $\dfrac{44}{48}$ 12. $\dfrac{0.6}{9}$ $\dfrac{0.4}{6}$

8. $\dfrac{32}{63}$ $\dfrac{4}{9}$ 13. $\dfrac{0.5}{0.25}$ $\dfrac{0.4}{0.2}$

9. $\dfrac{8}{1.2}$ $\dfrac{2}{0.3}$ 14. $\dfrac{0.3}{0.5}$ $\dfrac{3}{4.5}$

10. $\dfrac{3.5}{4.2}$ $\dfrac{10}{14}$ 15. $\dfrac{50.4}{100}$ $\dfrac{4.2}{9}$

11. $\dfrac{10.8}{6}$ $\dfrac{3.6}{2}$ 16. $\dfrac{75}{81}$ $\dfrac{2.5}{2.7}$

Set B   Solve and check.

17. $\dfrac{a}{20} = \dfrac{6}{8}$ 25. $\dfrac{0.75}{1} = \dfrac{30}{x}$

18. $\dfrac{11}{33} = \dfrac{c}{15}$ 26. $\dfrac{r}{14} = \dfrac{0.7}{10}$

19. $\dfrac{12}{d} = \dfrac{4}{3}$ 27. $\dfrac{5}{0.9} = \dfrac{s}{36}$

20. $\dfrac{24}{9} = \dfrac{8}{f}$ 28. $\dfrac{x}{1.4} = \dfrac{2.4}{2.8}$

21. $\dfrac{x}{5} = \dfrac{3}{4}$ 29. $\dfrac{0.03}{0.5} = \dfrac{t}{0.1}$

22. $\dfrac{16}{g} = \dfrac{10}{2}$ 30. $\dfrac{0.06}{v} = \dfrac{0.3}{4}$

23. $\dfrac{3}{5} = \dfrac{h}{7}$ 31. $\dfrac{y}{1.6} = \dfrac{1.5}{4.8}$

24. $\dfrac{24}{25} = \dfrac{6}{w}$ 32. $\dfrac{0.25}{0.3} = \dfrac{100}{x}$

Related Problems

The ratio of height to width on a standard printed billboard is 1 to 2.25.

33. If the height is 8 meters, find the width.

34. Could a standard printed billboard be 4 meters high and 9 meters wide?

Writing Percents, Decimals, and Fractions

> Percent means hundredths.
> $1\% = 0.01 = \frac{1}{100}$

Problem A

From the real estate section of his newspaper, Sonny Gillespie learned that the cost of new homes in his city has increased by a factor of 0.575 over the past 5 years.

Write 0.575 as a percent.

Solution

$0.575 = 57.5\%$ Move the decimal point two places to the right and write a percent sign.

As a percent, 0.575 is 57.5%.

Problem B

The Gillespies have saved enough money to pay about $\frac{3}{8}$ of the cost of a house.

Write $\frac{3}{8}$ as a percent.

Solution

First write $\frac{3}{8}$ as a decimal.

$$
\begin{array}{r}
0.375 \\
8\overline{)3.000} \\
\underline{2\,4} \\
60 \\
\underline{56} \\
40 \\
\underline{40} \\
0
\end{array}
$$
    Divide the numerator by the denominator.

$\frac{3}{8} = 0.375$

Then write the decimal as a percent.

$0.375 = 37.5\%$

As a percent, $\frac{3}{8}$ is 37.5%.

Problem C

Sonny read that mortgage interest rates are $5\frac{1}{4}\%$ higher than they were five years ago.

Write $5\frac{1}{4}\%$ as a decimal.

Solution

$5\frac{1}{4}\% = 5.25\%$ Write $5\frac{1}{4}$ as a decimal.

$5.25\% = 0.0525$ Drop the percent sign and move the decimal point 2 places to the left.

As a decimal, $5\frac{1}{4}\%$ is 0.0525.

Problem D

Often, 20% of the cost of a home is required as a down payment.

Write 20% as a fraction.

Solution

$20\% = \frac{20}{100}$ Drop the percent sign and write the number over 100.

$\frac{20}{100} = \frac{1}{5}$ Rename the fraction in lowest terms.

As a fraction, 20% is $\frac{1}{5}$.

Exercises

Set A   Write as a percent.

1. 0.43	**6.** 0.314	**11.** 0.0745
2. 0.71	**7.** 0.225	**12.** 0.0375
3. 0.09	**8.** 0.468	**13.** 1.25
4. 0.1	**9.** 0.1975	**14.** 3.74
5. 0.027	**10.** 0.2325	**15.** 2.465

Set B Write as a percent.

16. $\frac{3}{4}$ **21.** $\frac{17}{25}$ **26.** $\frac{9}{16}$

17. $\frac{1}{2}$ **22.** $\frac{27}{50}$ **27.** $\frac{12}{32}$

18. $\frac{1}{4}$ **23.** $\frac{1}{20}$ **28.** $\frac{1}{8}$

19. $\frac{4}{5}$ **24.** $\frac{2}{25}$ **29.** $\frac{11}{5}$

20. $\frac{8}{20}$ **25.** $\frac{5}{8}$ **30.** $\frac{27}{4}$

Set C Write as a decimal.

31. 23%   **36.** 9.25%   **41.** $32\frac{1}{4}$%

32. 7%   **37.** 8.75%   **42.** $12\frac{1}{10}$%

33. 2%   **38.** 24.8%   **43.** 135%

34. 14%   **39.** $3\frac{1}{2}$%   **44.** 216%

35. 13.5%   **40.** $4\frac{3}{4}$%   **45.** 107%

Set D Write as a fraction in lowest terms.

46. 10%   **51.** 75%   **56.** 18%

47. 70%   **52.** 60%   **57.** 61%

48. 25%   **53.** 35%   **58.** 93%

49. 50%   **54.** 21%   **59.** 109%

50. 40%   **55.** 47%   **60.** 107%

Related Problems

Use this information for problems 61–64.

> Mortgage payments now take $0.35 of each income dollar.

> Real estate taxes rose 22% in 6 years.

> In 6 years, repair and maintenance costs have increased by $\frac{3}{4}$.

61. Write the increase in real estate taxes as a decimal.

62. Write the increase in real estate taxes as a fraction in lowest terms.

63. Write the increase in repair and maintenance costs as a percent.

64. Mortgage payments take what percent of the income?

Using Percent

Problem A

Nita Singh determines the markup for items in a retail store. The markup is the difference between the store's cost and the selling price. The markup rate is a percent of the store's cost. Find the markup on a shirt that cost the store $6.75 if the markup rate is 45%.

Solution

Write an equation and solve it.

First write the information in this form:

___ % of ___ is _____.

<u>45%</u> of <u>cost</u> is <u>markup</u>.

$0.45 \times 6.75 = m$

$3.0375 = m$

$3.04 \approx m$ Round to the next higher cent.

The markup is $3.04.

Problem B

Find the markup rate for plant food if the store's cost was $1.90 and the markup is $0.76.

Solution

___ % of ___ is _____.

___ % of <u>cost</u> is <u>markup</u>.

$r \times 1.90 = 0.76$ Write an equation and solve it.

$\dfrac{r \times 1.90}{1.90} = \dfrac{0.76}{1.90}$

$r = 0.4$

$0.4 = 40\%$ Write 0.4 as a percent.

The markup rate is 40%.

Problem C

An ad says, "20% off our regular price. Save $39!" What is the regular price?

Solution

___% of _____ is_____.

20% of regular price is amount saved.

$0.20 \times p = 39$ Write an equation and solve it.

$$\frac{0.20p}{0.20} = \frac{39}{0.20}$$

$$p = 195$$

The regular price is $195.

Exercises

Set A

1. 35% of 40 is ____.

2. 3% of 75 is ____.

3. 12.5% of 20 is ____.

4. 6.3% of 37 is ____.

5. Find 14% of 231.

6. Find $2\frac{1}{2}$% of 300.

7. Find 85% of 25.

8. Find 125% of 44.

9. 30% of 140 is what number?

10. 16% of 28 is what number?

11. What number is 4.75% of 15?

12. What number is $5\frac{1}{4}$% of 80?

Set B

13. ____% of 15 is 9.

14. ____% of 48 is 7.2.

15. ____% of 88 is 77.44.

16. ____% of 60 is 2.1.

17. What percent of 20 is 15?

18. What percent of 64 is 40?

19. What percent of 25 is 2?

20. What percent of 10 is 19?

21. 12 is what percent of 80?

22. 21 is what percent of 350?

23. 675 is what percent of 1000?

24. 28 is what percent of 32?

Set C

25. 95% of _____ is 38.

26. 11% of _____ is 22.

27. 86% of _____ is 77.4.

28. $6\frac{1}{4}$% of _____ is 7.5.

29. 8% of what number is 36?

30. 40% of what number is 22?

31. 52% of what number is 5.72?

32. 20.2% of what number is 13.13?

33. 21 is 70% of what number?

34. 110 is 125% of what number?

35. 36 is 25% of what number?

36. 2.5 is 40% of what number?

Mixed Practice

37. 25% of 68 is _____.

38. ____% of 55 is 33.

39. 5% of _____ is 8.

40. $12\frac{1}{2}$% of 24 is _____.

41. 4% of _____ is 14.

42. 37.5% of 40 is _____.

43. ____% of 24 is 18.

44. 14% of _____ is 10.5.

45. ____% of 500 is 235.

46. $62\frac{1}{2}$% of 64 is _____.

47. 180% of _____ is 26.1.

48. ____% of 7.95 is 1.59.

Related Problems

Find the markup for each item. Round to the next higher cent.

	Item	Store's cost	Markup rate
49.	Red begonias	$0.89	40%
50.	Wood stain	$7.86	27%
51.	Shampoo	$1.16	14%
52.	Slacks	$7.99	46%

53. A store's cost for batteries was $0.48 and the markup was $0.10. Find the markup rate to the nearest percent.

54. A sale is advertised as follows: "25% off our regular price. Save $8." What is the regular price?

55. Janice bought shoes on sale at 10% off the regular price of $29. How much did she save?

56. A store's cost for jeans was $7.50 and the markup was $3.75. What was the markup rate?

57. As an employee, Nita is given a 15% discount on all items in the store. She bought a table and saved $21. What was the regular price of the table?

58. Nita used her 15% discount when she bought a lamp. If the regular price of the lamp was $36, how much did she save?

59. There is a 75% markup rate for curtains. If the store's cost is $8.50, find the markup and the selling price.

60. A camera that regularly sells for $45 is on sale for 25% off. Find the sale price.

Break Time

There are 3 boxes of flowers. One box has 1 dozen roses, one has 1 dozen carnations, and one has 6 roses and 6 carnations. Each cover is labeled, but someone has switched all the covers.

Select a box. With your eyes closed, open the box, take out a flower, and close the lid. When you open your eyes and see the flower you took, how can you tell which flowers are in which box?

37

CALCULATOR APPLICATIONS

Retail stores are often given discounts when they order large quantities of goods. One wholesale firm offers a $20\frac{3}{4}$% discount to retail stores on orders up to $400. If the total amount of the order is more than $400, an additional discount is given. This discount is $5\frac{1}{4}$% of the cost after the first discount. Find the net cost of a $765 order.

Total amount of order: $765

Amount of 1st discount: $765 × 0.2075 = $158.7375 ≈ $158.74
Cost after 1st discount: $765 − $158.74 = $606.26

Amount of 2nd discount: $606.26 × 0.0525 = $31.82865 ≈ $31.83
Cost after 2nd discount: $606.26 − $31.83 = $574.43

The net cost is $574.43.

For each problem, use the discounts described above to find the net cost of the order. The total amount of the order is given.

1. $945	**4.** $328	**7.** $1847.24
2. $475.30	**5.** $627.90	**8.** $1329.67
3. $847.29	**6.** $1023	**9.** $3216.42

Another firm offers a single 25% discount on orders over $200. Buyers pay an additional $\frac{1}{2}$% of the net cost for insurance. For each problem, find the total amount of the order, the net cost, and the final cost including insurance.

10. $179.48	**11.** $429.37	**12.** $821.18
$565.55	$65.42	$651.33
$739.15	$517.16	$47.24

Chapter 2 Review

**Addition and subtraction
equations, pages 24–25**

Solve and check.

1. $d + 3.5 = 8$

2. $15.8 = m + 7.3$

3. $f - 0.74 = 7.25$

4. $5.8 = g - 2.15$

**Multiplication and division
equations, pages 26–27**

Solve and check.

5. $8x = 424$

6. $17.5 = 2.5t$

7. $\dfrac{b}{9} = 0.24$

8. $3a + 9a = 48$

**Two-step equations,
pages 28–29**

Solve and check.

9. $7c + 2 = 37$

10. $23 = 5y - 17$

11. $\dfrac{a}{4} - 9 = 8$

12. $\dfrac{x}{2} + 2 = 5$

**Ratio and proportion,
pages 30–31**

Find the cross-products. Tell
whether the ratios are equal.

13. $\dfrac{50}{65}$ $\quad \dfrac{4}{5}$

14. $\dfrac{9}{24}$ $\quad \dfrac{1.2}{3.2}$

Solve and check.

15. $\dfrac{c}{56} = \dfrac{3}{7}$

16. $\dfrac{0.25}{2} = \dfrac{11}{t}$

**Writing percents, decimals, and
fractions, pages 32–33**

Write as a percent.

17. 0.06

18. 0.465

19. $\dfrac{19}{25}$

20. $\dfrac{5}{16}$

Write as a decimal.

21. 57%

22. $5\tfrac{3}{4}\%$

Write as a fraction in lowest
terms.

23. 41%

24. 38%

**Using percent,
pages 34–37**

25. Find 6% of 527.

26. $37\tfrac{1}{2}\%$ of 64 is what
number?

27. 9 is what percent
of 60?

28. What percent of
56 is 49?

29. 24% of what number
is 10.8?

30. 18 is 12% of what
number?

Chapter 2 Test

Solve and check.

1. $a + 7 = 11$

2. $14.7 = x + 4$

3. $p - 6 = 5.2$

4. $9 = h - 12$

5. $6t = 162$

6. $4.2 = 3a$

7. $\frac{d}{7} = 0.14$

8. $4t + 5t = 36$

9. $6x + 4 = 22$

10. $31 = 9b - 14$

11. $\frac{r}{6} - 8 = 3$

12. $\frac{s}{3} + 2 = 6$

Find the cross-products. Tell whether the ratios are equal.

13. $\frac{3}{8}$ $\frac{12}{32}$

14. $\frac{5.6}{8.1}$ $\frac{8}{9}$

Solve and check.

15. $\frac{2}{3} = \frac{n}{39}$

16. $\frac{3.2}{d} = \frac{16}{7}$

Write as a percent.

17. 0.24

18. 0.327

19. $\frac{3}{20}$

20. $\frac{7}{8}$

Write as a decimal.

21. 49%

22. $21\frac{1}{2}\%$

Write as a fraction in lowest terms.

23. 39%

24. 24%

Compute.

25. Find 8% of 43.

26. $12\frac{1}{2}\%$ of 88 is what number?

27. 7 is what percent of 25?

28. What percent of 125 is 15?

29. 18% of what number is 4.5?

30. 36 is 30% of what number?

Chapter 3 Measurement and Statistics

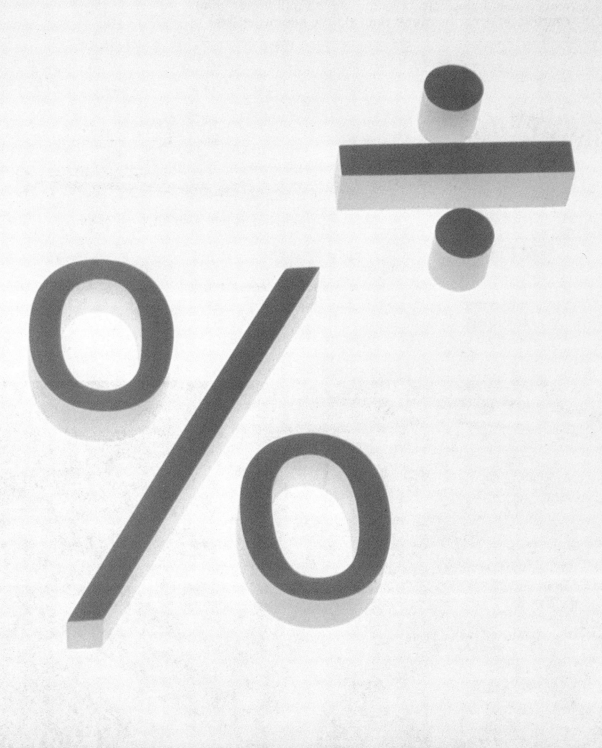

Metric Units of Length

Commonly used metric units of length are the **millimeter** (mm), the **centimeter** (cm), the **meter** (m), and the **kilometer** (km).

Objects are not shown actual size.

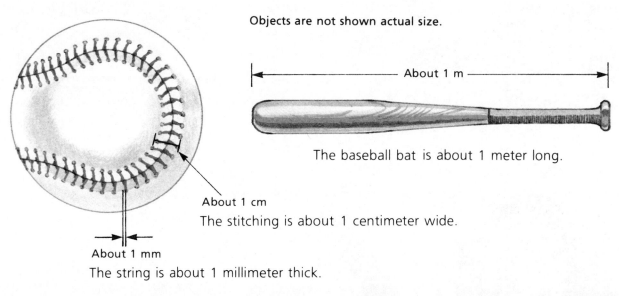

About 1 m

The baseball bat is about 1 meter long.

About 1 cm
The stitching is about 1 centimeter wide.

About 1 mm
The string is about 1 millimeter thick.

One kilometer is about 9 times around a baseball diamond.

There are 1000 millimeters in 1 meter.
There are 100 centimeters in 1 meter.
There are 1000 meters in 1 kilometer.

Problem A

Gina plans to make a suit. She estimated the length of the material needed.

Choose the most sensible measure for the length of the material needed.

4 mm   4 cm   4 m

Solution

Use the information on page 42 to make a sensible selection.

The length of the material needed is about 4 m.

Problem B

The Walkers are planning a trip from New York to Chicago. They estimated the distance one way.

Choose the most sensible measure for the distance from New York to Chicago.

1353 km   26 km   2 km

Solution

Use the information on page 42 to make a sensible selection.

The distance from New York to Chicago is about 1353 km.

Exercises

Set A   Choose the most sensible measure.

1. Average depth of the Atlantic Ocean
   3.87 cm   3.87 m   3.87 km

2. Height of a giant redwood tree
   110 cm   110 m   110 km

3. Length of a peanut
   14 mm   14 cm   14 m

4. Height of a toaster
   18 mm   18 cm   18 m

5. Distance from Denver to New Orleans
   2130 cm   2130 m   2130 km

Set B   Choose the most sensible measure.

6. Diameter of a long-playing record
   0.8 cm   12 cm   30 cm

7. Length of a hockey rink
   60 m   300 m   1000 m

8. Width of a lane on an expressway
   0.5 m   3.0 m   30.0 m

9. Distance from New York to Los Angeles
   6 km   250 km   4590 km

10. Thickness of this book
    25 mm   100 mm   500 mm

Related Problems

11. Estimate the length of your classroom in meters.

12. Estimate the width of your classroom in meters.

13. Estimate the height of the blackboard in centimeters.

14. Estimate the length of a paper clip.

15. Estimate the height of your teacher.

Area and Volume

Some metric units of area are the square millimeter (mm²), the square centimeter (cm²), the square meter (m²), and the square kilometer (km²).

Some metric units of volume are the cubic millimeter (mm³), the cubic centimeter (cm³), and the cubic meter (m³).

Problem A

What is the area of the front face of this concrete block?

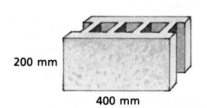

200 mm

400 mm

Solution

The **area** of a rectangle is the length times the width.

$A = l \times w$

$A = 400 \times 200$

$A = 80,000$

The area is 80,000 mm².

Problem B

What is the area of one triangular face of this roof?

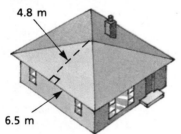

4.8 m

6.5 m

Solution

The area of a triangle is $\frac{1}{2}$ times the base times the height.

$A = \frac{1}{2} \times b \times h$

$A = \frac{1}{2} \times 6.5 \times 4.8$

$A = 15.6$

The area is 15.6 m².

Problem C

What is the volume of this brick? Round the answer to the nearest tenth of a cubic centimeter.

5.5 cm

9.0 cm

19.5 cm

Solution

The **volume** of a rectangular prism is the length times the width times the height.

$V = l \times w \times h$

$V = 19.5 \times 9.0 \times 5.5$

$V \approx 965.3$

The volume is about 965.3 cm³.

Exercises

Set A
Use the given dimensions to find the area of each rectangle to the nearest tenth.

	Length	Width
1.	28 mm	14 mm
2.	6.2 m	3.5 m
3.	4.1 km	2.3 km
4.	17.3 cm	25.9 cm
5.	11.6 m	27.8 m

Set B
Use the given dimensions to find the area of each triangle to the nearest tenth.

	Base	Height
6.	23 m	16 m
7.	35 mm	12 mm
8.	1.5 cm	1.0 cm
9.	11.2 m	6.5 m
10.	34.5 cm	11.5 cm

Set C
Use the given dimensions to find the volume of each rectangular prism to the nearest tenth.

	Length	Width	Height
11.	37 mm	13 mm	17 mm
12.	8.0 m	4.0 m	2.3 m
13.	9.0 cm	2.7 cm	4.3 cm
14.	8.1 m	6.2 m	3.7 m
15.	27.7 cm	21.5 cm	1.9 cm

Related Problems

16. Find the area of a rectangular driveway that measures 15.2 m by 5.5 m.

17. How many cubic meters of sand are needed to fill a sandbox 1.7 m long, 1.5 m wide, and 0.3 m deep? Round the answer to the nearest tenth.

18. Hoffmans' patio is shaped like a triangle. The base of the triangle is 6.1 m, and the height is 6.1 m. What is the area of the patio to the nearest tenth?

Break Time

Copy this picture. Try to place eight dots on the diagram so that two dots are on each circle and two dots are on each straight line.

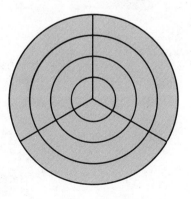

Metric Units of Capacity and Mass

Commonly used metric units of capacity are the **liter** (L) and the **milliliter** (mL).

Commonly used metric units of mass are the **kilogram** (kg), the **gram** (g), and the **milligram** (mg).

The mass of your math book is about 1 kilogram.

The amount of orange juice in this jar is 1 liter.

The amount of liquid in an eyedropper is about 1 milliliter.

The mass of a shoestring is about 1 gram.

The mass of one grain of sand is about 1 milligram.

There are 1000 milliliters in 1 liter.

There are 1000 milligrams in 1 gram.
There are 1000 grams in 1 kilogram.

Problem A

Tina's car is almost out of gas. She estimated the amount of gas the tank will hold.

Choose the more sensible measure for the capacity of a gas tank in a car.

60 mL   60 L

Solution

Use the information on page 46 to make a sensible selection.

The capacity of a gas tank is about 60 L.

Problem B

Chris plans to ship a lawn mower to a relative. He estimated the mass of the lawn mower.

Choose the most sensible measure for the mass of a lawn mower.

5 kg   35 kg   1000 kg

Solution

Use the information on page 46 to make a sensible selection.

The mass of a lawn mower is about 35 kg.

Exercises

Set A   Choose the more sensible measure of capacity.

1. Glass of milk
   250 mL   250 L

2. Bottle of antifreeze
   2 mL   2 L

3. Washing machine
   40 mL   40 L

4. Can of paint
   4 L   25 L

5. Tube of toothpaste
   15 mL   150 mL

Set B   Choose the most sensible measure for the mass of each object.

6. Brick
   2 kg   150 kg   900 kg

7. Car key
   0.8 g   85 g   8500 g

8. Paper clip
   0.5 mg   5 mg   500 mg

9. Hockey puck
   165 mg   165 g   165 kg

10. TV set
    50 mg   50 g   50 kg

Related Problems

Give the most sensible unit of measure for each of these items.

11. Capacity of an aquarium

12. Mass of a tennis ball

13. Capacity of a spoon

14. Mass of a portable typewriter

15. Mass of a letter

Renaming Metric Units of Measure

To rename a larger metric unit of measure as a smaller unit, *multiply* by a number such as 10, 100, or 1000.

To rename a smaller metric unit of measure as a larger unit, *divide* by a number such as 10, 100, or 1000.

The chart below lists the metric prefixes and their values.
It can help you to find equal metric measures.

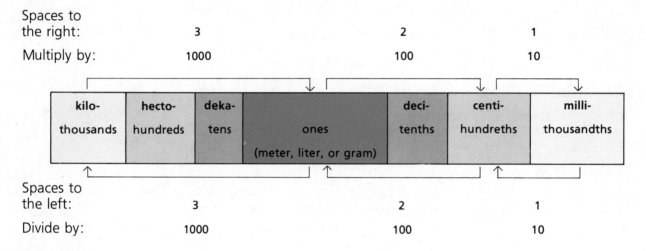

Spaces to the right:	3		2	1
Multiply by:	1000		100	10

kilo-	hecto-	deka-	ones	deci-	centi-	milli-
thousands	hundreds	tens	(meter, liter, or gram)	tenths	hundreths	thousandths

Spaces to the left:	3		2	1
Divide by:	1000		100	10

Problem A

Dick completed a 20-kilometer running race. How many meters did he run?

20 km = ⬚ m

Solution

Changing from kilometers to meters is like moving 3 places to the right on the chart. So multiply by 1000.

1000 × 20 = 20,000

20 km = 20,000 m

Dick ran 20,000 meters.

Problem B

Lynn needs 150 centimeters of ribbon, but the ribbon is sold only by the meter. How many meters of ribbon should she buy?

150 cm = ⬚ m

Solution

Changing from centimeters to meters is like moving 2 places to the left on the chart. So divide by 100.

150 ÷ 100 = 1.5

150 cm = 1.5 m

Lynn should buy 1.5 meters of ribbon.

Exercises

Set A

1. 5 m = ▒ cm

2. 0.8 km = ▒ m

3. 9.3 cm = ▒ mm

4. 2.1 m = ▒ mm

5. 12.75 m = ▒ cm

6. 3 L = ▒ mL

7. 0.5 L = ▒ mL

8. 45 kg = ▒ g

9. 2.1 g = ▒ mg

10. 0.84 kg = ▒ g

Set B

11. 935 m = ▒ km

12. 160.4 cm = ▒ m

13. 429 mm = ▒ m

14. 1250 m = ▒ km

15. 67 mm = ▒ cm

16. 1578 mL = ▒ L

17. 84 mL = ▒ L

18. 716 g = ▒ kg

19. 1375 mg = ▒ g

20. 42.6 g = ▒ kg

Mixed Practice

21. 23 km = ▒ m

22. 971 m = ▒ km

23. 18 cm = ▒ mm

24. 3.5 m = ▒ mm

25. 6 cm = ▒ m

26. 14 L = ▒ mL

27. 250 mL = ▒ L

28. 837 g = ▒ kg

29. 1296 mg = ▒ g

30. 8.3 kg = ▒ g

Related Problems

Use this recipe to answer problems 31–34.

Lasagna   Serves 8
1 kg ground beef
1 L spaghetti sauce
350 g ricotta cheese
450 g mozzarella cheese
100 mL grated Parmesan cheese
500 g lasagna noodles

31. How many grams of ground beef are needed?

32. How many liters of Parmesan cheese are needed?

33. Perry plans to make lasagna for 4 people. How many milliliters of spaghetti sauce does he need?

34. Anne plans to make a double recipe. How many kilograms of noodles does she need?

Temperature

Temperature can be measured with several different scales. The Celsius scale is commonly used in countries that use the metric system.

Problem

Ben plans to make an ice-skating rink in his backyard. To decide whether the conditions are suitable, he first estimates the outdoor temperature.

Choose the more sensible temperature in degrees Celsius (°C) for a winter day in Gary, Indiana.

$^-5$°C   25°C

Solution

Consult the Celsius thermometer shown at the right.

The more sensible temperature is $^-5$°C.

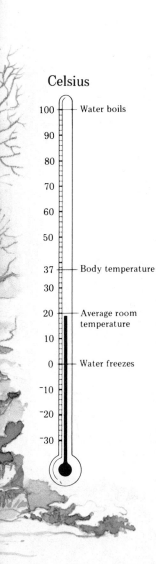

Celsius

100	Water boils
90	
80	
70	
60	
50	
37	Body temperature
30	
20	Average room temperature
10	
0	Water freezes
-10	
-20	
-30	

Exercises

Choose the more sensible temperature.

1. Frozen orange juice
   0°C   20°C

2. Hot summer day
   32°C   15°C

3. Snowball
   18°C   3°C

4. Sauna
   22°C   60°C

5. Warm dinner rolls
   50°C   125°C

6. Ocean water
   118°C   18°C

7. Sick person
   39.8°C   100.4°C

8. Setting on a home thermostat
   50°C   20°C

9. Cold milk
   10°C   50°C

10. Melted cheese
   ⁻5°C   40°C

Related Problems

Use the wind-chill index for problems 11–15.

Wind-Chill Index

Wind speed (km/h)	Thermometer reading (°C)								
	0	⁻5	⁻10	⁻15	⁻20	⁻25	⁻30	⁻35	⁻40
	Wind chill (°C) (equivalent temperature)								
Calm	0	⁻5	⁻10	⁻15	⁻20	⁻25	⁻30	⁻35	⁻40
10	⁻4	⁻10	⁻15	⁻21	⁻27	⁻32	⁻38	⁻43	⁻49
15	⁻8	⁻14	⁻20	⁻26	⁻32	⁻38	⁻45	⁻51	⁻57
20	⁻10	⁻17	⁻23	⁻30	⁻37	⁻43	⁻50	⁻56	⁻63
25	⁻12	⁻19	⁻26	⁻33	⁻40	⁻47	⁻54	⁻61	⁻68
30	⁻14	⁻21	⁻28	⁻36	⁻43	⁻50	⁻57	⁻64	⁻71
35	⁻16	⁻23	⁻30	⁻38	⁻45	⁻52	⁻60	⁻67	⁻74
40	⁻17	⁻24	⁻32	⁻39	⁻47	⁻54	⁻62	⁻69	⁻77
45	⁻18	⁻25	⁻33	⁻41	⁻48	⁻56	⁻64	⁻71	⁻79
50	⁻19	⁻26	⁻34	⁻42	⁻50	⁻57	⁻65	⁻73	⁻81
55	⁻19	⁻27	⁻35	⁻43	⁻51	⁻59	⁻67	⁻74	⁻82
60	⁻20	⁻28	⁻36	⁻44	⁻52	⁻60	⁻68	⁻76	⁻83

Little danger   Increasing danger   Great danger

11. The thermometer reading is ⁻10°C and the wind speed is 30 km/h. Find the wind chill.

12. The thermometer reading is ⁻5°C and the wind speed is 45 km/h. Find the wind chill.

13. If the wind chill is ⁻34°C and the wind speed is 50 km/h, what is the thermometer reading?

14. If the thermometer reading is ⁻30°C and the wind chill is ⁻50°C, what is the wind speed?

15. At one time the wind chill was ⁻20°C. An hour later the wind chill was ⁻16°C. If the thermometer reading was 0°C at both times, what was the difference in wind speeds?

Time

The abbreviation "A.M." represents the time from midnight to noon; "P.M." represents the time from noon to midnight.

Problem A

A trip to Crystal Lake took 4 hours 45 minutes by train plus 2 hours 30 minutes by bus. How long did the trip take?

Add 4 hours 45 minutes and 2 hours 30 minutes.

Solution

First add the minutes. Then add the hours.

$$\begin{array}{r} 4 \text{ hours } 45 \text{ minutes} \\ + \ 2 \text{ hours } 30 \text{ minutes} \\ \hline 6 \text{ hours } 75 \text{ minutes} \end{array}$$

There are 60 minutes in 1 hour. Since 75 minutes = 1 hour 15 minutes, 6 hours 75 minutes is the same as 7 hours 15 minutes.

The trip took 7 hours 15 minutes.

Problem B

The departure time on a flight from New York to Miami was 11:20 A.M. If the flight took 2 hours 25 minutes, what was the arrival time in Miami?

Add 2 hours 25 minutes to 11:20 A.M.

Solution

First add the hours to the departure time. Remember that the first hour after 12:00 noon is 1:00 P.M.

11:20 A.M. + 2 hours ⟶ 1:20 P.M.

Then add the minutes.

1:20 + 25 minutes ⟶ 1:45 P.M.

The arrival time was 1:45 P.M.

Problem C

Mr. Bedoni left St. Louis at 10:30 A.M. and drove to Chicago. He arrived in Chicago at 5:15 P.M. How long did Mr. Bedoni drive?

Find how much time there is from 10:30 A.M. to 5:15 P.M.

Solution

First find the number of hours. Remember that the first hour after 12:00 noon is 1:00 P.M.

10:30 A.M. to 4:30 P.M. ⟶ 6 hours

Then find the number of minutes remaining.

4:30 P.M. to 5:15 P.M. ⟶ 45 minutes

Mr. Bedoni drove 6 hours 45 minutes.

Exercises
Set A   Add.

1. 3 hours 15 minutes + 5 hours 20 minutes

2. 2 hours 35 minutes + 7 hours 50 minutes

3. 4 hours 25 minutes + 3 hours 55 minutes

4. 5 hours 45 minutes + 5 hours 15 minutes

Set B

5. Add 3 hours 20 minutes to 8:15 A.M.

6. Add 6 hours 5 minutes to 9:25 A.M.

7. Add 8 hours 15 minutes to 10:10 P.M.

8. Add 12 hours 35 minutes to 12:05 P.M.

Set C

9. How much time is there from 4:30 P.M. to 7:40 P.M.?

10. How much time is there from 7:15 A.M. to 3:35 P.M.?

11. How much time is there from 11:45 A.M. to 6:20 P.M.?

12. How much time is there from 1:30 A.M. to 12:45 P.M.?

Related Problems

13. Pete and Liz drove to Yosemite National Park. Pete drove 3 hours 20 minutes. Liz drove 4 hours 45 minutes. What was the total driving time?

14. A car was parked in a parking lot from 8:50 A.M. until 9:20 P.M. the same day. How long was the car parked?

15. Joe went sailing with some friends. They left at 10:30 A.M. and returned 5 hours 45 minutes later. What time did they return?

Bar Graphs and Line Graphs

Problem A

Paul Marcello is planning a national advertising campaign. He needs to make a **bar graph** that shows the estimated advertising expenditures for 1979.

Make a bar graph for this set of data.

1979 estimated advertising expenditures

Newspapers	$14 billion
Magazines	$3 billion
Television	$10 billion
Radio	$4 billion
Direct mail	$7 billion
Other	$10 billion

Solution

List the six types of advertising on the vertical scale.

Units on the horizontal scale can be billions of dollars. Since the largest number is 14, the scale can stop at 15.

Draw bars to show the billions of dollars spent for each type of advertising.

Write a title for the graph.

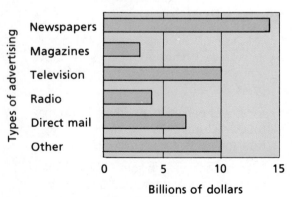

Problem B

Kathy Odina is doing research on school enrollment trends. She needs to make a **line graph** that shows the number of students enrolled in high schools for the years 1973 to 1979.

Make a line graph for this set of data.

High school enrollment, 1973–1979

1973	15.3 million
1974	15.4 million
1975	15.7 million
1976	15.7 million
1977	15.8 million
1978	15.5 million
1979	15.1 million

Solution

Draw and label the vertical and horizontal scales. The broken vertical scale means that numbers are missing.

Find the line for 1973. Mark a point on that line for 15.3.

Locate the points for the other years. Connect the points with a line.

Write a title for the graph.

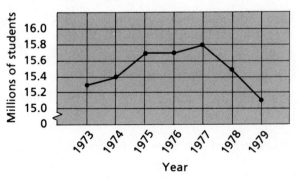

Exercises

Set A Make a bar graph for each set of data.

1. Average personal income in 1979 by region

Northeast	$8900
North Central	$8800
Southeast	$8200
South Central	$7600
West	$9000

2. U.S. birth rates per 1000 people

1970	18.4	1975	14.8
1971	17.2	1976	14.8
1972	15.6	1977	15.4
1973	14.9	1978	15.3
1974	14.9	1979	15.8

Set B Make a line graph for each set of data.

3. Number of work stoppages (strikes) in the U.S.

1970	5716	1975	5031
1971	5138	1976	5648
1972	5010	1977	5506
1973	5353	1978	4230
1974	6074		

4. Existing single-family houses sold

1973	2,334,000
1974	2,272,000
1975	2,452,000
1976	3,002,000
1977	3,547,000
1978	3,863,000
1979	3,701,000

Related Problems

Use the bar graph below for problems 5–7.

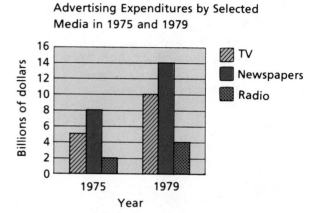

Advertising Expenditures by Selected Media in 1975 and 1979

5. How much more was spent on television advertising in 1979 than in 1975?

6. How many times as much was spent on newspaper advertising as on radio advertising in 1975? in 1979?

7. What was the total amount spent on advertising for these selected media in 1975? in 1979?

8. Erica Schmidt works for an international airline. She wants to make a graph that shows the number of travelers to and from the U.S. for each year from 1974 to 1979. Make two line graphs on the same grid for this set of data. Use one line graph to show the travelers to the U.S. and the other to show the travelers from the U.S. Label each line graph.

	To the U.S.	From the U.S.
1974	3.7 million	6.4 million
1975	3.6 million	6.3 million
1976	4.4 million	6.8 million
1977	4.5 million	7.3 million
1978	5.7 million	7.7 million
1979	7.2 million	7.8 million

Circle Graphs

Problem A

Ann Winters read a report in a news magazine that included the **circle graph** below. It shows the countries with the greatest energy usage. The total amount of energy used worldwide was estimated at 8,020,000,000 metric tons. About how many metric tons of energy were used by the United States?

Countries with Greatest Energy Usage

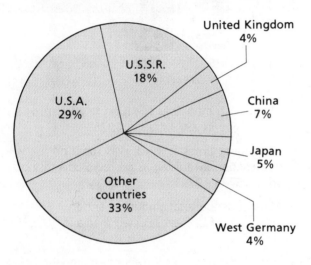

Solution

Read the circle graph to find what percent of the energy was used by the United States.

29%

Then find 29% of 8,020,000,000.

$0.29 \times 8,020,000,000 = 2,325,800,000$

The United States used about 2,325,800,000 metric tons of energy.

Problem B

Jorge Alvaro is preparing a report on the cost of living. He wants to make a circle graph that shows how a typical family's income is spent.

Make a circle graph for this set of data.

Living expenses

Category	Percent of income
Food	25%
Housing	30%
Utilities	10%
Travel	12%
Clothing	8%
Miscellaneous	15%

Solution

Multiply 360° by each percent to find the size of each **central angle.** Round each answer to the nearest degree.

Food	$0.25 \times 360° = 90°$
Housing	$0.30 \times 360° = 108°$
Utilities	$0.10 \times 360° = 36°$
Travel	$0.12 \times 360° \approx 43°$
Clothing	$0.08 \times 360° \approx 29°$
Miscellaneous	$0.15 \times 360° = 54°$

Draw a circle. Then use a protractor to draw each central angle. Label each section. Write a title for the graph.

Living Expenses

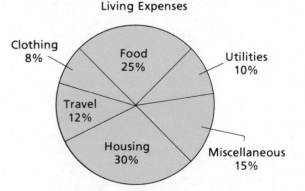

Exercises

Set A
Use the circle graph in problem A for exercises 1–6. About how many metric tons were used by each of the following?

1. U.S.S.R.
2. United Kingdom
3. China
4. Japan
5. West Germany
6. Other countries

Use the circle graph in problem B for exercises 7–12. If the Wilsons' income was $17,500, about how much was spent in each category?

7. Housing
8. Travel
9. Clothing
10. Food
11. Utilities
12. Miscellaneous

Set B
Make a circle graph for each set of data.

13. Land owned by the federal government in 1979

Type (use)	Percent of total
Forest and wildlife	60%
Grazing	21%
Parks	9%
Military	3%
Other	7%

14. Major issues causing work stoppages in 1978

Issue	Percent of work stoppages
Wages and benefits	67%
Working conditions and hours	2%
Job security	3%
Union organization	6%
Plant administration	12%
Other	10%

15. Estimated voting population by age in 1980

Age	Percent of population
18–24 years	18.1%
25–44 years	38.9%
45–64 years	27.3%
65 years and over	15.7%

Related Problems

Lisa Sadler made the circle graph below to show the distribution of workers by occupation throughout the country. The total number of employed persons in 1979 was about 97,000,000.

Distribution of Workers by Occupation in 1979

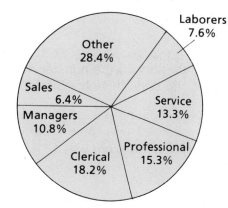

16. About how many more clerical workers were there than professional workers?

17. About how many more managers were there than laborers?

18. About what was the total number of workers in sales occupations or in service occupations?

19. About what percent of the total number of employed persons were clerical workers or laborers?

Mean, Median, and Mode

The sum of a set of numbers divided by the number of addends is the average, or the **mean.** When a set of numbers is arranged in order, the middle number is the **median.** In a set of numbers, the number that appears most often is the **mode.**

Problem A

Ricky Doran bowled 132, 146, 121, 118, and 138. What was his mean score?

Find the mean for these numbers.

Solution

Add the bowling scores.

```
   132
   146
   121
   118
 + 138
   655
```

Then divide the sum by the number of addends. In this case, there are 5 addends.

```
    131
5) 655
```

Ricky's mean bowling score was 131.

Problem B

A girls' basketball team played seven games this season. Their scores were 56, 59, 61, 56, 64, 43, and 81. A boys' basketball team played eight games this season. Their scores were 95, 41, 78, 81, 69, 102, 59, and 75. What was the median score for each team?

Find the median for each set of numbers.

Solution

Arrange the girls' scores in order.

43, 56, 56, **59,** 61, 64, 81

The middle number is 59.

Arrange the boys' scores in order.

41, 59, 69, **75, 78,** 81, 95, 102

In this set of numbers there are two middle numbers, 75 and 78. The median is the average of 75 and 78.

$75 + 78 = 153$ $153 \div 2 = 76.5$

The median score for the girls' team was 59. The median score for the boys' team was 76.5.

Problem C

During the golf season, Norma shot 85, 86, 97, 102, 86, 93, 91, 97, and 86. What was the mode of her golf scores?

Find the mode for these numbers.

Solution

Arrange the numbers in order.

85, **86, 86, 86,** 91, 93, 97, 97, 102

86 appears most often.

The mode of her golf scores was 86.

Some sets of numbers, such as 16, 19, 20, 21, 25, and 27, have no mode. Some sets of numbers, such as 6, 6, 8, 9, 11, 11, and 14, have more than one mode.

Exercises

Set A Find the mean for each set of numbers.

1. 8, 9, 7, 2, 3, 7, 6

2. 9, 7, 13, 5, 3, 11

3. 47, 21, 89, 12, 21

4. 73, 87, 78, 69, 73, 58

5. 29, 23, 21, 25, 24, 31, 29

6. 309, 305, 309, 301, 301

7. 116, 132, 116, 104, 132, 126

8. 21, 18, 14, 15, 15, 18, 20, 15

9. 10.3, 10.1, 10.2, 10.6, 10.3

10. 2.2, 2.3, 2.5, 2.4, 2.6, 2.4

Set B Exercises 11–20. Find the median for each set of numbers in Set A.

Set C Exercises 21–30. Find the mode for each set of numbers in Set A.

Related Problems

In bowling, a handicap is the number of points given to the player with the lower mean score to equalize the chances of winning. The amount of the handicap is the difference in the mean scores of the players.

For each problem, find the mean score for each player. Then tell which player should get the handicap. Indicate the amount of the handicap.

31. Bob's scores: 119, 131, 127, 147
    Matt's scores: 172, 136, 165, 151

32. Jill's scores: 127, 131, 146, 136
    Sue's scores: 96, 107, 85, 120

33. Bev's scores: 113, 117, 121, 117, 127
    John's scores: 114, 105, 136, 99, 121

CALCULATOR APPLICATIONS

Finding the Mean

Find the mean for each set of numbers. Round each answer to the nearest tenth.

1. 282, 919, 464, 737

2. 1537, 2491, 1764, 3248, 2073

3. 1234, 5678, 6789

4. 1122, 3344, 5566, 7788, 9900

5. 27,634   47,092
   90,185   53,264
   36,243

6. 364,257   423,765
   170,843   857,091
   963,251

7. 84,076.3   65,308.7
   58,732.1   42,435.4
   93,457.8

8. 525.371   976.32
   624.57   425.09
   139.84   840.16

9. 532.96   4.308
   647.91   17.852
   3.54

10. 17.562   3.354
    23.98   22.731
    104.16   0.634

Find the mean for each set of data. Round each answer to the nearest whole number.

11. Number of students attending school during a one-week period

Monday	1842
Tuesday	1730
Wednesday	1753
Thursday	1813
Friday	1647

12. Salaries in one department

Baker	$6,790
Carson	$13,500
Mason	$8,470
Omachi	$20,620
Pena	$18,575
Roberts	$7,250
Thomas	$10,825

13. Attendance at football games

Sept. 22	62,153
Sept. 29	48,139
Oct. 6	57,204
Oct. 13	64,379
Oct. 20	35,702
Oct. 27	71,428

14. U.S. motor vehicle factory sales

1976	11,480,000
1977	12,642,000
1978	12,871,000
1979	11,456,000

Chapter 3 Review

Metric units of length, pages 42–43

Choose the most sensible measure.

1. Length of a paper clip
3 mm   3 cm   3 m

2. Width of a desk
1 m   4 m   10 m

Area and volume, pages 44–45

3. Find the area of a rectangle 7.0 m by 4.8 m.

4. Find the area of a triangle with a base of 9.4 cm and a height of 11.0 cm.

5. Find the volume of a rectangular prism 14.3 cm by 7.2 cm by 5.6 cm to the nearest tenth.

Metric units of capacity and mass, pages 46–47

Choose the more sensible measure.

6. Gas tank of a motorcycle
13 mL   13 L

7. Can of peaches
25 g   600 g

Renaming metric units of measure, pages 48–49

8. 7.63 kg = ▓ g   **9.** 34 cm = ▓ m

Temperature, pages 50–51

10. Choose the more sensible temperature for melted wax.
20°C   80°C

Time, pages 52–53

11. Add. 6 hours 20 minutes + 3 hours 45 minutes.

12. Add 4 hours 10 minutes to 3:55 P.M.

13. How much time is there from 10:35 A.M. to 2:20 P.M.?

Bar graphs and line graphs, pages 54–55

14. Make a bar graph for this set of data.

New housing units started, 1976–1979

| 1976 | 1550 million | 1978 | 2020 million |
| 1977 | 1990 million | 1979 | 1750 million |

15. Make a line graph for the data in problem 14.

Circle graphs, pages 56–57

Use the circle graph for problem 16.

Households Using Fuel Oil in 1979

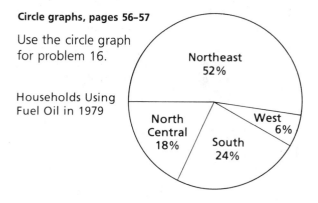

Northeast 52%
North Central 18%
South 24%
West 6%

16. In 1979, the total number of households using fuel oil to heat their homes was about 17,000,000. How many of these were in the Northeast?

17. Make a circle graph for this set of data.

Distribution of families by number of children under 18 years (1979)

Number of children	Percent of total
0	48%
1	21%
2	19%
3 or more	12%

Mean, median, and mode, pages 58–59

For problems 18–20, use this set of numbers.

21, 15, 23, 10, 14, 28, 21, 12

Find the

18. mean.   **19.** median.   **20.** mode.

Chapter 3 Test

Choose the most sensible measure.

1. Length of a canoe
4 mm   4 cm   4 m

2. Length of a wrench
1 cm   26 cm   315 cm

3. Find the area of a rectangle 3.0 m by 7.2 m.

4. Find the area of a triangle with a base of 8.6 cm and a height of 13.0 cm.

5. Find the volume of a rectangular prism 11.4 cm by 5.7 cm by 7.1 cm to the nearest tenth.

Choose the more sensible measure.

6. Carton of grapefruit juice
900 mL   900 L

7. Whole chicken
1.2 kg   24.5 kg

8. 3.7 m = ▦ cm   **9.** 482 g = ▦ kg

10. Choose the more sensible temperature for a warm shower.
30°C   80°C

11. Add. 8 hours 15 minutes + 4 hours 55 minutes.

12. Add 3 hours 45 minutes to 9:45 A.M.

13. How much time is there from 1:10 P.M. to 5:45 P.M.?

14. Make a bar graph for this set of data.

Value of farm real estate, 1977–1980
1977 $470 billion   1979 $580 billion
1978 $510 billion   1980 $670 billion

15. Make a line graph for the data in problem 14.

Use the circle graph below for problem 16.

Households Using Electricity in 1979

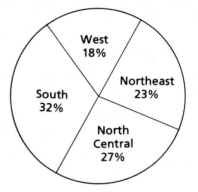

16. In 1979, the total number of households using electricity to heat their homes was about 80,000,000. How many of these were in the South?

17. Make a circle graph for this set of data.

Persons employed in health occupations in 1979

Type	Percent of total
Physicians, dentists, and pharmacists	15%
Registered nurses	25%
Technicians	10%
Other	50%

For problems 18–20, use this set of numbers.

15, 22, 23, 16, 22, 12, 16

Find the

18. mean.   **19.** median.   **20.** mode.

Unit 1 Test

Choose the best answer.

1. Round 4753 to the nearest hundred.

   A 5000 **C** 4700

   B 4800 **D** 4750

2. $96.27 - 64.83$

   A 161.10 **C** 31.44

   B 32.64 **D** 32.34

3. 783×94

   A 73,602 **C** 66,502

   B 68,592 **D** 72,602

4. 8.32×4.7

   A 3.8104 **C** 39.104

   B 381.04 **D** 38.104

5. $28.236 \div 3.9$

   A 0.724 **C** 7.31

   B 0.731 **D** 7.24

6. Rename $\frac{12}{20}$ in lowest terms.

   A $\frac{6}{10}$ **C** $\frac{4}{5}$

   B $\frac{3}{4}$ **D** $\frac{3}{5}$

7. $5\frac{3}{5} \div 2\frac{1}{3}$

   A $10\frac{3}{15}$ **C** $13\frac{1}{15}$

   B $2\frac{2}{5}$ **D** $\frac{5}{12}$

8. $3\frac{3}{4} + 1\frac{1}{6}$

   A $4\frac{11}{12}$ **C** $4\frac{4}{10}$

   B $3\frac{4}{10}$ **D** $3\frac{1}{8}$

9. Solve. $d - 25.1 = 34.7$

   A $d = 59.8$ **C** $d = 11.6$

   B $d = 9.6$ **D** $d = 10.4$

10. Solve. $384 = 16y$

    A $y = 6144$ **C** $y = 24$

    B $y = 368$ **D** $y = 400$

11. Solve. $8b + 42 = 138$

    A $b = 12$ **C** $b = 14.5$

    B $b = 22.5$ **D** $b = 16$

12. Solve. $\frac{6}{c} = \frac{21}{28}$

    A $c = 4.5$ **C** $c = 9$

    B $c = 8$ **D** $c = 98$

13. Write 8% as a decimal.

    A 0.8 **C** 8

    B 0.008 **D** 0.08

14. Find 15% of 90.

    A 1350 **C** 600

    B 13.5 **D** 135

15. Choose the most sensible measure for the length of an adult's hand.

A 19 mm   **C** 19 m

B 19 cm   **D** 19 km

16. Find the area of a rectangle that measures 6.0 meters by 9.7 meters.

A 582 m²   **C** 474 m²

B 47.4 m²   **D** 58.2 m²

17. Choose the most sensible measure for a container of liquid bleach.

A 0.003 L   **C** 4 L

B 125 L   **D** 68 L

18. 3476 g = ▦ kg

A 0.3476   **C** 3.476

B 347.6   **D** 34.76

19. Choose the most sensible water temperature for outdoor swimming.

A 23°C   **C** 79°C

B 4°C   **D** 101°C

20. Add 3 hours 25 minutes to 4:15 P.M.

A 7:30 P.M.   **C** 7:40 P.M.

B 1:10 P.M.   **D** 8:40 P.M.

21. How many more TV sets per 1000 population are there in Australia than in France?

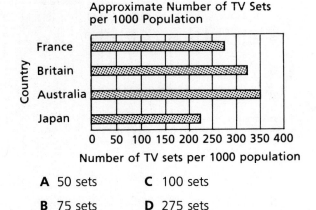

Approximate Number of TV Sets per 1000 Population

Number of TV sets per 1000 population

A 50 sets   **C** 100 sets

B 75 sets   **D** 275 sets

22. Read the circle graph below and find the cost of labor on a home that costs $78,000 to build.

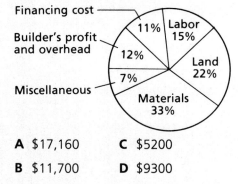

Major Cost Items in Building a House

A $17,160   **C** $5200

B $11,700   **D** $9300

23. Find the mean for this set of numbers.

13, 18, 4, 15, 9, 18, 21

A 15   **C** 18

B 98   **D** 14

Break Time

Here is a method of adding a long column of one-digit numbers in which you use your fingers to show the tens. First look at the usual way of adding these numbers.

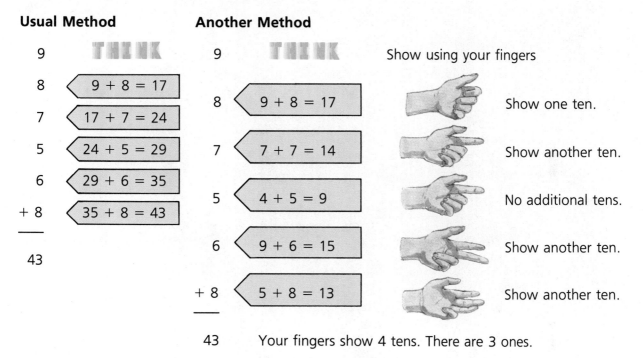

Usual Method

9

8   9 + 8 = 17

7   17 + 7 = 24

5   24 + 5 = 29

6   29 + 6 = 35

+ 8   35 + 8 = 43
___

43

Another Method

9

8   9 + 8 = 17

7   7 + 7 = 14

5   4 + 5 = 9

6   9 + 6 = 15

+ 8   5 + 8 = 13
___

43

Show using your fingers

Show one ten.

Show another ten.

No additional tens.

Show another ten.

Show another ten.

Your fingers show 4 tens. There are 3 ones.

Add, using your fingers to show the tens. Write only the answer.

1. 5 + 8 + 8 + 7 + 3 + 9 + 4

2. 7 + 4 + 9 + 5 + 3 + 9 + 4 + 6

3. 6 + 8 + 9 + 4 + 6 + 2 + 9 + 7 + 4

4. 5 + 7 + 9 + 3 + 6 + 9 + 7 + 8 + 2

5. 3 + 9 + 9 + 5 + 8 + 6 + 8 + 7 + 5 + 1 + 7

6. 9 + 7 + 8 + 2 + 7 + 5 + 1 + 4 + 9 + 8 + 7 + 5

7. 3 + 3 + 8 + 2 + 9 + 7 + 5 + 6 + 9 + 1 + 7 + 9

8. 5 + 5 + 5 + 6 + 6 + 6 + 7 + 7 + 7 + 8 + 8 + 8

9. 3 + 7 + 9 + 1 + 7 + 8 + 4 + 9 + 7 + 8 + 2 + 9 + 4 + 4 + 8

10. 6 + 9 + 1 + 3 + 6 + 8 + 2 + 5 + 8 + 7 + 4 + 8 + 3 + 9 + 2

Unit 2 Income, Banking, and Credit

Chapter 4   Income

Hourly Rate and Overtime Rate

Ruben Betances is a mailer for a stereo manufacturer. He usually works 8 hours a day, 5 days a week.

When he works more than 8 hours in one day, Ruben is paid at an **overtime rate** for the extra hours. The overtime rate is 1.5 times the regular hourly rate. This is called **time and a half.**

Ruben's **gross pay** is the sum of his regular pay and his overtime pay.

Problem

One week Ruben worked his regular 40 hours and 4.75 hours of overtime. If his regular hourly rate is $5.50 per hour, what was his gross pay for the week?

Solution

Strategy
• Multiply hourly rate by 40 to find regular pay.

$40 \times \$5.50 = \$220.00$

• Multiply hourly rate by 1.5 to find overtime rate.

$1.5 \times \$5.50 = \$8.25$

• Multiply by 4.75 to find overtime pay. Round to the nearest cent.

$4.75 \times \$8.25 \approx \$39.19$

• Add to find gross pay.

$\$220.00 + \$39.19 = \$259.19$

Conclusion
Ruben's gross pay was $259.19.

Related Problems

Complete the table to find the gross pay for each employee. Round each amount to the nearest cent.

	Job	Regular hours	Regular hourly rate	Regular pay	Overtime hours	Overtime rate (time and a half)	Overtime pay	Gross pay
	Mailer	40	$5.50	$220.00	4.75	$8.25	$39.19	$259.19
1.	Steamfitter	40	$10.10		0	————	————	
2.	Sheet-metal worker	38	$10.39		0	————	————	
3.	Power truck operator	40	$6.50		5			
4.	Operating engineer	40	$9.50		6			
5.	Floor molder	40	$6.20		8			
6.	Millwright	40	$8.72		12			
7.	Machinist	40	$8.02		2.25			
8.	Ironworker	40	$10.85		15			
9.	Tool and die maker	40	$8.53		3.5			
10.	Electroplater	40	$6.75		6.75			
11.	Instrument maker	40	$8.03		5.25			

12. Ann Altaha is a stationary engineer. Her regular hourly rate is $7.93 for a 40–hour week. She is paid double time (two times the hourly rate) for each hour she works on holidays. She is paid time and a half for all other overtime. One week Ann worked 53.5 hours, including 8 hours on a holiday. Find her gross pay for that week. Round each amount to the nearest cent.

Hourly Rate Plus Tips

Earl Johnson is a waiter in a large restaurant in Chicago. His weekly pay is determined by both his hourly rate and the tips he earns. Earl gives part of his tips to other employees who help him serve his customers.

Problem

Earl is paid $4.15 an hour for a 40–hour week. One week he worked 40 hours and earned $215 in tips. Earl kept 75% of his tips and gave the other 25% of his tips to the other employees. What was Earl's gross pay for the week?

Solution

Strategy

• Multiply to find regular pay.

$40 \times \$4.15 = \$166.00$

• Multiply his tips by 75% to find his share of the tips.

$0.75 \times \$215 = \$161.25$

• Add to find gross pay.

$\$166.00 + \$161.25 = \$327.25$

Conclusion

Earl's gross pay was $327.25.

Related Problems

Find each person's gross pay for the week.

	Name	Hourly rate	Hours worked	Tips		Gross pay
				Amount	Percent kept	
1.	Linda Taylor	$4.00	40	$250	100%	
2.	Phillip Witt	$4.35	25	$115	100%	
3.	David Glenn	$4.18	40	$164	80%	
4.	Vicki Farnsworth	$4.75	35	$183	75%	
5.	Dick Grove	$6.20	40	$212	85%	
6.	Irene Luciano	$4.90	36.4	$148	85%	
7.	Clyde Beagle	$7.10	34.7	$143	90%	

8. Roger Marks is a porter. He earns $4.75 an hour plus tips. He worked 35 hours and earned $175 in tips. What was his gross pay?

9. Sue Bowersox is a barber. She charges $7.50 for each haircut. She gave 65 haircuts and earned $62.50 in tips. What was her gross pay?

10. Ray Inada is a musician earning $6.75 an hour for a 40-hour week. He makes time and a half for overtime. One week Ray worked 45 hours and made $185 in tips. Find his gross pay. Round each amount to the nearest cent.

Break Time

A farmer planted 10 trees in 5 rows of 4 each. Two ways are shown. Draw three other ways.

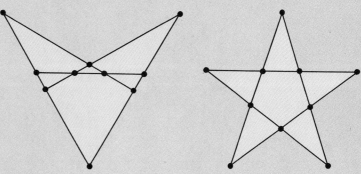

Straight Commission

Wendy McClure works part time selling products for Home Cosmetics, Inc. She is paid a **commission,** or a certain portion of the money from the sales, as her pay.

Since this commission is the only pay that Wendy earns, it is called **straight commission.**

Problem

One customer ordered two bottles of cologne that cost $5.49 each. Wendy's commission on the cologne was 43%. How much did Wendy earn on this sale?

Solution

Strategy
• Multiply to find the total amount of the sale.

$2 \times \$5.49 = \$10.98$

• Multiply by 43% to find the earnings. Round to the nearest cent.

$0.43 \times \$10.98 \approx \$4.72$

Conclusion
Wendy earned $4.72 on this sale.

Related Problems

Find the amount of commission for each item. Round each answer to the nearest cent.

	Item	Price	Commission
1.	Night cream	$3.50	45%
2.	Cleansing cream	$2.69	45%
3.	Eyeshadow	$2.99	43%
4.	Mascara	$2.49	43%
5.	Blush	$4.49	37%

	Item	Price	Commission
6.	Moisturizer	$3.29	35%
7.	Lipstick	$1.99	41%
8.	After-shave lotion	$6.99	33%
9.	Air freshener	$1.49	25%
10.	Jewelry case	$16.99	45%

Complete the table. The commission for each item is 40%. Round each answer to the nearest cent.

	Item	Quantity	Price each	Total price	Commission earned
11.	Bath crystals	2	$5.99		
12.	Suntan lotion	3	$2.99		
13.	Eyeliner	1	$2.29		
14.	Hand lotion	2	$2.99		
15.	Perfumed soap	3	$1.50		
16.	Hair spray	2	$2.49		
17.	Bath talc	4	$2.99		

18. Find the total amount of the sale and the total commission earned for problems 11–17.

Bookkeeper

Career Cluster: Business Detail Carolyn Tarahata owns Business Services, Inc. Her firm prepares payroll information for Becker's Home Center. Carolyn computes the gross pay for each employee.

Problem

Greg Ritter is paid $125 a week plus a commission of 1.5% on all sales delivered. Last week, he sold $7400 worth of furniture. Orders totaling $475 were canceled. What was Carolyn's computation of Greg's gross pay for the week?

Solution

Strategy

- Subtract the canceled sales from the total sales to find the sales delivered.

  $7400 - $475 = $6925

- Multiply by 1.5% to find the commission earnings. Round to the nearest cent.

  $0.015 \times $6925 \approx 103.88

- Add to find gross pay.

  $125.00 + $103.88 = $228.88

Conclusion

Carolyn's computation of Greg's gross pay was $228.88.

Related Problems

Find the gross pay for each of the Becker employees.
Round each amount to the nearest cent.

	Name	Total sales	Cancellations	Commission	Weekly salary	Gross pay
1.	Mary Andrulewicz	$8,500	——	1.5%	$115	
2.	Gloria Wren	$7,860	——	1.5%	$120	
3.	Bill Bowen	$10,432	$357	2%	$135	
4.	Jay Baldwin	$9,136	$425	2%	$100	
5.	Lorraine Hill	$11,089	$718	1.5%	$110	
6.	Tom Gill	$9,976	$387	1.5%	$110	
7.	Carol Reynolds	$7,659	$195	3%	$95	
8.	Mike Merrill	$8,564	$87	2%	$100	

9. Jerry Cohen sells mattresses and springs. He receives a salary of $255 a week plus a commission of 2% on all sales over $800. Last week he sold $1500 worth of bedding. Find his gross pay.

10. Neil McCall receives a salary of $330 a week plus a commission of 1.5% on all sales over $1800. Last week he sold $3700 worth of carpeting. Find his gross pay.

11. Shannon Michaels sells major appliances. Her salary is $680 per month plus a commission of 3.5% on all sales over $8000. Find her gross pay for the month if her sales were $12,400.

12. Dick Nair sells tires for a monthly salary of $840 plus a 2% commission on all sales over $4800. If he sold $4650 worth of tires last month, what was his gross pay?

Graduated Commission

Scott Palmer sells pipe and steel products for large construction projects. He is paid a monthly salary plus a **graduated commission.** His commission rate depends upon his total sales.

Problem

Scott's monthly salary is $350. In addition, he receives 5% commission on the first $9000 of his sales and 6% commission on all sales over $9000.

Last month Scott sold $17,000 worth of products. What was his gross pay?

Solution

Strategy
• Multiply $9000 by 5% to find the earnings on the first $9000 of his sales.

  $0.05 \times \$9000 = \$450$

• Subtract $9000 from the total sales to find the amount that earns commission at 6%.

  $\$17,000 - \$9000 = \$8000$

• Multiply $8000 by 6% to find the earnings on sales over $9000.

  $0.06 \times \$8000 = \$480$

• Add to find the gross pay.

  $\$350 + \$450 + \$480 = \$1280$

Conclusion
Scott's gross pay was $1280.

Related Problems

For each problem, find the gross pay from the total sales and the commission given.

	Salary	Commission	Total sales
1.	$500	5% of first $5000; 6% of sales over $5000	$9,500
2.	$535	4% of first $2000; 5.5% of sales over $2000	$9,200
3.	$475	8% of first $5000; 10% of sales over $5000	$8,500
4.	$525	5.5% of first $8500; 7% of sales over $8500	$9,450
5.	$0	10% of all sales plus 5% of sales over $4300	$9,865
6.	$0	4% of first $1500; 5% of next $1500; 7% of sales over $3000	$19,800

CALCULATOR APPLICATIONS

Employers may use selling-cost percent to compare the work of their salespeople. The lower the selling-cost percent, the more efficient the salesperson.

Selling-cost percent can be found by dividing the total earnings by the total sales and then expressing that quotient as a percent.

Emily Fiene sold $87,000 worth of goods last year. Her salary was $12,300 plus a commission of 2% of her sales.

$0.02 \times \$87,000 = \$1740$ Commission earnings

$\$12,300 + \$1740 = \$14,040$ Total earnings

$\$14,040 \div \$87,000 \approx 0.161$ Rounded to 3 decimal places

Emily's selling-cost percent is 16.1%.

Find each selling-cost percent to the nearest tenth.

	Salesperson	Salary	Commission	Sales	Total earnings	Selling-cost percent
	Emily Fiene	$12,300	2% of all sales	$87,000	$14,040	16.1%
1.	Tom Auer	$5,823	5% of all sales	$65,000		
2.	Carole Nitz	$7,123	7.25% of all sales	$88,500		
3.	Pete Vaughn	$6,100	6.135% of all sales	$74,865		
4.	Andy Ricco	$5,036	3.35% of first $1800; 4.7% of sales over $1800	$89,547		
5.	Dan Statz	$4,538	5.5% of first $20,000; 8.5% of sales over $20,000	$133,457		
6.	Vicky Sayo	$5,200	6.7% of first $25,000; 9.2% of sales over $25,000	$189,419		
7.	Ben Griffin	$0	10.23% straight commission	$158,889		
8.	Mike Ryan	$0	11.85% straight commission	$126,453		
9.	Jenny Fox	$3,500	11.21% straight commission	$117,582		
10.	Liz Wille	$7,400	3.47% of first $25,000; 6.23% of next $25,000; 7.35% of sales over $50,000	$298,468		
11.	Dave Bock	$6,000	3.73% of first $45,000; 6.85% of next $45,000; 7.35% of sales over $90,000	$215,386		

12. Which three people had the best selling-cost percents?

Net Pay

Each pay period, employers subtract a specified amount from employees' gross pay for federal income tax.

The amount deducted is determined by an employee's gross pay, marital status, and number of **exemptions.** An exemption is a member of the family or a person who lived in the employee's home as a member of the family for the whole year.

The Internal Revenue Service of the United States Treasury Department provides tables which employers use to determine the amount to withhold for federal income tax. The tables are on pages 402–405.

SINGLE Persons—WEEKLY Payroll Period

And the wages are—		Exemptions claimed			
At least	But less than	0	1	2	3
		The amount of income tax to be withheld shall be—			
$135	$140	$19.00	$15.30	$11.80	$8.40
140	145	20.00	16.20	12.70	9.30
145	150	21.10	17.10	13.60	10.20
150	160	22.60	18.60	15.00	11.50
160	170	24.70	20.70	16.80	13.30
370	380	83.60	77.10	70.50	64.50
380	390	87.00	80.50	73.90	67.50
390	400	90.40	83.90	77.30	70.80
400	410	93.80	87.30	80.70	74.20
410	420	97.20	90.70	84.10	77.60

Problem

Marge Schaffer is single and earns $375.55 a week. She claims exemptions for herself and her father. How much is withheld from her paycheck each week for federal income tax?

Solution

Strategy
- Use the table for single persons and find the amounts that the salary is between.

  $375.55 is "at least $370 but less than $380."

- Follow the table across for the amount listed under 2 exemptions.

  $70.50

Conclusion
$70.50 is withheld from Marge's paycheck for federal income tax.

Related Problems

Use the appropriate table from pages 402–405 to find the amount withheld each week for federal income tax.

	Gross pay	Marital status	Exemptions claimed			Gross pay	Marital status	Exemptions claimed
1.	$125	Single	1		**9.**	$418	Married	6
2.	$98	Single	1		**10.**	$287	Married	5
3.	$175	Single	2		**11.**	$247	Single	1
4.	$437	Single	1		**12.**	$415	Married	4
5.	$437	Single	3		**13.**	$170	Married	3
6.	$437	Married	2		**14.**	$343	Single	1
7.	$437	Married	3		**15.**	$542	Married	5
8.	$323	Married	2					

Each pay period, part of most employees' paychecks is withheld under the Federal Insurance Contributions Act (FICA). The federal government uses this money to provide retirement income, survivors' benefits, and medical-cost benefits to qualified persons.

Most employed persons pay *6.65% of the first $29,700 of their gross income* to the federal government for **social security** (FICA deductions). Nothing is withheld for amounts over $29,700.

Problem

Marge's paycheck shows that her gross pay to date totaled $12,017.60. This week, her gross pay was $375.55. How much was withheld this week for social security?

Solution

Strategy
• Check that the year's total gross pay is less than $29,700.

$12,017.60 < $29,700

• Multiply the week's gross pay by 6.65% to find the amount withheld for social security. Round to the nearest cent.

$0.0665 \times \$375.55 \approx \$24.97$

Conclusion
$24.97 was withheld from Marge's paycheck for social security.

Related Problems

Find the amount withheld from each paycheck for social security. Round each answer to the nearest cent.

	Gross pay to date	Gross pay this paycheck
16.	$6358.07	$138.81
17.	$2009.18	$94.65
18.	$197.67	$46.73
19.	$7885.60	$226.80
20.	$5421.45	$500.00
21.	$4960.48	$181.53
22.	$10,965.00	$674.26
23.	$12,376.14	$1547.02
24.	$25,980.90	$885.46
25.	$31,664.00	$938.17

Scott, Foresman and Company ▼ 258491

08

394-42-4945	8-7-81	10.73	2		2		
SOCIAL SECURITY	PERIOD ENDING	RATE	REG. PAID AND EX.	EXTRA FED. TAX WITHHELD	ST. ALLOW AND EX.	EXTRA STATE TAX WITHHELD	DEPT. AND EMPLOYEE NUMBER

EARNINGS	HOURS	CURRENT	YEAR TO DATE	DEDUCTIONS	CURRENT	YEAR TO DATE
REGULAR PAY	35 00	375 55	12 017 60	FICA	24 97	799 04
OVERTIME PAY				FEDERAL	70 50	2 256 00
PERSONAL SICK				STATE	9 39	300 48
VACATION				HOSPITAL	3 88	124 16
HOLIDAY				DENTAL		
TIME AND A HALF						
TOTAL PAY		375 55	12 017 60	NET PAY	266 81	8 537 92

Net pay, also called **take-home pay,** is the amount left after all deductions have been subtracted from the gross pay.

Some states require deductions for state or local income tax. Sometimes other deductions, such as union dues or insurance payments, are also made.

Problem

Gerry's salary is $641.67 per week. He is single and claims one exemption. His gross pay to date is $6858.37. He pays $16.04 state tax. What is Gerry's net pay?

Solution

Strategy

- Use the tables on pages 402–405 to find the amount of federal income tax withheld.
  $178.50

- Check that the year's gross pay is less than $29,700.
  $6858.37 < $29,700

- Multiply the week's gross pay by 6.65% to find the amount withheld for social security. Round to the nearest cent.
  $0.0665 \times \$641.67 \approx \$42.67$

- Add to find the total deductions.
  $178.50 + $42.67 + $16.04 = $237.21

- Subtract to find net pay.
  $641.67 − $237.21 = $404.46

Conclusion
Gerry's weekly net pay is $404.46.

Related Problems

Find the amounts withheld from each paycheck for federal income tax (use the tables on pages 402–405) and social security.
Then find the net pay. Round each amount to the nearest cent.

| | Marital status | Exemptions claimed | Gross pay to date | This week's paycheck | | | | |
				Gross pay	Federal tax	Social security	Other deductions	Net pay
	Single	1	$6858.37	$641.67	$178.50	$42.67	$16.04	$404.46
26.	Single	1	$8695.00	$202.21			———	
27.	Married	2	$11,560.09	$235.92			———	
28.	Married	3	$7543.81	$179.60			$5.75	
29.	Single	1	$14,000.00	$311.11			$9.16	
30.	Married	4	$22,820.00	$447.45			$13.87	
31.	Single	1	$19,865.32	$389.51			$15.43	

Jobs in Classified Ads

Bobbi Gill is looking for a job as a secretary. She uses the "help wanted" section of the classified ads in her daily paper.

Problem

Bobbi found these two ads that interest her. Which job pays more? How much more per year does it pay?

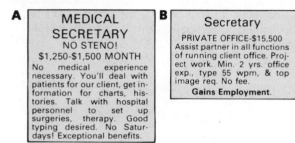

A
MEDICAL SECRETARY
NO STENO!
$1,250-$1,500 MONTH
No medical experience necessary. You'll deal with patients for our client, get information for charts, histories. Talk with hospital personnel to set up surgeries, therapy. Good typing desired. No Saturdays! Exceptional benefits.

B
Secretary
PRIVATE OFFICE-$15,500
Assist partner in all functions of running client office. Project work. Min. 2 yrs. office exp., type 55 wpm, & top image req. No fee.
Gains Employment.

Solution

Strategy

• Multiply the monthly salary of Job A by 12 to find the yearly salary.
$12 \times \$1250 = \$15,000$

• The yearly salary for Job B is given in the ad.
$15,500

• Compare the yearly salaries.
$\$15,000 < \$15,500$

• Subtract to find the difference in salaries.
$\$15,500 - \$15,000 = \$500$

Conclusion
Job B pays $500 more per year than Job A.

Related Problems

Use these ads and the strategies from the previous lessons in this chapter to solve problems 1–10.

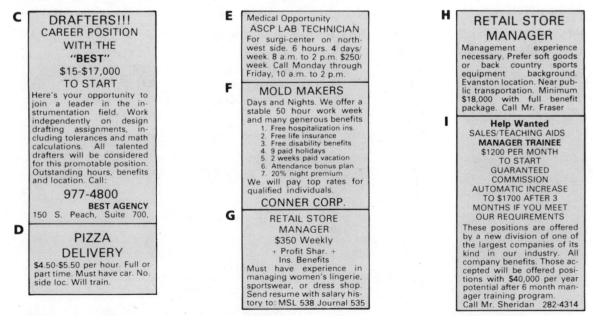

C
DRAFTERS!!!
CAREER POSITION WITH THE
"BEST"
$15-$17,000
TO START
Here's your opportunity to join a leader in the instrumentation field. Work independently on design drafting assignments, including tolerances and math calculations. All talented drafters will be considered for this promotable position. Outstanding hours, benefits and location. Call:
977-4800
BEST AGENCY
150 S. Peach, Suite 700,

D
PIZZA DELIVERY
$4.50-$5.50 per hour. Full or part time. Must have car. No side loc. Will train.

E
Medical Opportunity
ASCP LAB TECHNICIAN
For surgi-center on northwest side. 6 hours. 4 days/week. 8 a.m. to 2 p.m. $250/week. Call Monday through Friday, 10 a.m. to 2 p.m.

F
MOLD MAKERS
Days and Nights. We offer a stable 50 hour work week and many generous benefits
1. Free hospitalization ins.
2. Free life insurance
3. Free disability benefits
4. 9 paid holidays
5. 2 weeks paid vacation
6. Attendance bonus plan
7. 20% night premium
We will pay top rates for qualified individuals.
CONNER CORP.

G
RETAIL STORE MANAGER
$350 Weekly
+ Profit Shar. +
Ins. Benefits
Must have experience in managing women's lingerie, sportswear, or dress shop. Send resume with salary history to: MSL 538 Journal 535

H
RETAIL STORE MANAGER
Management experience necessary. Prefer soft goods or back country sports equipment background. Evanston location. Near public transportation. Minimum $18,000 with full benefit package. Call Mr. Fraser

I
Help Wanted
SALES/TEACHING AIDS
MANAGER TRAINEE
$1200 PER MONTH
TO START
GUARANTEED
COMMISSION
AUTOMATIC INCREASE
TO $1700 AFTER 3
MONTHS IF YOU MEET
OUR REQUIREMENTS
These positions are offered by a new division of one of the largest companies of its kind in our industry. All company benefits. Those accepted will be offered positions with $40,000 per year potential after 6 month manager training program.
Call Mr. Sheridan 282-4314

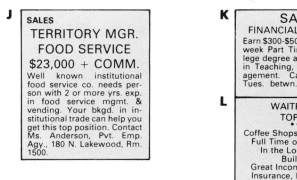

J SALES

TERRITORY MGR. FOOD SERVICE
$23,000 + COMM.
Well known institutional food service co. needs person with 2 or more yrs. exp. in food service mgmt. & vending. Your bkgd. in institutional trade can help you get this top position. Contact Ms. Anderson, Pvt. Emp. Agy., 180 N. Lakewood, Rm. 1500.

K SALES
FINANCIAL PLANNING
Earn $300-$500 in comm. per week Part Time, prefer college degree and background in Teaching, Sales or Management. Call Mon. and Tues. betwn. 9 & 5 Ms. Haas

L WAITRESSES
TOP TIPS
• • • •
Coffee Shops & Dining Rms Full Time or Lunch Only In the Loop's Finest Buildings Great Income & Benefits Insurance, Free Meals & Uniforms 55 E Apple, Rm 3533,

M Secretary LEARN
WORD PROCESSING
$1,333-$1,416 MONTH
Train to use the latest in our client's word processing equipment. Just good office skills, some secretarial background and desire to get into interesting, higher paying field. Any familiarity with word processing is a plus

N WORD-PROCESSOR: $14,560
Expanding Corp. Hdqr's. client seeking exp. word-proc. to join progressive dept. Definite promotion opp't's. Min 6 mo's. exp. & typing 60 wpm req. No fee. 943-6676. Gains Employment.

1. Charles is looking for a job as a word processor. Which of the jobs advertised pays more per year? How much more does it pay?

2. Danny is looking for a delivery job. How much more would he make in a 40–hour week if he is offered the highest pay rather than the lowest pay in the ad?

3. Mona is looking for a job as a retail store manager. Which of the jobs advertised pays more per year? How much more does it pay? (Use 52 weeks for 1 year.)

4. Barbara was hired as a manager trainee in sales of teacher aids. She met the requirements to receive the automatic increase. What was her salary for the first six months?

5. Cheryl was hired as a drafter at the lowest salary in the ad. After 6 months she received a 15% raise. What was her gross pay for the year?

6. Bob was hired as a mold maker on the night shift. The position of mold maker pays $10.50 per hour for the first 40 hours and time and a half for the additional hours. What is Bob's weekly gross pay?

7. Bernard accepted the position as a lab technician. He is single and claims 1 exemption. Along with federal income tax and social security, $6.25 is deducted from each check for state tax. What is his net pay per week?

8. Jack was hired for the sales/financial planning position for a straight commission of 16%. His first week's sales were $585, $1128, $456, and $298. How much did he earn from these sales? Did he receive the advertised commission?

9. Kelly received the position as territory manager of a food service. She received 4% commission on the first $20,000 in sales, and 6.5% commission on all sales over $20,000. What was her gross pay for the year if the sales were $32,500?

10. Carla interviewed for the job as a waitress. She would earn $5.50 an hour and work 7 hours a day, 5 days a week, in the coffee shop. She was told that tips averaged $18 per day. A position in the dining room paid $200 for a 5-day week. Tips averaged $35 a day. At which place could Carla earn more money? How much more could she earn?

Skills Tune-Up

Rounding whole numbers and decimals, pages 4–5

Round each number to the nearest thousand, nearest hundred, and nearest ten.

1. 668

2. 923

3. 1246

4. 7958

5. 5042

6. 2003

7. 65,191

8. 71,544

9. 87,897

10. 28,028

Round each number to the nearest whole number, nearest tenth, and nearest hundredth.

11. 3.283

12. 11.754

13. 74.521

14. 20.196

15. 152.802

16. 647.033

17. 391.475

18. 18.912

19. 84.666

20. 100.349

21. 478.977

Subtracting whole numbers and decimals, pages 6–7

1. 47 − 16

2. 84 − 27

3. 74 − 8

4. 83 − 6

5. 26 − 17

6. 59 − 55

7. 44.2 − 31.7

8. 63.4 − 4.8

9. 45.34 − 32.63

10. 64.43 − 37.83

11. 80.41 − 64.6

12. 52.83 − 43.5

13. 6.092 − 2.61

14. 63.944 − 16.35

15. 83.364 − 66.019

16. 97.087 − 34.521

17. 0.45 − 0.097

18. 48.04 − 12.07

19. 18.5 − 17.9

20. 8.07 − 7.44

21. 8.103 − 3

22. 79.002 − 63

23. 93 − 21.6

24. 24 − 0.8

25. 5 − 0.61

26. 65 − 32.05

27. 61.5 − 48.984

Multiplying whole numbers, pages 8–9

1. 30 × 50

2. 90 × 40

3. 70 × 600

4. 200 × 800

5. 900 × 600

6. 8000 × 60

7. 90 × 2000

8. 500 × 6000

9. 43 × 7

10. 17 × 26

11. 1700 × 2000

12. 50 × 91

13. 9 × 873

14. 430 × 800

15. 425 × 5

16. 855 × 37

17. 5100 × 700

18. 49 × 63

19. 84 × 48

20. 490 × 99

21. 68 × 506

22. 240 × 600

23. 9478 × 23

24. 892 × 7172

25. 9075 × 894

26. 100 × 460

27. 594 × 3652

Chapter 4 Review

Hourly rate and overtime rate, pages 68–69

1. Don Marcy makes $4.86 per hour. Find his gross pay for 40 hours.

2. Kay Soto earns $4.50 per hour for a 40-hour work week and time and a half for overtime. One week she worked 56 hours. Find her gross pay for the week.

Hourly rate plus tips, pages 70–71

3. Mary Harvey makes $3.50 per hour plus tips. One week she worked 35 hours and earned $39.20 in tips. She kept 85% of her tips. Find her gross pay for the week.

Straight commission, pages 72–73

4. Dwayne Johnson makes 15% straight commission. One week he had sales of $1560. Find his gross pay for the week.

Bookkeeper, pages 74–75

5. Dottie Koontz receives a salary of $150 per week plus a commission of 5% on all sales delivered. Last week she had sales of $3000 and cancellations of $1200. Find her gross pay for the week.

Graduated commission, page 76

6. Dale Keller is paid $350 per month plus a commission of 3% of the first $2000 of his sales, and 4.5% of all his sales over $2000. He sold $4500 worth of lumber last month. Find his gross pay for the month.

Net pay, pages 78–81

7. Max Steiner is married and claims 3 exemptions. He makes $289.46 per week. Use the table below to find the amount withheld from his weekly paycheck for federal income tax.

And the wages are—		Exemptions claimed			
At least	But less than	0	1	2	3
		The amount of income tax to be withheld shall be—			
250	260	36.50	32.50	28.50	24.80
260	270	38.60	34.60	30.60	26.60
270	280	40.70	36.70	32.70	28.60
280	290	42.80	38.80	34.80	30.70
290	300	45.10	40.90	36.90	32.80

8. Donna Adamson's gross pay for last week was $365.48. 6.65% was withheld for social security. Find the amount withheld. Round to the nearest cent.

9. Dick Laba's gross pay is $256.72 a week. $28.50 is withheld for federal income tax, $17.07 for social security, and $3.15 for insurance. Find his net pay.

Jobs in classified ads, pages 82–83

10. Use the ads shown. Which job pays more? How much more does it pay per year?

A
Receptionist
FRONT DESK
PEOPLE MEETER
$11,400 TO START
Plush offices! Lots of variety! A chance to polish your office basics! Our client anxious to hire!
JAROSZ PERSONNEL
985 Nash, Suite 315
Oak Brook
Des Plaines

B
Help Wanted
RECEPTIONIST
TELEPHONE
Growing food company near Loop needs a telephone receptionist with light typing. Must have good phone voice. $985/mo.

Chapter 4 Test

1. Sheila makes $4.95 per hour. Find her gross pay for 40 hours.

2. Eric earns $6.50 per hour for a 40-hour work week and time and a half for overtime. One week he worked 54 hours. Find his gross pay for the week.

3. Rick makes $3.85 per hour plus tips. One week he worked 30 hours and earned $86.40 in tips. He kept 85% of the tips. Find his gross pay for the week.

4. Elaine makes 25% straight commission. One week she had sales of $1840. Find her gross pay for the week.

5. Kristen receives a salary of $110 per week plus a commission of 8% of all sales delivered. Last week she had sales of $4000 and cancellations of $1700. Find her gross pay for the week.

6. Marjorie is paid $125 per week plus a commission of 3% on the first $3000 of sales, and 5.5% of all sales over $3000. She sold $4000 worth of appliances. Find her gross pay for the week.

7. Julio is single and claims 1 exemption. He makes $198.53 per week. Use the table below to find the amount withheld from his weekly paycheck for federal income tax.

And the wages are—		Exemptions claimed			
At least	But less than	0	1	2	3
		The amount of income tax to be withheld shall be—			
170	180	26.80	22.80	18.80	15.10
180	190	28.90	24.90	20.90	16.90
190	200	31.00	27.00	23.00	18.90
200	210	33.60	29.10	25.10	21.00
210	220	36.20	31.20	27.20	23.10

8. Jim's gross pay for last week was $219.87. 6.65% was withheld for social security. Find the amount withheld. Round to the nearest cent.

9. Julie's gross pay is $369.24 a week. $57.30 is withheld for federal income tax, $24.55 for social security, and $5.85 for insurance. Find her net pay.

10. Use the ads shown. Which job pays more? How much more does it pay per year?

Chapter 5 Personal Banking

Deposit Slips

James Morrison has a checking account. The money that he puts into his account is called a **deposit**. Often when making a deposit, he keeps some cash for spending money. The **net deposit** is the actual amount that is put into the account.

Problem

James is making a deposit. He has checks for $237.31 and $176.25. He wants to keep $50 in cash. Find his net deposit.

Solution

Strategy

• List each check separately on the deposit slip.

• Add to find the total.

• Subtract the cash received from the total to find the net deposit.

	DEPOSIT TICKET			
	JAMES C. MORRISON 1765 SHERIDAN DR. YOUR CITY, U.S.A. 60618			

DEPOSIT TICKET

JAMES C. MORRISON
1765 SHERIDAN DR.
YOUR CITY, U.S.A.   60618

DATE *October 23* 19 81

James C. Morrison

Glenview State Bank
GLENVIEW, ILLINOIS 60025

	|CASH| CURRENCY			
		COIN		
LIST CHECKS SINGLY			237	31
			176	25
TOTAL FROM OTHER SIDE				
TOTAL			413	56
LESS CASH RECEIVED			50	00
NET DEPOSIT			363	56

70-2030
719

USE OTHER SIDE FOR ADDITIONAL LISTING

BE SURE EACH ITEM IS PROPERLY ENDORSED

SAMPLE-VOID
DELUXE CHECK PRINTERS. INC.

⑂ 123 456 7⑂

DELUXE H03   CHECKS AND OTHER ITEMS ARE RECEIVED FOR DEPOSIT SUBJECT TO THE PROVISIONS OF THE UNIFORM COMMERCIAL CODE OR ANY APPLICABLE COLLECTION AGREEMENT.

Conclusion

James's net deposit was $363.56.

Related Problems

Complete each deposit slip.

1.

CASH	CURRENCY		
	COIN		
LIST CHECKS SINGLY		478	23
		36	42
TOTAL FROM OTHER SIDE			
TOTAL			
LESS CASH RECEIVED		60	00
NET DEPOSIT			

2.

CASH	CURRENCY		
	COIN		
LIST CHECKS SINGLY		715	95
		139	24
		78	78
TOTAL FROM OTHER SIDE			
TOTAL			
LESS CASH RECEIVED		80	00
NET DEPOSIT			

3.

CASH	CURRENCY		
	COIN	7	86
LIST CHECKS SINGLY		18	84
		27	36
		16	25
TOTAL FROM OTHER SIDE			
TOTAL			
LESS CASH RECEIVED			
NET DEPOSIT			

4.

CASH	CURRENCY		
	COIN	18	56
LIST CHECKS SINGLY		205	16
		19	43
		8	62
TOTAL FROM OTHER SIDE			
TOTAL			
LESS CASH RECEIVED		32	00
NET DEPOSIT			

5.

CASH	CURRENCY		
	COIN	54	75
LIST CHECKS SINGLY		218	97
		108	29
		37	17
TOTAL FROM OTHER SIDE			
TOTAL			
LESS CASH RECEIVED		75	00
NET DEPOSIT			

6.

CASH	CURRENCY		
	COIN	37	17
LIST CHECKS SINGLY		49	26
		123	47
		35	91
TOTAL FROM OTHER SIDE			
TOTAL			
LESS CASH RECEIVED		65	00
NET DEPOSIT			

7. Roy had checks to deposit for the following amounts: $23.78, $116.29, $108.25, and $8.75. He wanted $75 in cash. What was his net deposit?

8. Linda had checks to deposit for the following amounts: $97.18, $208.36, $29.16, and $8.64. She wanted $35 in cash. What was her net deposit?

9. Rosa had checks to deposit for the following amounts: $327.67, $53.77, $184.23, and $3.85. She wanted $100 in cash. What was her net deposit?

10. Marc had checks to deposit for the following amounts: $1025.76, $879.24, $548.92, and $353.88. He wanted $75 in cash. What was his net deposit?

Checks and Check Stubs

To whom check is payable   Date   Check number

JAMES C. MORRISON
1765 SHERIDAN DR.
YOUR CITY, U.S.A.   60618

No.   **101**

Sept. 19 19 **81**   70-2030
719

Pay to the order of   *The Hecht Company* $ *36.50*

Thirty-six and 50/100 ———————— DOLLARS

Glenview State Bank
GLENVIEW, ILLINOIS 60025

SAMPLE-VOID
DELUXE CHECK PRINTERS, INC.

Memo   *outside paint*   *James C. Morrison*

⑆07920300⑈ ⑈123 456 7⑈ 0101   DELUXE AQ

Purpose of check   Account number   Authorizing signature   Amount of check

The amount of a check is written in both words and
numbers. If there is a difference in these amounts, the bank
would honor the amount written in words.

Problem

How should $457.17 be written in words on a check?

Solution

Always use ink and fill the entire space so that no one can
change the amount that is written.

Four hundred fifty-seven and 17/100 ——— DOLLARS

Related Problems

Write each amount in words as it would appear on a check.

1. $27.81   **4.** $72.54   **7.** $395.13

2. $45.63   **5.** $15.00   **8.** $639.00

3. $60.00   **6.** $18.08   **9.** $1002.30

When James wrote the check to the Hecht Company, he filled in the attached **check stub**. The stub is a record of the check. When completed, the stub shows how much money is left in the account.

Problem

If the balance brought forward was $347.59 and a deposit of $63.20 was made, what was the new balance after James wrote the check shown on page 90?

Solution

Strategy
- List the balance brought forward from the last stub.

- List all deposits.

- Add the balance brought forward and all deposits made since the last stub was completed to find the total.

- Subtract the amount of this check from the total to find the new balance to be carried forward to the next stub.

Conclusion
The new balance was $374.29.

101	$ 36.50	
Sept. 19 19 81		
TO The Hecht Co. (paint)		
	DOLLARS	CENTS
BAL. FOR'D	347	59
DEPOSITS	63	20
"		
TOTAL	410	79
THIS PAYMENT	36	50
OTHER DEDUCTIONS		
BAL. FOR'D	374	29

Related Problems

Complete each check stub.

10.

	DOLLARS	CENTS
BAL. FOR'D	65	29
DEPOSITS		
"		
TOTAL		
THIS PAYMENT	18	40
OTHER DEDUCTIONS		
BAL. FOR'D		

11.

	DOLLARS	CENTS
BAL. FOR'D	86	20
DEPOSITS	37	50
"	23	16
TOTAL		
THIS PAYMENT	48	95
OTHER DEDUCTIONS		
BAL. FOR'D		

12.

	DOLLARS	CENTS
BAL. FOR'D	17	86
DEPOSITS	39	42
"	8	63
TOTAL		
THIS PAYMENT	15	29
OTHER DEDUCTIONS		
BAL. FOR'D		

13. On a check stub the balance brought forward was $475.80. Deposits of $163.20 and $87.25 were made. The amount of this check is $287.45. Find the balance carried forward to the next stub.

Check Registers

Many people use a **check register** rather than check stubs to record their checks. The same information is written on both.

Problem

David Halstead had a balance of $431.18 in his account. On September 29, he wrote check number 342 for $289.00. This check was made out to Realty Associates to pay his rent. What was the balance after David wrote this check?

Solution

Strategy
• Write the check number, date, description of check, and amount of check in the check register.

• Subtract the amount of the check from the old balance to find the new balance.

NUMBER	DATE	DESCRIPTION OF TRANSACTION	PAYMENT/DEBIT (−)	√ T	FEE (IF ANY) (−)	DEPOSIT/CREDIT (+)	BALANCE
							$ 431 18
342	9/29	*Realty Associates (rent)*	$ 289 00		$	$	289 00
							142 18

Conclusion
The balance was $142.18.

92

Problem

David made a deposit of $203.14 on October 2. Find the new balance.

Solution

Strategy
- Write the date and the amount of deposit in the check register.
- Add the old balance and the deposit to find the new balance.

NUMBER	DATE	DESCRIPTION OF TRANSACTION	PAYMENT/DEBIT (−)	√ T	FEE (IF ANY) (−)	DEPOSIT/CREDIT (+)	BALANCE
						$	$ 431 18
342	9/29	Realty Associates (rent)	$ 289 00	$	$		289 00
							142 18
	10/2	Deposit (paycheck)				203 14	203 14
							345 32

Conclusion
The new balance is $345.32.

Related Problems

Find each new balance. The last balance on each page of the partial check register becomes the beginning balance for the next page of the check register.

	NUMBER	DATE	PAYMENT/DEBIT (−)	√ T	FEE (IF ANY) (−)	DEPOSIT/CREDIT (+)	BALANCE
						$	$ 345 32
1.	343	10/3	$ 63 10	$	$		63 10
2.	344	10/6	12 38				12 38
3.	345	10/6	25 00				25 00
4.		10/9				203 14	203 14
5.		10/10				80 89	80 89
6.	346	10/10	33 56				33 56
7.	347	10/13	36 15				36 15
8.	348	10/13	27 96				27 96

	NUMBER	DATE	PAYMENT/DEBIT (−)	√ T	FEE (IF ANY) (−)	DEPOSIT/CREDIT (+)	BALANCE
						$	$
9.	349	10/15	$ 57 66	$	$		57 66
10.		10/16				203 14	203 14
11.	350	10/19	144 34				144 34
12.	351	10/19	109 20				109 20
13.	352	10/19	18 48				18 48
14.	353	10/22	50 00				50 00
15.		10/23				203 14	203 14
16.	354	10/27	73 56				73 56

93

Reconciling a Bank Statement

Each month David Halstead receives a **bank statement** for his checking account. He also receives the checks that the bank has paid from his account during the month. These are called **canceled checks**.

David **reconciles** the bank statement with his check register. This means that he determines if the check register agrees with the bank statement.

Sometimes David has recorded deposits and checks in his check register that are not listed on the bank statement. These are called **outstanding deposits** and **outstanding checks**.

The service charge is the amount the bank charges for handling the account.

BALANCE LAST STATEMENT	DEPOSITS AND CREDITS		CHECKS AND DEBITS		SERVICE CHARGE	BALANCE THIS STATEMENT
	NO.	TOTAL AMOUNT	NO.	TOTAL AMOUNT		
142.18	4	690.31	9	418.63	4.75	409.11

CHECKING ACCOUNT TRANSACTIONS

DATE	DEBITS	CREDITS	DESCRIPTION
10/02		203.14	DEPOSIT
10/09		203.14	DEPOSIT
10/10		80.89	DEPOSIT
10/16		203.14	DEPOSIT
10/30	4.75		SERVICE CHARGE

CHECKS

DATE	CHECK NO	AMOUNT	DATE	CHECK NO	AMOUNT
10/08	343	63.10	10/13	344	12.38
10/14	345	25.00	10/19	346	33.56
10/20	347	36.15	10/23	348	27.96
10/26	349	57.66	10/28	350	144.34
10/29	352	18.48			

Problem

The balance in David's check register is $384.24. He determined that he has an outstanding deposit of $203.14 and that check #351 for $109.20, check #353 for $50.00, and check #354 for $73.56 are outstanding. Does his check register agree with his bank statement? Find the actual amount in his checking account.

Solution

Strategy

- Complete the form on the back of the bank statement to reconcile the bank statement with the check register.

BALANCE YOUR CHECK BOOK
by doing these things

Fill in Below Amounts from Your BANK STATEMENT and CHECK BOOK

Balance shown on
BANK STATEMENT . . . $ *409.11*

Add Deposits
Not on Statement $ *203.14*

Sub-Total . . . . . $ *612.25*

Subtract Checks Issued But
Not on Statement:
$ *109.20*
50.00
73.56

Total . . . . . . $ *232.76*

BALANCE . . . . $ *379.49*

Balance shown in
Your CHECK Book . . . $ *384.24*

Add any Deposits Not
Already Entered in
Check Book . . . . $

Sub-Total . . . . . $ *384.24*

Subtract Service Charges
and other Bank Charges
Not in Check Book

$ *4.75*

Total . . . . $ *4.75*

BALANCE . . . . . $ *379.49*

- Since the adjusted statement balance and the adjusted check register are the same, the statement is reconciled.

- Subtract the service charge from the previous balance in the check register to find the actual amount. $384.24 - $4.75 = $379.49

Conclusion

The check register and the bank statement agree. The actual amount in David's account was $379.49.

Related Problems

Reconcile the bank-statement information with the check-register balance. Find the actual amount in each checking account.

1. Statement ending balance: $41.27
Outstanding deposits: $27.70, $12.30
Outstanding check: $9.98
Service charge: $4.21
Check-register balance: $75.50

2. Statement ending balance: $151.93
Outstanding deposit: $100.00
Outstanding checks: $10.00, $24.13, $200.00
Service charge: $6.60
Check-register balance: $24.40

3. Statement ending balance: $67.38
Outstanding deposits: $15.45, $12.55
Outstanding checks: $18.45, $17.12, $20.20
Service charge: $5.50
Check-register balance: $45.11

4. Statement ending balance: $235.00
Outstanding deposits: $12.00, $13.00
Outstanding checks: $9.75, $11.25, $10.00
Service charge: $6.00
Check-register balance: $235.00

5. Statement ending balance: $392.41
Outstanding deposits: $32.41, $50.12, $49.46
Outstanding checks: $42.75, $73.12, $63.30, $88.71, $81.80
Service charge: $7.15
Check-register balance: $181.87

6. A portion of Joe Sanchez's check register is shown. Find the actual amount in Joe's checking account on August 30. You may find arithmetic errors in Joe's check register. The bank statement showed an ending balance of $73.47; a deposit of $45.00; check #981, check #982, and check #983; and a service charge of $5.50.

NUMBER	DATE	DESCRIPTION OF TRANSACTION	PAYMENT/DEBIT (−)	√ T	FEE (IF ANY) (−)	DEPOSIT/CREDIT (+)	BALANCE $ 120	00
981	8/5	Sadkin Hardware (tools)	$ 10 25	$	$		10	25
							109	75
	8/8	Deposit				45 00	45	00
							154	75
982	8/10	Granger's Store (for groceries)	25 35				25	35
							129	40
983	8/15	Tony Navarro (for car repair)	50 43				50	43
							79	97
	8/27	Deposit				52 60	52	60
							132	57
984	8/30	Northwest Telephone	32 52				32	52
							100	05

CALCULATOR APPLICATIONS

Checking Accounts

Many people use the single-line method of recording entries in their check registers. Each new balance is written on the same line as the entry to which it corresponds.

Find each new balance. The last balance on each page of the check register becomes the beginning balance for the next page of the check register.

NUMBER	DATE	PAYMENT/DEBIT (-)	√T	FEE (IF ANY) (-)	DEPOSIT/CREDIT (+)	BALANCE
						1005 07
719	8/26	$103 82		$	$	901 25
1. 720	8/28	111 26				
2. 721	8/28	273 69				
3.	8/31				887 51	
4. 722	9/1	386 89				
5. 723	9/3	270 93				
6. 724	9/9	521 57				
7. 725	9/11	211 40				

NUMBER	DATE	PAYMENT/DEBIT (-)	√T	FEE (IF ANY) (-)	DEPOSIT/CREDIT (+)	BALANCE
8.	9/15	$		$	$428 60	
9. 726	9/21	219 74				
10. 727	9/24	202 55				
11.	9/30				628 35	
12. 728	9/30	77 78				
13. 729	10/2	35 40				
14. 730	10/2	187 65				

15. Reconcile the check register above with this bank statement.
Find the actual amount in the checking account.

BALANCE LAST STATEMENT	DEPOSITS AND CREDITS		CHECKS AND DEBITS		SERVICE CHARGE	BALANCE THIS STATEMENT
	NO.	TOTAL AMOUNT	NO.	TOTAL AMOUNT		
1005.07	2	1316.11	8	2082.11	6.80	232.27

```
CHECKING ACCOUNT TRANSACTIONS
DATE         DEBITS        CREDITS      DESCRIPTION

09/01                      887.51       DEPOSIT
09/16                      428.60       DEPOSIT
09/30        6.80                       SERVICE CHARGE

CHECKS
 DATE      CHECK NO    AMOUNT     DATE      CHECK NO    AMOUNT
09/01        719       103.82    09/02        720       111.26
09/04        721       273.69    09/08        722       386.89
09/11        723       270.93    09/15        724       521.57
09/21        725       211.40    09/28        727       202.55
```

Personal Banking Representative

Career Cluster: Business Contact Debbie Haverl is a personal banking representative for the Edgar State Bank. She advises customers on the various services offered by the bank. John and Andrea Warren want to open a savings account. The amount the Warrens deposit is called the **principal**. The amount that the bank will pay the Warrens for leaving their money in a savings account is called the **interest**.

Debbie uses the simple interest formula to find the amount of interest that will be paid.

$$I = P \times R \times T$$

Interest Principal Rate Time

Problem

The Warrens opened a savings account by depositing $300. After 3 months, what was the amount of interest at $5\frac{1}{2}\%$ per year?

Solution

Strategy
• Write the percent as a decimal.

$5\frac{1}{2}\% = 0.055$

• Write the time as part of a year.

3 months is $\frac{3}{12}$, or $\frac{1}{4}$, year. $\frac{1}{4} = 0.25$

• Use the formula. Round to the nearest cent.

$I = P \times R \times T$
$I = \$300 \times 0.055 \times 0.25$
$I \approx \$4.13$

Conclusion
The interest earned was $4.13.

Related Problems

Compute the simple interest for each savings account. Round each amount to the nearest cent.

	Principal	Interest rate	Time
1.	$50	5%	6 mo.
2.	$200	$5\frac{3}{4}$%	1 yr.
3.	$350	6.5%	18 mo.
4.	$175	6.25%	9 mo.
5.	$348	$5\frac{1}{2}$%	15 mo.
6.	$225	4.75%	30 mo.
7.	$285	5.35%	27 mo.
8.	$615	$6\frac{1}{2}$%	2 yr.
9.	$425	5.25%	39 mo.
10.	$3210	6%	1 yr. 9 mo.
11.	$3750	$6\frac{1}{4}$%	3 mo.
12.	$2940	4.8%	2 yr. 3 mo.
13.	$5000	5.65%	3 yr. 3 mo.
14.	$1290	$6\frac{3}{4}$%	2 yr. 6 mo.
15.	$720	6.2%	3 yr. 9 mo.

Break Time

Use each number and operation symbol to form an equation.

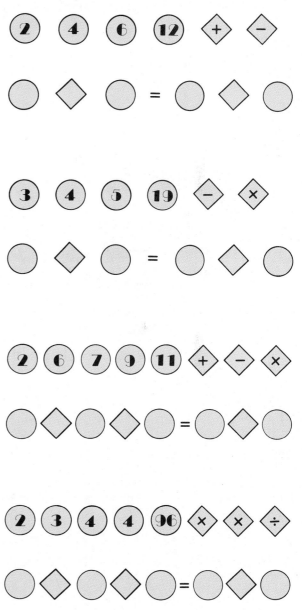

Compound Interest

Huang Ching put his money into a savings account that paid **compound interest**. This means that the interest is computed on the sum of the principal *and* the previously earned interest.

Problem

Huang put $1000 in a savings account that paid 8% interest compounded annually. How much interest was earned in 2 years?

Solution

Strategy
- Huang made the table below by using the simple interest formula.
- Find the interest for the first year.

Year	Principal plus previous interest	Interest for the year $P \times R \times T = I$
1	$1000	$1000 \times 0.08 \times 1 = $80.00
2	$1000 + $80 = $1080	$1080 \times 0.08 \times 1 = $86.40

- Add the principal and the interest. Then find the interest for the second year.
- Add the interest earned each year to find the total interest.
  $80.00 + $86.40 = $166.40

Conclusion
The interest earned in 2 years was $166.40.

Related Problems

Compute the interest earned by the amount in each of these savings accounts. The interest is compounded annually. Round each answer to the nearest cent.

1. $100 at 7% for 4 years

2. $500 at 8% for 3 years

3. $300 at 6% for 5 years

4. $250 at 6.5% for 2 years

5. $1000 at 7.5% for 3 years

6. $3000 at 7.75% for 3 years

Interest compounded semiannually is computed every 6 months.
Interest compounded quarterly is computed every 3 months.

Problem

Alicia Melendez put $1500 in a savings account that paid 8% interest compounded quarterly. How much interest was earned in 1 year?

Solution

Strategy
• Alicia made the table below using the simple interest formula.

• Find the interest for the first quarter.

Qtr.	Principal plus previous interest	Interest for the year $P \times R \times T = I$
1	$1500	$1500 × 0.08 × 0.25 = $30
2	$1500.00 + $30.00 = $1530.00	$1530.00 × 0.08 × 0.25 = $30.60
3	$1530.00 + $30.60 = $1560.60	$1560.60 × 0.08 × 0.25 ≈ $31.21
4	$1560.60 + $31.20 = $1591.80	$1591.80 × 0.08 × 0.25 ≈ $31.84

• Add the principal and the interest. Then find the interest for the next 3 quarters. Round to the nearest cent.

• Add the interest earned each quarter to find the total interest.
  $30.00 + $30.60 + $31.21 + $31.84 = $123.65

Conclusion
The interest earned in one year was $123.65.

Related Problems

Find the interest earned by each amount for the given time. Round each answer to the nearest cent.

7. $400 at 7% compounded quarterly for 1 year

8. $300 at 6% compounded semiannually for 2 years

9. $560 at 8% compounded semiannually for 3 years

10. $220 at 7% compounded quarterly for 1 year

11. $1000 at 6.5% compounded semiannually for 2 years

12. $500 at 6% compounded quarterly for 1 year

13. $500 at 6% compounded semiannually for 1 year

14. $500 at 6% compounded annually for 1 year

Compound Interest Tables

Compound interest tables are designed to allow people to compute compound interest without extensive calculating.

No. of Periods	1.5%	2%	2.5%	3%	3.5%	4%	5%	6%	7%	8%
					COMPOUND INTEREST TABLE					
1	1.0150	1.0200	1.0250	1.0300	1.0350	1.0400	1.0500	1.0600	1.0700	1.0800
2	1.0302	1.0404	1.0506	1.0609	1.0712	1.0816	1.1025	1.1236	1.1449	1.1664
3	1.0457	1.0612	1.0769	1.0927	1.1087	1.1248	1.1576	1.1910	1.2250	1.2597
4	1.0614	1.0824	1.1038	1.1255	1.1475	1.1699	1.2155	1.2625	1.3108	1.3605
5	1.0773	1.1041	1.1314	1.1593	1.1877	1.2167	1.2763	1.3382	1.4026	1.4693
6	1.0934	1.1262	1.1597	1.1941	1.2293	1.2653	1.3401	1.4186	1.5007	1.5869
7	1.1098	1.1487	1.1887	1.2299	1.2723	1.3159	1.4071	1.5036	1.6058	1.7138
8	1.1265	1.1717	1.2184	1.2668	1.3168	1.3686	1.4775	1.5938	1.7182	1.8059
9	1.1434	1.1951	1.2489	1.3048	1.3629	1.4233	1.5513	1.6895	1.8385	1.9990
10	1.1605	1.2190	1.2801	1.3439	1.4106	1.4802	1.6289	1.7908	1.9672	2.1589
11	1.1779	1.2434	1.3121	1.3842	1.4600	1.5395	1.7103	1.8983	2.1049	2.3316
12	1.1956	1.2682	1.3449	1.4258	1.5111	1.6010	1.7959	2.0122	2.2522	2.5182
13	1.2136	1.2936	1.3785	1.4685	1.5640	1.6651	1.8856	2.1329	2.4098	2.7196
14	1.2318	1.3195	1.4130	1.5126	1.6187	1.7317	1.9799	2.2609	2.5785	2.9372
15	1.2502	1.3459	1.4483	1.5580	1.6753	1.8009	2.0789	2.3966	2.7590	3.1722
16	1.2690	1.3728	1.4845	1.6047	1.7340	1.8730	2.1829	2.5404	2.9522	3.4259
17	1.2880	1.4002	1.5216	1.6528	1.7947	1.9479	2.2920	2.6928	3.1588	3.7000
18	1.3073	1.4282	1.5597	1.7024	1.8575	2.0258	2.4066	2.8543	3.3799	3.9960
19	1.3270	1.4568	1.5987	1.7535	1.9225	2.1068	2.5270	3.0256	3.6165	4.3157
20	1.3469	1.4859	1.6386	1.8061	1.9898	2.1911	2.6533	3.2071	3.8697	4.6610
21	1.3671	1.5157	1.6796	1.8603	2.0594	2.2788	2.7860	3.3996	4.1406	5.0338
22	1.3876	1.5460	1.7216	1.9161	2.1315	2.3699	2.9253	3.6035	4.4304	5.4365
23	1.4084	1.5769	1.7646	1.9736	2.2061	2.4647	3.0715	3.8198	4.7405	5.8715
24	1.4295	1.6084	1.8087	2.0328	2.2833	2.5633	3.2251	4.0489	5.0724	6.3412
25	1.4509	1.6407	1.8539	2.0938	2.3673	2.6658	3.3864	4.2919	5.4274	6.8485

Problem

Ginny Leatherman had $550 in a savings account that paid 7% interest compounded semiannually. How much interest was earned in 3 years?

Solution

Strategy
• Divide 7% by the number of times the interest is compounded each year.

$7 \div 2 = 3.5$

• Multiply the number of years by the number of times the interest is compounded each year to find the total number of periods.

$2 \times 3 = 6$

• Read the entry from the table.
1.2293

• Multiply by the principal to find the total amount in the account. Round to the nearest cent.

$\$550 \times 1.2293 \approx \$676.12$

• Subtract the principal from the total amount to find the interest.

$\$676.12 - \$550.00 = \$126.12$

Conclusion
The interest earned was $126.12.

Related Problems

Use the compound interest table to find the interest earned by each amount for the given time. Round each answer to the nearest cent.

1. $100 at 6% compounded annually for 4 years
2. $370 at 7% compounded annually for 5 years
3. $750 at 8% compounded annually for 15 years
4. $435 at 5% compounded annually for 8 years
5. $400 at 10% compounded semiannually for 3 years
6. $850 at 7% compounded semiannually for 8 years
7. $575 at 8% compounded semiannually for 11 years
8. $1000 at 6% compounded semiannually for 12 years
9. $2000 at 8% compounded quarterly for 5 years
10. $1500 at 6% compounded quarterly for 6 years
11. $1800 at 10% compounded quarterly for 4 years
12. $2500 at 12% compounded quarterly for 3 years

Break Time

The picture below shows both the top view and the front view of a three-dimensional figure. Draw the side view.

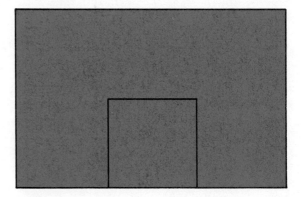

Skills Tune-Up

Multiplying decimals, pages 10-11

1. 0.5×0.7
2. 0.6×0.4
3. 0.08×0.2
4. 0.06×0.1
5. 0.03×0.06
6. 0.8×0.04
7. 0.002×0.04
8. 0.11×0.003
9. 700×0.2
10. 0.6×900
11. 800×0.04
12. 0.05×110
13. 0.003×700
14. 600×0.008
15. 0.005×0.004
16. 0.002×0.007
17. 4000×0.0011
18. 8.3×1.7
19. 8.32×4.2
20. 9.1×3.46
21. 13.5×0.018
22. 5.661×6.46
23. 80.33×1.911
24. 7.49×0.6008
25. 49.217×0.032
26. 4.627×0.0037
27. 0.054×31.5
28. 0.014×782.3

Ratio and proportion, pages 30-31

Find the cross-products. Tell whether the ratios are equal.

1. $\dfrac{2}{40}$ $\quad$ $\dfrac{3}{60}$
2. $\dfrac{3}{13}$ $\quad$ $\dfrac{5}{15}$
3. $\dfrac{4}{12}$ $\quad$ $\dfrac{12}{35}$
4. $\dfrac{1.4}{0.6}$ $\quad$ $\dfrac{7}{3}$
5. $\dfrac{0.32}{0.05}$ $\quad$ $\dfrac{0.66}{0.20}$
6. $\dfrac{15.3}{25.5}$ $\quad$ $\dfrac{0.3}{0.5}$

Solve and check.

7. $\dfrac{4}{5} = \dfrac{n}{45}$
8. $\dfrac{15}{a} = \dfrac{3}{20}$
9. $\dfrac{x}{54} = \dfrac{5}{18}$
10. $\dfrac{14}{3} = \dfrac{7}{c}$
11. $\dfrac{16}{d} = \dfrac{3.2}{4.2}$
12. $\dfrac{1.4}{0.7} = \dfrac{a}{0.45}$
13. $\dfrac{0.04}{0.36} = \dfrac{9}{y}$
14. $\dfrac{42}{x} = \dfrac{26}{0.13}$

Writing percents, decimals, and fractions, pages 32-33

Write as a decimal.

1. 17%
2. 8%
3. 1%
4. 25%
5. 96%
6. 3%
7. 99%
8. $6\frac{1}{4}\%$
9. 7.75%
10. 15.6%
11. $12\frac{1}{2}\%$
12. 1.5%
13. 6.75%
14. $1\frac{1}{2}\%$
15. 32.8%
16. 8.5%
17. $5\frac{3}{4}\%$
18. $16\frac{1}{8}\%$
19. 103%
20. 924%
21. 856%
22. 160%
23. $\frac{1}{4}\%$
24. $\frac{2}{5}\%$

Write as a fraction in lowest terms.

25. 50%
26. 90%
27. 35%
28. 75%
29. 60%
30. 37%
31. 24%
32. 83%
33. 20%
34. 15%
35. 9%
36. 56%
37. 33%
38. 5%
39. 45%
40. 87%
41. 95%
42. 67%
43. $37\frac{1}{2}\%$
44. $16\frac{1}{2}\%$
45. 110%
46. 675%
47. 350%
48. 140%

Chapter 5 Review

Deposit slips, pages 88-89

1. Find the total and the net deposit for this deposit slip.

CASH	CURRENCY		
	COIN	8	75
LIST CHECKS SINGLY		29	80
		37	40
		5	23
TOTAL FROM OTHER SIDE			
TOTAL			
LESS CASH RECEIVED		25	00
NET DEPOSIT			

Checks and check stubs, pages 90-91

2. Write $38.72 in words as it would appear on a check.

3. Find the balance carried forward for this check stub.

	DOLLARS	CENTS
BAL. FOR'D	93	57
DEPOSITS	95	76
''	17	29
TOTAL		
THIS PAYMENT	75	20
OTHER DEDUCTIONS		
BAL. FOR'D		

Check registers, pages 92-93

For problems 4 and 5, find each new balance.

NUMBER	DATE	PAYMENT/DEBIT (-)	V T	FEE (IF ANY) (-)	DEPOSIT/CREDIT (+)	BALANCE	
		$		$		$ 283	26
	10/8	$			$ 136 18	136	18
4.							
127	10/9	34 70				34	70
5.							

Reconciling a bank statement, pages 94-96

6. Reconcile the bank-statement information with the check-register balance. Find the actual amount in the checking account.

Statement ending balance: $196.50
Outstanding deposit: $57.56
Outstanding checks: $19.70, $125.25
Service charge: $4.75
Check-register balance: $113.86

Personal banking representative, pages 98-99

7. A savings account paid 6.5% simple interest. Find the amount of interest that $1200 earned in 9 months.

Compound interest, pages 100-101

8. Sylvia put $800 in a savings account that paid 6% interest compounded annually. Find the interest earned in 2 years.

9. Carl put $1000 in a savings account that paid 8% interest compounded quarterly. Find the interest earned in 1 year. Round to the nearest cent.

Compound interest tables, pages 102-103

10. Use the table below to find the amount of interest earned on $400 at 6% interest compounded semiannually for 5 years.

No. of Periods	1.5%	2%	2.5%	3%
1	1.0150	1.0200	1.0250	1.0300
2	1.0302	1.0404	1.0506	1.0609
7	1.1098	1.1487	1.1887	1.2299
8	1.1265	1.1717	1.2184	1.2668
9	1.1434	1.1951	1.2489	1.3048
10	1.1605	1.2190	1.2801	1.3439

Chapter 5 Test

1. Find the total and the net deposit for this deposit slip.

CASH	CURRENCY		
	COIN		
LIST CHECKS SINGLY		18	50
		43	82
		459	27
TOTAL FROM OTHER SIDE			
TOTAL			
LESS CASH RECEIVED		35	00
NET DEPOSIT			

2. Write $52.43 in words as it would appear on a check.

3. Find the balance carried forward for this check stub.

	DOLLARS	CENTS
BAL. FOR'D	100	69
DEPOSITS	47	29
"	126	35
TOTAL		
THIS PAYMENT	225	80
OTHER DEDUCTIONS		
BAL. FOR'D		

For problems 4 and 5, find each new balance.

	NUMBER	DATE	PAYMENT/DEBIT (−)	√ T	FEE (IF ANY) (−)	DEPOSIT/CREDIT (+)	BALANCE	
			$		$		$ 114	53
		11/20	$			$ 126 74	126	74
4.								
5.	311	11/24	78 16				78	16

6. Reconcile the bank-statement information with the check-register balance. Find the actual amount in the checking account.

Statement ending balance: $147.80
Outstanding deposit: $57.26
Outstanding checks: $37.86, $105.24
Service charge: $6.25
Check-register balance: $68.21

7. A savings account paid 7.5% simple interest. Find the amount of interest that $700 earned in 6 months.

8. Joan put $500 in a savings account that paid 7% interest compounded annually. Find the interest earned in 2 years.

9. Ray put $2000 in a savings account that paid 8% interest compounded semiannually. Find the interest earned in 1 year.

10. Use the table below to find the amount of interest earned on $5000 at 8% interest compounded quarterly for 4 years.

No. of Periods	1.5%	2%	2.5%	3%
1	1.0150	1.0200	1.0250	1.0300
2	1.0302	1.0404	1.0506	1.0609

16	1.2690	1.3728	1.4845	1.6047
17	1.2880	1.4002	1.5216	1.6528
18	1.3073	1.4282	1.5597	1.7024
19	1.3270	1.4568	1.5987	1.7535
20	1.3469	1.4859	1.6386	1.8061

Chapter 6 Consumer Credit

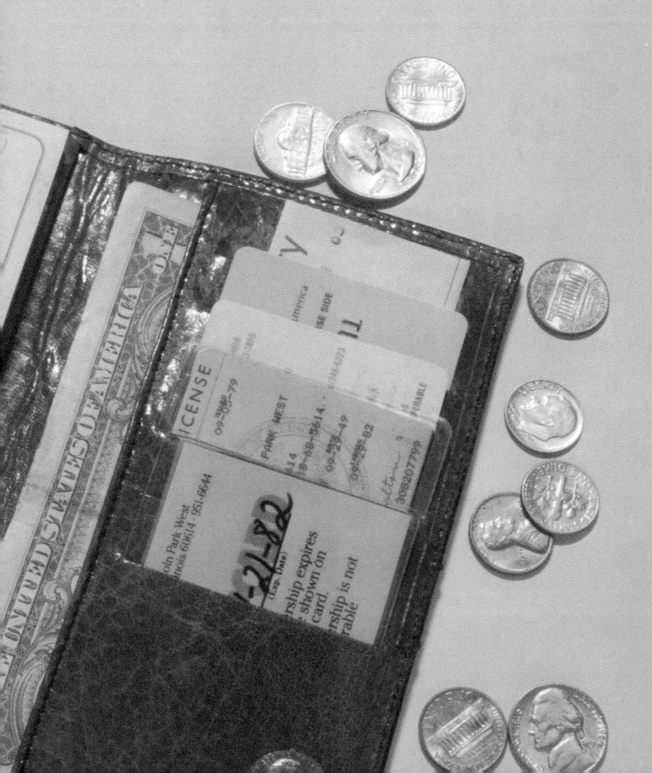

Promissory Notes

When Dennis Nelson borrowed money from his bank, the bank required that he sign a **promissory note.** In the note, he agreed to repay the **principal,** or the amount borrowed, along with the **interest,** by a certain date. The interest is the amount the bank charges for the use of the money.

The bank used the simple interest formula to compute the amount of interest due.

$$I = P \times R \times T$$

| | | | |
| Interest | Principal | Rate | Time |

Problem

Dennis signed a promissory note for $2500 at an interest rate of 17.5% per year. The note is due in 120 days. Find the amount of interest and the total amount due. Use 360 days for 1 year.

Solution

Strategy

• Express the interest rate and time as fractions.

$17.5\% = 0.175 = \frac{175}{1000}$

120 days is $\frac{120}{360}$, or $\frac{1}{3}$, year.

• Use the simple interest formula to compute the interest due. Round to the nearest cent.

$I = P \times R \times T$

$I = \$2500 \times \frac{175}{1000} \times \frac{1}{3}$

$I \approx \$145.83$

• Add the principal and the interest to find the total amount due.

$\$2500 + \$145.83 = \$2645.83$

Conclusion

Dennis will pay $145.83 in interest. The total amount due will be $2645.83.

Related Problems

Find the amount of interest due. Round to the nearest cent.

1. $850 at 18% for 90 days
2. $1100 at 15% for 30 days
3. $730 at 14.5% for 60 days
4. $1500 at 13.5% for 120 days
5. $2000 at 20% for 1 day

6. $600 at 17.5% for 15 days
7. $2300 at 15% for 4 months
8. $1350 at 18.5% for 8 months
9. $500 at 17% for 15 months
10. $4850 at 18% for 18 months

For each promissory note, find the amount of interest due.
Round to the nearest cent. Then find the total amount due.

11. _120 days_ AFTER DATE I, WE, OR EITHER OF US, PROMISE TO
PAY TO THE ORDER OF _First National Bank_
One thousand eight hundred and °°/100 DOLLARS
WITH INTEREST FOR VALUE RECEIVED AT _18_ % PER YEAR.

12. _1 yr. 3 mo._ AFTER DATE I, WE, OR EITHER OF US, PROMISE TO
PAY TO THE ORDER OF _Prairie State Bank_
Nine hundred twenty-five and °°/100 DOLLARS
WITH INTEREST FOR VALUE RECEIVED AT _18.5_ % PER YEAR.

13. _2 yr. 6 mo._ AFTER DATE, I, WE, OR EITHER OF US, PROMISE TO
PAY TO THE ORDER OF _Lincoln Bank_
Two thousand four hundred and °°/100 DOLLARS
WITH INTEREST FOR VALUE RECEIVED AT _14_ % PER YEAR.

14. _50 days_ AFTER DATE I, WE, OR EITHER OF US, PROMISE TO
PAY TO THE ORDER OF _Northeast National Bank_
Nine hundred seventy-five and °°/100 DOLLARS
WITH INTEREST FOR VALUE RECEIVED AT _17.5_ % PER YEAR.

Credit Card Finance Charges

Marilyn Running Deer has a credit card that allows her to charge all of her purchases at Engel's, a local department store. Once a month, she receives a statement of the balance due on her account.

When Marilyn pays less than the full amount owed, she has to pay a **finance charge** the next month. The finance charge is the amount that the store charges for the privilege of delaying payment.

Engel's computes the finance charge on the balance that remains after payments have been subtracted from the unpaid balance. Engel's does not charge its customers a finance charge on new purchases.

Problem

Marilyn's unpaid balance from last month is $87.50. This month she has made a payment of $20 and charged purchases totaling $23.18. The finance charge is 1.5% per month. What is the new balance?

Solution

Strategy
• Subtract to find the balance after payment.

  $87.50 − $20.00 = $67.50

• Multiply by 1.5% to find the finance charge on the balance after payment. Round to the nearest cent.

  $0.015 \times \$67.50 \approx \$1.01$

• Add to find the new balance.

Balance after payment	Finance charge	Purchases	New balance
$67.50	+ $1.01	+ $23.18	= $91.69

Conclusion
The new balance is $91.69.

Related Problems

Complete the table. The finance charge is 1.5% per month of the balance after payments. Round the finance charge to the nearest cent.

	Unpaid balance	Payments	Balance after payments	Finance charge	Purchases	New balance
1.	$47.16	$0			$0	
2.	$79.62	$0			$46.13	
3.	$126.38	$20.00			$0	
4.	$148.18	$25.00			$30.57	
5.	$72.33	$50.00			$9.98 $14.68	
6.	$342.75	$10.00			$6.23 $10.39	
7.	$183.77	$10.00			$17.43 $12.21	
8.	$234.90	$36.00			$18.95 $19.34	
9.	$83.21	$83.21			$20.94	
10.	$223.14	$10.00 $13.14			$0	
11.	$158.19	$8.19			$35.60	
12.	$0	$0			$12.00 $16.49 $49.40	

Break Time

A farmer counted the number of cows and chickens by counting heads and legs. If he counted 35 heads and 78 legs, how many cows and chickens did he have?

Credit Counselor

Career Cluster: Social Service Lee Jones is a counselor for a consumer protection agency. She helps people understand the cost of buying on credit.

Jim Nawrocki has a credit card from a company that uses the **average daily balance** to compute finance charges. The company computes the unpaid balance in the account each day of the month. The finance charge is based on the average of these daily unpaid amounts. Ms. Jones showed Jim how a weighted balance was used to find the average daily balance in his account.

Problem

Jim's unpaid balance on April 1 was $132.40. He charged $23.14 on April 15 and made a payment of $20 on April 21. The finance charge was 1.8% per month of the average daily balance. There was no finance charge on new purchases. What were the finance charge and the new balance as of April 30?

Solution

Strategy

- Multiply to find each weighted balance. Add to find the total.

Dates	Payment	Unpaid balance	Days	Weighted balance (unpaid balance × days)
April 1–20	——	$132.40	20	$2648.00
April 21	$20	$112.40	1	$112.40
April 22–30	——	$112.40	9	$1011.60
		Total	30	$3772.00

- Divide to find the average daily balance to the nearest cent.

Total weighted balance ÷ Total days ≈ Average daily balance

$3772 ÷ 30 ≈ $125.73

- Multiply to find the finance charge to the nearest cent.

Monthly rate × Average daily balance ≈ Finance charge

0.018 × $125.73 ≈ $2.26

- Subtract to find the balance after payment.

$$\begin{array}{ll} \$132.40 & \text{Unpaid balance} \\ -\ \ \ 20.00 & \text{Payment} \\ \hline \$112.40 & \text{Balance after payment} \end{array}$$

- Add to find the new balance.

$$\begin{array}{ll} \$112.40 & \text{Balance after payment} \\ 2.26 & \text{Finance charge} \\ +\ \ \ 23.14 & \text{Purchases} \\ \hline \$137.80 & \text{New balance} \end{array}$$

Conclusion

The finance charge was $2.26. The new balance was $137.80.

Related Problems

On June 1, the unpaid balance in Jim's account was $147.19. On June 11, he made a $25 payment. A purchase of $19.82 was made on June 17.

Complete this table to find the total weighted balance.

	Dates	Payment	Unpaid balance	Days	Weighted balance (unpaid balance × days)
1.	June 1–10	———	$147.19		
2.	June 11	$25			
3.	June 12–30	———			
4.			Total		

5. Use the information in the table to find Jim's average daily balance to the nearest cent.

6. The finance charge is 1.8% of the average daily balance. There is no finance charge on new purchases. Find Jim's finance charge to the nearest cent.

7. What is the balance after payment?

8. Find the new balance in Jim's account on June 30.

Find the finance charge to the nearest cent and the new balance at the end of the month. The finance charge is 1.8% per month of the average daily balance. There is no finance charge on new purchases.

9. Jan. 1: Unpaid balance of $34
Jan. 7: Payment of $10
New purchase of $18

10. Sept. 1: Unpaid balance of $88.14
Sept. 22: Payment of $25
No new purchases

11. Aug. 1: Unpaid balance of $108.75
Aug. 21: Payment of $60
New purchase of $32.98

12. May 1: Unpaid balance of $235.89
No payment during the month
New purchases of $76.54 and
$33.65

CALCULATOR APPLICATIONS

Some companies *include* new purchases when they determine a customer's average daily balance. They do this only when the customer has an unpaid balance from the previous month.

Alice Chen has a credit card from a company that uses this method. The finance charge is 1.8% per month. Complete the chart below to find the amount of the finance charge and the new balance in Alice's account on December 31.

	Dates	Payments	Purchases	Unpaid balance	Days	Weighted balance (unpaid balance × days)
	Dec. 1–8	——	——	$435.78	8	$3486.24
1.	Dec. 9	——	$23.97	$459.75	1	
2.	Dec. 10	$50.00	——	$409.75		
3.	Dec. 11–14	——				
4.	Dec. 15	——	$12.31			
5.	Dec. 16–23	——	——			
6.	Dec. 24	——	$18.99			
7.	Dec. 25–28	——	——			
8.	Dec. 29	——	$15.79			
9.	Dec. 30–31	——	——			
10.	Total			——	31	

11. Find the average daily balance to the nearest cent.

Total weighted balance		Total days		Average daily balance
▦	÷	31	≈	▦

12. Find the amount of the finance charge to the nearest cent.

Monthly rate		Average daily balance		Finance charge
0.018	×	▦	≈	▦

13. Find the new balance in the account.

	$435.78	Unpaid balance
−	▦	Total of payments
	▦	Balance after payments

	▦	Balance after payments
	▦	Total of purchases
+	▦	Finance charge
	▦	New balance

114

Minimum Payments on Charge Accounts

Most credit companies require that the customer make a **minimum payment** on the account each month. The amount of this payment depends upon the balance in the account.

A minimum-payment schedule may look like this.

New balance	Minimum payment
$0–$10	100% of balance
$10.01–$100	$10
$100.01–$200	$20
$200.01–$400	15% of balance
Over $400	20% of balance

Problem

Claire Thompson's charge-account statement showed an unpaid balance of $198.42. During the month, she made a payment of $150 and charged purchases of $227.65. The finance charge on the statement was $0.73. What was her new balance at the end of the month? What was the minimum payment required?

Solution

Strategy

- Subtract to find the balance after payment.

$198.42	Unpaid balance
− 150.00	Payment
$ 48.42	Balance after payment

- Add to find the new balance.

$ 48.42	Balance after payment
0.73	Finance charge
+ 227.65	Purchases
$276.80	New balance

- Read the schedule for minimum-payment terms.   15% of balance

- Multiply to find the minimum payment.   0.15 × $276.80 = $41.52

Conclusion

The new balance was $276.80. The minimum payment required was $41.52.

Related Problems

Complete the table. Use the minimum-payment schedule above. Round to the nearest cent.

	Unpaid balance	Payment	Balance after payment	Finance charge	Purchases	New balance	Minimum payment
1.	$52.16	$10.00		$0.78	$11.76		
2.	$85.49	$10.00		$1.13	$76.35		
3.	$127.36	$20.00		$1.61	$85.50		
4.	$178.28	$20.00		$2.37	$107.00		
5.	$225.93	$35.00		$2.86	$0		
6.	$418.73	$125.00		$4.41	$0		
7.	$129.68	$120.00		$0.15	$0		
8.	$629.58	$629.58		$0	$9.55		

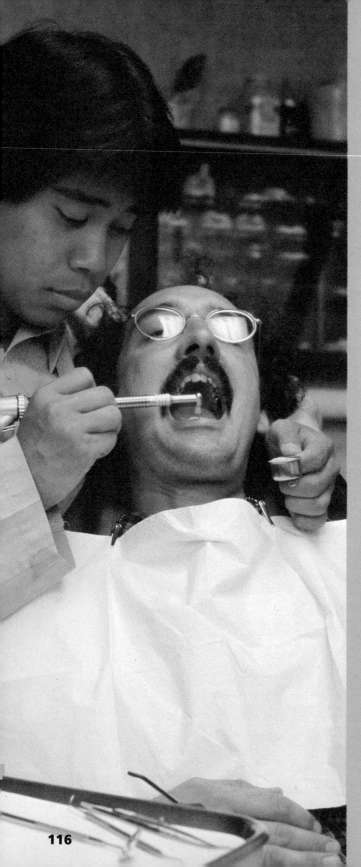

Level-Payment Loans

For many people, the best credit arrangement is a **level-payment loan.** This type of loan is repaid in equal monthly payments.

The calculations needed to determine the amount of each payment are very complicated, so lenders use a table like the one on page 401. Part of the table is shown below.

	Monthly Payment per $1 Borrowed			
Annual rate	Number of equal monthly payments			
	6	12	18	24
16%	0.17453	0.09073	0.06286	0.04896
16.5%	0.17478	0.09097	0.06309	0.04920
17%	0.17503	0.09120	0.06333	0.04944

Problem

Don Delfonso wants to borrow $300 for 6 months to pay dental bills. The annual interest on the level-payment loan will be 16% of the unpaid balance. How much will each monthly payment be?

Solution

Strategy
• Read the table for 16% with 6 payments.
  0.17453

• Multiply to find the monthly payment on $300. Round to the nearest cent.
  0.17453 × $300 ≈ $52.36

Conclusion
Each monthly payment will be $52.36.

Related Problems

Use the table on page 401 to find the amount of the monthly payment for each level-payment loan. Round to the nearest cent.

1. $500 at 18.5% for 6 months

2. $350 at 16% for 12 months

3. $700 at 15.5% for 6 months

4. $875 at 12% for 36 months

5. $300 at 22% for 30 months

6. $1100 at 14% for 24 months

7. $950 at 16% for 24 months

8. $950 at 16% for 36 months

9. $2500 at 18% for 18 months

10. $2500 at 16.5% for 18 months

Problem

Each month, part of Don's payment is used to repay one month's interest. The rest of the payment reduces the amount owed on the loan. How much will Don still owe on his $300 loan after the first payment of $52.36?

Solution

Strategy
- Use the simple interest formula to find the amount of interest at 16% per year for 1 month ($\frac{1}{12}$ year).

$$I = P \times R \times T$$

$$I = \$300 \times \frac{16}{100} \times \frac{1}{12}$$

$$I = \$4$$

- Add the amount of the loan and the interest to find the total amount owed.

$$\$300 + \$4 = \$304$$

- Subtract $52.36 to find the amount owed after the first payment.

$$\$304.00 - \$52.36 = \$251.64$$

Conclusion
Don will still owe $251.64 after the first payment.

Related Problems

Complete the table to find Don's schedule for repaying his loan. Round to the nearest cent.

	End of month	Amount owed	Interest for the month	Total owed	Payment	Amount still owed
	1	$300.00	$4.00	$304.00	$52.36	$251.64
11.	2	$251.64			$52.36	
12.	3				$52.36	
13.	4				$52.36	
14.	5				$52.36	
15.	6				$52.36	
16.	Total	——		——		——

Installment Buying

Instead of paying full price for an item at the time of purchase, people often pay only part of the price, or the **down payment.** The remainder is **financed** and paid in monthly **installments.** Buying on an installment plan is similar to borrowing money with a level-payment loan.

Like all credit arrangements, buying an item on installment costs more than paying in full at the time of purchase. The additional cost is the finance charge.

Problem

The Jamisons bought a color television set. The price, including tax, was $736.70. They signed an installment contract agreeing to pay 15% of the price as a down payment. The remainder, plus a finance charge, will be paid in 18 monthly installments of $41.16 each. What is the amount of the finance charge on the Jamisons' account?

Solution

Strategy
• Multiply the price by 15% to find the down payment. Round to the nearest cent.
  $0.15 \times \$736.70 \approx \$110.51$

• Subtract to find the amount financed.
  $\$736.70 - \$110.51 = \$626.19$

• Multiply the monthly installment by 18 to find the total amount paid in installments.
  $18 \times \$41.16 = \$740.88$

• Subtract to find the amount of the finance charge.
  $\$740.88 - \$626.19 = \$114.69$

Conclusion
The amount of the finance charge is $114.69.

Related Problems

Complete the table. Round to the nearest cent.

	Item	Cash price	Down payment	Amount financed	Installments Number of months	Installments Monthly payment	Installments Total paid in installments	Finance charge
	TV set	$736.70	$110.51	$626.19	18	$41.16	$740.88	$114.69
1.	Tool set	$249.50	——	$249.50	12	$23.11		
2.	Lawn mower	$269.15	——	$269.15	18	$17.43		
3.	Refrigerator	$829.95	$100.00		24	$37.15		
4.	Rug	$151.25	$25.00		12	$11.69		
5.	Water heater	$199.20	$25.00		30	$7.43		
6.	Typewriter	$289.16	$30.00		24	$13.19		
7.	Furniture	$615.23	10%		36	$20.58		
8.	Air conditioner	$499.85	20%		24	$20.35		
9.	Oven	$289.67	30%		36	$7.53		
10.	Sewing machine	$385.35	10%		30	$14.78		

Complete the table. Round to the nearest cent. To find the monthly payment for these installment plans, use the strategy from the previous lesson and the table on page 401.

	Amount financed	Annual rate	Installments Number of months	Installments Monthly payment	Installments Total paid in installments	Finance charge
11.	$500	18%	12			
12.	$500	18%	24			
13.	$500	18%	36			
14.	$500	21%	12			
15.	$500	21%	24			
16.	$500	21%	36			
17.	$500	21.5%	24			
18.	$500	21.5%	36			

Comparing Credit Plans

People can often choose from a variety of credit plans to finance a major purchase. They should compare the plans before deciding which one to use.

Problem

Victor Lopez wants to buy a piano for $1289. He can borrow $1289 from his credit union at an annual rate of 15%. He would repay the credit union $44.69 per month for 36 months.

Victor can also finance the $1289 through the piano dealer at an annual rate of 21%. He would repay the dealer $84.09 per month for 18 months.

What is the cost of credit for each plan? Which plan costs less?

Solution

Strategy
• Multiply to find the total amount to be repaid to the credit union.

$36 \times \$44.69 = \$1608.84$

• Subtract to find the cost of borrowing the money from the credit union.

$\$1608.84 - \$1289.00 = \$319.84$

• Multiply to find the total amount to be repaid to the dealer.

$18 \times \$84.09 = \$1513.62$

• Subtract to find the cost of financing through the dealer.

$\$1513.62 - \$1289.00 = \$224.62$

Conclusion
The cost of credit for borrowing the money from the credit union is $319.84. The cost of credit for financing through the dealer is $224.62. Financing the piano through the dealer costs less.

Related Problems

Use strategies from previous lessons to solve these problems.

Two stores are offering the same model home freezer for $469.95.

1. Ace Appliance Store will finance the purchase over 18 months with monthly payments of $31.12. What is the cost of credit for this plan?

2. Lakeview Department Store offers a 24-month payment plan with monthly payments of $23.92. What is the cost of credit for this plan?

3. Which store's plan costs less?

Al Marvin wants to borrow $800 to buy carpentry tools.

4. He can borrow $800 on a level-payment loan and repay it in 6 monthly installments of $141.22. What is the cost of credit for this plan?

5. He can borrow $800 on a promissory note at 18% interest for 6 months. What is the cost of credit for this plan?

6. Which plan costs less?

Gladys Smith needs to borrow $2800 for medical expenses. Use the table on page 401.

7. She can borrow $2800 at 18% for 30 months on a level-payment loan. What is the monthly payment? Round to the nearest cent.

8. She can borrow $2800 at 17% for 36 months on a level-payment loan. What is the monthly payment?

9. Gladys knows that the most she can repay is $100 per month. Which credit plan will fit into her budget?

George Menendez is buying a canoe for $357.88.

10. He can use his credit card to make the purchase. Use the schedule on page 115 to find the amount of his minimum monthly payment for the first month. Round to the nearest cent.

11. He can buy the canoe on an installment plan. The contract calls for no down payment and 18 monthly payments at an annual rate of 22%. Use the table on page 401 to find the monthly payment.

12. Which first-month payment is less?

Emily Franconi owes $400 on a credit card account.

13. She could borrow $400 from a savings and loan association and repay the loan in 4 equal payments of $104.11 each. What is the cost of credit for this plan?

14. She could pay $100 per month on her account and pay finance charges of 2% per month on the balance after payment. Complete the table to find the cost of credit for this plan. Round to the nearest cent.

Unpaid balance	Payment	Balance after payment	Finance charge (2%)	New balance
$400	$100	$300	$6	$306
$306	$100			
	$100			
	$100			
		$0	$0	$0
Total	——	——		——

15. Which plan costs less?

Skills Tune-Up

Dividing whole numbers, pages 12–13

1. $7812 \div 3$
2. $3124 \div 9$
3. $1098 \div 6$
4. $5642 \div 7$
5. $6614 \div 4$
6. $1997 \div 4$
7. $3885 \div 87$
8. $2059 \div 19$
9. $5971 \div 57$
10. $8274 \div 42$
11. $2716 \div 66$
12. $2488 \div 28$
13. $6412 \div 14$
14. $4880 \div 86$
15. $8176 \div 39$
16. $8449 \div 71$
17. $3266 \div 72$
18. $77,765 \div 24$
19. $45,493 \div 67$
20. $45,049 \div 58$
21. $65,971 \div 29$
22. $468,635 \div 81$
23. $299,641 \div 82$
24. $513,122 \div 62$
25. $971,169 \div 86$
26. $563,806 \div 802$
27. $64,737 \div 743$
28. $829,740 \div 283$

Dividing decimals, pages 12–13

Find the quotient to the nearest hundredth.

1. $14.69 \div 8$
2. $47.13 \div 7$
3. $20.34 \div 31$
4. $34.02 \div 41$
5. $4.154 \div 46$
6. $1.741 \div 67$
7. $6.5 \div 1.2$
8. $87.2 \div 0.6$
9. $0.7 \div 6.5$
10. $1.6 \div 4.4$
11. $48.58 \div 7.6$
12. $10.23 \div 4.8$
13. $0.731 \div 0.16$
14. $3.261 \div 0.57$
15. $56 \div 0.2$
16. $35 \div 0.7$
17. $8.7 \div 1.54$
18. $2.56 \div 8.75$
19. $6.41 \div 8.17$
20. $7.32 \div 4.75$
21. $0.1531 \div 2.87$
22. $0.614 \div 0.314$
23. $0.851 \div 0.613$
24. $0.3498 \div 0.071$
25. $0.6649 \div 0.092$
26. $0.9368 \div 0.045$

Multiplying fractions and mixed numbers, pages 16–17

1. $\frac{2}{3} \times \frac{1}{5}$
2. $\frac{3}{8} \times \frac{1}{2}$
3. $\frac{4}{5} \times \frac{1}{4}$
4. $\frac{1}{3} \times \frac{1}{2}$
5. $\frac{5}{8} \times \frac{4}{5}$
6. $\frac{7}{12} \times \frac{3}{7}$
7. $\frac{4}{9} \times 15$
8. $30 \times \frac{3}{10}$
9. $\frac{4}{5} \times 2\frac{1}{4}$
10. $1\frac{7}{8} \times \frac{4}{5}$
11. $5\frac{5}{7} \times \frac{7}{8}$
12. $2\frac{1}{2} \times 2\frac{1}{4}$
13. $\frac{1}{2} \times 6\frac{1}{4}$
14. $2 \times 3\frac{5}{7}$
15. $5\frac{1}{3} \times 1\frac{1}{8}$
16. $1\frac{1}{2} \times 8\frac{1}{2}$
17. $14 \times 1\frac{1}{8}$
18. $9\frac{2}{7} \times 2\frac{4}{5}$
19. $\frac{5}{8} \times \frac{16}{21} \times \frac{3}{4}$
20. $7 \times 2\frac{4}{7} \times \frac{3}{5}$
21. $\frac{2}{5} \times 10 \times 4\frac{1}{6}$

Chapter 6 Review

Promissory notes, pages 108–109

1. A promissory note for $1500 at 18% interest per year is due in 3 months. What is the total amount due?

Credit card finance charges, pages 110–111

2. The unpaid balance in an account was $127.30. A payment of $20 was made. The finance charge is 1.5% per month of the balance after payment. What is the new balance? (Round the finance charge to the nearest cent.)

Credit counselor, pages 112–113

3. On June 1, the unpaid balance in a charge account was $120. On June 15, a payment of $75 was made. There were no new purchases made. What was the average daily balance in the account during the month of June? (June has 30 days.)

4. The average daily balance in an account for the month of February was $130.50. The finance charge was 1.8% per month of the average daily balance. What was the finance charge for February to the nearest cent?

Minimum payments on charge accounts, page 115

5. The unpaid balance in an account was $75. A $20 payment and purchases of $155 were made during the month. The finance charge was $1.83. What was the new balance in the account?

6. The new balance in an account is $255.68. Use the schedule below to find the minimum payment required. Round to the nearest cent.

New balance	Minimum payment
$0–$20	100% of balance
$20.01–$100	$20
$100.01–$300	20% of balance

Level-payment loans, pages 116–117

7. Use the table below to find the amount of the monthly payment on a level-payment loan of $800 at 16% for 18 months. Round to the nearest cent.

Monthly Payment per $1 Borrowed				
Annual rate	Number of equal monthly payments			
	6	12	18	24
16%	0.17453	0.09073	0.06286	0.04896

8. A level-payment loan of $500 is to be repaid in 12 monthly payments of $45.84 each. The annual interest is 18% of the unpaid balance. Part of each payment is used to repay one month's interest. The rest of each payment reduces the amount owed on the loan. How much will still be owed on the loan after the first payment?

Installment buying, pages 118–119

9. The cash price of a sofa was $429.50. The customer agreed to pay 20% of the price as a down payment. The remainder will be paid in 24 monthly installments of $17.15 each. What is the amount of the finance charge?

Comparing credit plans, pages 120–121

10. Jim Adolf needs to borrow $500. Plan A will allow him to repay the $500 in 18 monthly payments of $32.62 each. For Plan B, he can repay the loan in 12 monthly payments of $46.56 each. Which payment plan costs less?

Chapter 6 Test

1. A promissory note for $300 at 19% interest per year is due in 6 months. What is the total amount due?

2. The unpaid balance in an account was $175. A payment of $60 was made. The finance charge is 1.5% per month of the balance after payment. What is the new balance? (Round the finance charge to the nearest cent.)

3. On April 1, the unpaid balance in a charge account was $75. On April 21, a payment of $15 was made. There were no new purchases. What was the average daily balance in the account during the month of April? (April has 30 days.)

4. The average daily balance in an account for the month of September was $60.50. The finance charge was 1.8% per month of the average daily balance. What was the finance charge for September to the nearest cent?

5. The unpaid balance in an account was $65. A $25 payment and purchases of $89 were made during the month. The finance charge was $1.60. What was the new balance in the account?

6. The new balance in an account is $231.15. Use the schedule below to find the minimum payment required. Round to the nearest cent.

New balance	Minimum payment
$0–$25	100% of balance
$25.01–$100	$25
$100.01–$300	25% of balance

7. Use the table below to find the amount of the monthly payment on a level-payment loan of $2000 at 18% for 12 months.

	Monthly Payment per $1 Borrowed			
Annual rate	Number of equal monthly payments			
	6	12	18	24
18%	0.17553	0.09168	0.06381	0.04992

8. A level-payment loan of $600 is to be repaid in 18 monthly payments of $37.72 each. The annual interest is 16% of the unpaid balance. Part of each payment is used to repay one month's interest. The rest of each payment reduces the amount owed on the loan. How much will still be owed on the loan after the first payment?

9. The cash price of a refrigerator was $850. The customer agreed to pay $127.50 as a down payment. The remainder will be paid in 18 monthly installments of $46.79 each. What is the amount of the finance charge?

10. Nancy James needs to borrow $1000. Plan A will allow her to repay the $1000 in 6 monthly payments of $176.02 each. In Plan B, she can repay the loan in 18 monthly payments of $64.28 each. Which payment plan costs less?

Unit 2 Test

Choose the best answer.

1. Carol earns $5.25 per hour. What is her gross pay for a 38-hour week?

A $43.25   C $57.75

B $563   D $199.50

2. Nan kept 80% of her $195 in tips. How much did Nan keep?

A $39   C $245.50

B $156   D $175

3. Mr. Morrow sells cleaning supplies for a straight commission of 40%. How much did he earn on a sale of $982?

A $392.80   C $245.50

B $589.20   D $3928

4. Vince is paid $175 a week plus 4% of all sales delivered. Last week his total sales were $4500. Orders totaling $750 were canceled. Find Vince's gross pay for the week.

A $355   C $150

B $325   D $180

5. Maria earns $150 a month plus 8% of her first $1000 in sales and 15% of her sales over $1000. Maria's sales for the month were $5500. Find her gross pay.

A $590   C $905

B $825   D $1415

6. Dale Snowbird's gross pay is $375 a week. His deductions are $77.10 for federal tax and $24.94 for social security. What is his net pay?

A $102.04   C $272.96

B $297.90   D $477.04

7. Mert's Market has an opening for a job that pays $12,000 a year. At Gary's Grocery, the same job pays $948 a month. How much more does Mert's Market pay per year?

A $624   C $11,376

B $52   D $1000

8. Su Lin has checks for $135.48, $9.34, and $97.20 to deposit. If she wants $80 in cash, how much will she deposit in her account?

A $162.02   C $242.02

B $322.02   D $106.54

9. The balance forwarded on a check stub was $225.75. A deposit of $100 was made and a check for $50 was written. What was the balance carried forward?

A $325.75   C $150

B $275.75   D $175.75

10. Find the new balance in this account.

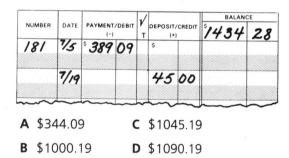

NUMBER	DATE	PAYMENT/DEBIT (-)	√T	DEPOSIT/CREDIT (+)		BALANCE
					$	1434 28
181	7/5	$ 389 09		$		
	7/19			45 00		

A $344.09   C $1045.19

B $1000.19   D $1090.19

11. The ending balance on a bank statement is $427.32. There is one outstanding deposit of $105.50 and one outstanding check of $39.84. What is the actual amount in the account?

A $361.66   C $281.98

B $572.66   D $492.98

12. A savings account of $1600 earns 7% simple interest per year. Find the interest earned in 9 months.

A $84   C $112

B $1008   D $1200

13. A savings account of $500 earns 9% interest compounded annually. Find the interest earned in 2 years.

A $594.05   C $49.05

B $545   D $94.05

14. Find the interest on $300 at 8% compounded semiannually for 1 year.

COMPOUND INTEREST TABLE					
No. of Periods	4%	5%	6%	7%	8%
1	1.0400	1.0500	1.0600	1.0700	1.0800
2	1.0816	1.1025	1.1236	1.1449	1.1664

A $324.48   C $24.48

B $49.92   D $349.92

15. A promissory note for $1500 at an interest rate of 18% per year is due in 30 days. Find the amount of interest due. Use 360 days for 1 year.

A $22.50   C $270

B $8100   D $225

16. The unpaid balance in an account was $95.50. A payment of $50 was made during the month. The finance charge is 1.5% per month of the balance after payments. Find the finance charge to the nearest cent.

A $1.43   C $0.75

B $0.68   D $0.71

17. In a charge account, the average daily balance for the month is $189.50. The finance charge is 1.8% per month of the average daily balance. Find the finance charge to the nearest cent.

A $341.11   C $34.72

B $3.41   D $192.91

18. A store requires a minimum payment of 20% of the balance in the account if the balance is over $200. Find the minimum payment on a balance of $330.20.

A $40   C $26.04

B $106.04   D $66.04

19. Find the amount of the monthly payment on a level-payment loan of $500 at 17% for 18 months. Round to the nearest cent.

Monthly Payment per $1 Borrowed			
Annual rate	Number of equal monthly payments		
	6	12	18
17%	0.17503	0.09120	0.06333

A $45.60   C $31.67

B $31.43   D $85

20. A loan of $850 will be repaid in 12 installments of $79.55 each. Find the finance charge.

A $104.60   C $954.60

B $745.40   D $929.55

21. Elsa financed a $2400 purchase with no down payment and 12 installments of $220.03 each. Find the total amount repaid.

A $240.36   C $2640.36

B $200   D $2620.03

Break Time

A jogging suit costs $17, and jogging shoes cost $24. Find the total cost mentally.

If one addend is a multiple of 10 (10, 20, 30, and so on), the addition is easier.

Here is one way to find 17 + 24 mentally.   Here is another way.

THINK   THINK

Add 3 to 17 to get a multiple of 10.   17 + 3 = 20
Add 20 and 24. 20 + 24 = 44
Subtract the 3 you added. 44 − 3 = 41

Subtract 4 from 24 to get a multiple of 10. 24 − 4 = 20
Add 20 and 17. 20 + 17 = 37
Add the 4 you subtracted. 37 + 4 = 41

The total cost is $41.

Use a *multiple-of-10* method to find each sum mentally. Write only the answer. In problems 22–28, add two numbers at a time.

1. 49 + 25	**8.** 79 + 14	**15.** 56 + 48	**22.** 36 + 44 + 8
2. 12 + 78	**9.** 27 + 39	**16.** 18 + 23	**23.** 27 + 19 + 12
3. 57 + 25	**10.** 44 + 66	**17.** 135 + 39	**24.** 16 + 58 + 11
4. 19 + 63	**11.** 66 + 95	**18.** 36 + 256	**25.** 57 + 18 + 51
5. 28 + 37	**12.** 77 + 77	**19.** 17 + 465	**26.** 63 + 49 + 77
6. 49 + 32	**13.** 23 + 98	**20.** 134 + 259	**27.** 38 + 89 + 12
7. 61 + 28	**14.** 84 + 48	**21.** 338 + 174	**28.** 23 + 99 + 36

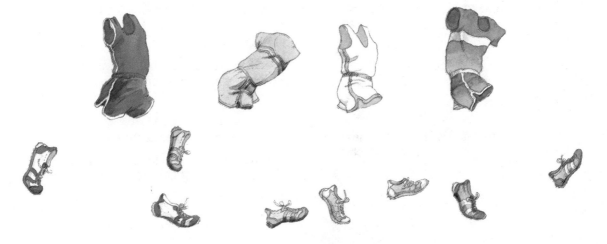

COMPUTER APPLICATIONS

Charge Accounts

Sylvia Bishop has a charge account at Meyer's Department Store. She received this bill.

```
        MEYER'S DEPARTMENT STORE
        CHARGE-ACCOUNT STATEMENT

BEGINNING OF JULY
  BALANCE                     87.5
PAYMENTS DURING JULY          20
FINANCE CHARGE ON
  BALANCE OF $ 67.5           1.01
CHARGES DURING JULY          23.18
NEW BALANCE                  91.69
```

The bill was prepared using the program shown on the next page.

Lines 30, 50, 70, and 90 Only these values need to be entered to prepare the bill.

Data required	Name
Name of month	M$
Balance at beginning of month	B
Total payments	P
Total charges	C

Lines 20, 40, 60, and 80 A PRINT statement before each INPUT statement shows what data to enter.

A semicolon at the end of the PRINT statement causes the computer to print the question mark for the INPUT statement on the same line.

All the calculations for preparing the bill are in the program.

Line 100 The unpaid balance (U) is calculated after the payment is made.

Line 110 The finance charge (F) is calculated using the unpaid balance and a rate of 1.5%.

Line 120 Many times the finance charge calculation will result in a part of a cent, so F must be rounded. Change F to a number of cents (*100). Add .5, then drop any tenths of a cent (INT), and then change F back to dollars and cents (/100).

Line 130 The unpaid balance, finance charge, and total charges are added. The sum is the new balance (N) to be used for next month.

Lines 140–230 After the bill is calculated, PRINT statements are used to print the bill.

Line 160 A PRINT statement with nothing following the word "PRINT" causes a blank line in the printout.

```
10 REM   MEYER'S CHARGE ACCOUNTS        130 LET N=U+F+C
20 PRINT "MONTH";                        140 PRINT TAB(8);"MEYER'S DEPARTMENT STORE"
30 INPUT M$                              150 PRINT TAB(8);"CHARGE-ACCOUNT STATEMENT"
40 PRINT "BEGINNING BALANCE";            160 PRINT
50 INPUT B                               170 PRINT "BEGINNING OF ";M$
60 PRINT "PAYMENT";                      180 PRINT "  BALANCE";TAB(30);B
70 INPUT P                               190 PRINT "PAYMENTS DURING ";M$;TAB(30);P
80 PRINT "CHARGES";                      200 PRINT "FINANCE CHARGE ON"
90 INPUT C                               210 PRINT "  BALANCE OF $";U;TAB(31);F
100 LET U=B-P                            220 PRINT "CHARGES DURING ";M$;TAB(30);C
110 LET F=.015*U                         230 PRINT "NEW BALANCE";TAB(30);N
120 LET F=INT(F*100+.5)/100              240 END
```

Give the output for the program above when

1. M$ is AUGUST, B is 211.85, P is 50.00, and C is 37.82.

2. M$ is SEPTEMBER, B is 748.53, P is 35.00, and C is 52.77.

3. M$ is JANUARY, B is 37.42, P is 37.42, and C is 23.51.

4. M$ is APRIL, B is 126.73, P is 25.00, and C is 0.

5. M$ is JUNE, B is 83.92, P is 40.00, and C is 27.35.

6. the balance at the beginning of May was $438.22, the payment was $62, and the charge was $16.87.

7. the balance at the beginning of February was $287.93, the payment was $35, and the charge was $29.68.

8. the balance at the beginning of November was $16.58, the payment was $16.58, and there were no new charges.

9. the balance at the beginning of October was $87.21, the payment was $10, and the charge was $19.58.

10. the balance at the beginning of March was $549.03, the payment was $20, and there were no new charges.

11. Modify the program so that it prints a statement about not receiving a payment.

12. Give the output when M$ is December, B is 237.45, P is 0, and C is 24.86.

13. Modify the program so that more than one purchase can be entered. Have the computer total the purchases.

14. Give the output when M$ is June, B is 356.92, P is 60.00, and C is 12.98, 45.87, and 123.66.

15. Modify the program so that credit for returned purchases can also be entered. Interest should not be charged on amounts to be credited.

16. Give the output when M$ is April, B is 20.72, P is 20.72, C is 0, and the $20.72 purchase is returned for credit.

17. Modify the program so that the rate of the finance charge is part of the input.

18. Give the output when M$ is January, B is 386.92, P is 50.00, C is 8.95 and 17.47, and the finance charge rate is 1.8%.

Unit 3 Transportation

Chapter 7 Buying a Car

New Car Sticker Price

The sticker price of a new car is the suggested retail price plus the cost of optional equipment plus the destination charge. A portion of a new car sticker and a sample price list for some options are shown below.

MODEL: Compact (2-door)
SUGGESTED RETAIL PRICE: $6833.49
Vehicle Identification Number:
3W18J2B675498

The following items are included at NO EXTRA CHARGE unless replaced by optional equipment.
- 2.5-liter L4 engine
- 4-speed manual transmission
- Fiberglass-belted blackwall tires
- Rack and pinion steering

Optional Equipment

Engines

2.8-liter V6 w/4-speed manual transmission	$125
2.5-liter L4 w/automatic transmission	$370
2.8-liter V6 w/automatic transmission	$495

Tires

Fiberglass-belted, whitewall	$75
Steel-belted, blackwall	
with 2.5-liter engine	$95
with 2.8-liter engine	$67
Steel-belted, whitewall	
with 2.5-liter engine	$110
with 2.8-liter engine	$78
Steel-belted, wide-oval, billboard-lettered	
with 2.5-liter engine	$135
with 2.8-liter engine	$119

Comfort and convenience

Power steering	$179
Power front disc brakes	$86
Air conditioner	$625
Electric rear-window defogger	$115
Cruise control	$145

Compact (2-door)

Entertainment

AM radio	$51
AM-FM radio	$68
AM-FM stereo radio with front and rear dual speakers	$100
AM-FM stereo radio with tape player and front and rear dual speakers	$174
AM-FM stereo radio with 40 channel CB	$413

Appearance and protection

Styled wheel covers	$59
Deluxe wire wheel covers	$129
Sunroof, tempered removable glass	$261
Landau top	$175
Vinyl top	$149
Protective body-side moldings	$44
Door-edge guards	$15
Bumper guards, front and rear	$38
Special-order paint	$181
Body-side accent stripe	$47
Sport-style mirrors, driver's remote	$53
Sport-style mirrors, both remote	$80

Problem

Jason Lee is buying a new 2-door compact car. The options on the car include automatic transmission (2.5-liter engine), AM-FM stereo radio with front and rear dual speakers, and steel-belted, whitewall tires. The destination charge is $285. Find the sticker price of Jason's new car.

Solution

Strategy
- Read the price list. Then add to find the sticker price.

$6833.49	Suggested retail price
370.00	Automatic transmission
100.00	AM-FM stereo radio
110.00	Steel-belted, whitewall tires
+ 285.00	Destination charge
$7698.49	

Conclusion
The sticker price of the car is $7698.49.

Related Problems

Use the suggested retail price and list of options given on page 132 for problems 1–10.

For problems 1–3, find the sticker price of a new compact car with the options given. The destination charge is $305.

1. AM-FM stereo radio with front and rear dual speakers
   Air conditioner
   Body-side accent stripe
   Fiberglass-belted, whitewall tires
   Landau top

2. 2.8-liter, V6 engine with automatic transmission
   Power steering
   Power front disc brakes
   AM-FM stereo radio and tape player with front and rear dual speakers
   Electric rear-window defogger
   Steel-belted, blackwall tires
   Bumper guards, front and rear

3. AM radio
   Sport-style mirrors, driver's remote
   Automatic transmission (2.5-liter engine)
   Air conditioner
   Cruise control
   Styled wheel covers
   Vinyl top
   Special-order paint

Nancy Parkins plans to buy a new compact car. She does not want to spend more than $8000. In problems 4 and 5, find the sticker price of a car with the options listed and a destination charge of $265. Then tell whether Nancy could buy either car.

4. AM-FM radio
   Air conditioner
   Electric rear-window defogger
   Steel-belted, whitewall tires (2.5-liter engine)
   Deluxe wire wheel covers
   Protective body-side moldings

5. Power steering
   AM-FM stereo radio with tape player and front and rear dual speakers
   Sport-style mirrors, both remote
   Steel-belted, wide-oval, billboard-lettered tires (2.5-liter engine)
   Sunroof, tempered removable glass
   Door-edge guards
   Body-side accent stripe

Jay Murphy wants to buy a new compact car. The options will include a 2.8-liter, V6 engine with 4-speed manual transmission, power steering, power front disc brakes, and styled wheel covers. The destination charge will be $285.

6. Find the sticker price of Jay's car.

7. Jay would also like a radio, sport-styled mirrors, and steel-belted tires. List the least expensive of each of these options.

8. What is the sticker price of the car Jay wants with the options in problem 7?

9. List the most expensive of each of the options in problem 7.

10. What is the sticker price of the car Jay wants with the options in problem 9?

Making an Offer for a Car

Walter Choi bought a new car. He bargained on the price of the car since he knows that the sticker price includes a profit for the dealer.

Walter used this guideline: Offer the dealer 10% less than the sticker price. Round the offer to the nearest hundred dollars.

Problem

Walter selected a new subcompact car. The sticker price was $6970. What was Walter's offer for the car?

Solution

Strategy

- Multiply the sticker price by 10% to find the price reduction.

$$0.10 \times \$6970 = \$697$$

- Subtract and round the answer to the nearest hundred to find the amount Walter offered.

$$\$6970 - \$697 \approx \$6300$$

Conclusion

Walter's offer for the car was $6300.

Related Problems

Use the guideline to find an offer for each car.

	Model	Sticker price
1.	Mid-sized	$9,200
2.	Subcompact	$7,300
3.	Full-sized	$9,780
4.	Sports car	$12,856
5.	Compact	$7,895
6.	Station wagon	$9,467
7.	Mid-sized	$9,386
8.	Full-sized	$10,212
9.	Subcompact	$7,480
10.	Compact	$8,427

Break Time

The hop-off at the Toad County Frog Jump featured four participants—Croaker, Longjump, Hopalong, and Gribbit.

After the contest, the following statements were made.

I won.
Hopalong came in second.
Hopalong beat Gribbit by 5cm.
Gribbit beat Longjump.

I won.
Croaker beat Gribbit.
Gribbit did better than Hopalong.
Hopalong beat Croaker.

I took first place.
Gribbit came in second.
Longjump came in third.
Croaker was a distant last.

I won.
Croaker came in second.
Hopalong beat Longjump.
Longjump finished last.

If each of the four participants made two true statements and told two lies, what was the order of finish in the race?

Finding Total Cost of a Car

Teri Bright plans to buy a used car. She must consider the total cost of the car. Besides price, the total cost includes sales tax, a title fee, a license-plate fee, and any repairs needed on the car.

Problem

The price of the used car Teri wants to buy is $1985. The state sales tax is 4% of the price of the car. There is a title fee of $5. The license-plate fee is $22. Teri took the car to a mechanic and found that the car needs a tune-up that would cost $92.45. What is the total cost of the car?

Solution

Strategy
- Multiply the price by 4% to find the sales tax.
  $0.04 \times \$1985 = \$79.40$

- Add to find the total cost of the car.

$1985.00	Price
79.40	Sales tax
5.00	Title fee
22.00	License-plate fee
+ 92.45	Repairs
$2183.85	

Conclusion
The total cost of the car is $2183.85.

Related Problems

Complete the table for each used car.

	Price	Sales tax	Amount of sales tax	Title fee	License–plate fee	Repairs	Total cost
	$1985	4%	$79.40	$5.00	$22	$92.45	$2183.85
1.	$825	5%		$8.00	$20	$142.50	
2.	$1495	4%		$4.00	$30	$81.45	
3.	$2295	3%		$5.50	$24	——	
4.	$1395	——	——	$10.00	$56	$163.79	
5.	$1845	7%		$6.00	$18	——	
6.	$2995	6%		$9.50	$75	$97.40	
7.	$3575	——	——	$7.00	$100	$56.95	
8.	$4350	4.5%		$12.50	$48	——	
9.	$2768	5.5%		$4.50	$35	$264.18	

Floyd Gates is comparing the total cost of different-sized used cars. His state has a 4% sales tax and a $6.50 title fee. Floyd can buy a 6-month license plate for $15. There is also a city sales tax of 1.5%.

The price of a used subcompact car is $1876.

10. Find the state sales tax.

11. Find the city sales tax.

12. The car needs new brakes that will cost $95.35. Find the total cost of the car.

The price of a used compact car is $2920.

13. Find the state sales tax.

14. Find the city sales tax.

15. This car needs new spark plugs. Floyd can do the work himself for a cost of $11.80. Find the total cost of the car.

16. Find the difference in the total cost of the subcompact car and the compact car.

Martha O'Brien wants to buy a new car. The state sales tax is 5%. The title fee is $6.

17. The sticker price of a new full-sized car is $8945. The license-plate fee is $34. What is the total cost of the car?

18. The sticker price of a new mid-sized car is $8250. The license-plate fee is $22. What is the total cost of the car?

19. Find the difference in the total cost of the full-sized car and the mid-sized car.

Shopping for a Car

Amy and Dudley Davis want to buy a new compact station wagon. They will receive a trade-in allowance from the dealer for their present car. The total cost less the trade-in allowance is the net price.

Problem

Amy and Dudley have shopped at three car dealerships and have found these prices for the same car.

Dealer	Selling price	Trade-in allowance
Penn Sales, Inc.	$8560	$1845
Richard Motors	$8500	$1830
Walker Motors, Ltd.	$8455	$1775

What is the lowest net price, and which car dealer offers it?

Solution

Strategy

- Subtract to find the net price at Penn Sales, Inc.
  $8560 - $1845 = $6715

- Subtract to find the net price at Richard Motors.
  $8500 - $1830 = $6670

- Subtract to find the net price at Walker Motors, Ltd.
  $8455 - $1775 = $6680

- Compare the net prices.
  $6670 < $6680 < $6715

Conclusion

The lowest net price is $6670, offered by Richard Motors.

Penn Sales, Inc. $8560   Richard Motors $8500   Walker Motors $8

Related Problems

Find the net price for each new car. Then indicate which dealer offers the lowest net price.

Subcompact model

Dealer	Selling price	Trade-in allowance
1. Suburban, Ltd.	$7385	$1260
2. Oak St. Motors	$7435	$1200
3. Field Sales	$7495	$1330

Compact model

Dealer	Selling price	Trade-in allowance
4. Pollard Motors	$8330	$1500
5. Central Sales	$8450	$1645
6. Colonial Motors	$8090	$1485

Mid-sized model

Dealer	Selling price	Trade-in allowance
7. Lutz Motor Co.	$9143	$2435
8. Oak Park Sales	$9328	$2470
9. Heritage, Ltd.	$9208	$2510

Full-sized model

Dealer	Selling price	Trade-in allowance
10. Cass St. Motors	$9842	$2580
11. Morris, Inc.	$9767	$2425
12. Wagner Motors	$9985	$2610

Luxury sedan

Dealer	Selling price	Trade-in allowance
13. Serota Motors	$11,204	$2665
14. Prospect Sales	$11,284	$2850
15. Viking Motors	$11,175	$2730

Sports car

Dealer	Selling price	Trade-in allowance
16. Village Imports	$13,529	$3135
17. Congress Motors	$13,589	$3375
18. Matulis Imports	$13,759	$3460

John Lauer is buying a new mid-sized car. The sticker price of the car is $8775.

19. The dealer agreed to John's offer to pay 8% less than the sticker price. Find the selling price.

20. The state sales tax is 7% of the selling price of the car. Find the amount of state sales tax.

21. The title fee is $6.50 and the license-plate fee is $28. Find the total cost of the car.

22. The trade-in allowance on the car he owns now is $2390. Find the net price.

Financing a Car

Bud Elliot must finance the new compact car he plans to buy. Financing a car is similar to buying on the installment plan.

The total down payment could include a trade-in allowance and a cash deposit made at the time the car is purchased. The remainder is the amount to be financed.

The sum of the down payment and the total paid in monthly installments is the total sale price, or deferred-payment price.

Problem

The total cost of the car Bud plans to buy is $8450. His total down payment is $1400. Bud can finance the rest of the cost for 36 months. His monthly payments will be $260.22. Find the finance charge on the loan. Then find the total sale price.

Solution

Strategy

- Subtract the down payment from the total cost to find the amount to be financed.

$8450 − $1400 = $7050

- Multiply the monthly installments by 36 to find the total paid in monthly installments.

36 × $260.22 = $9367.92

- Subtract the amount to be financed from the total paid in monthly installments to find the amount of the finance charge.

$9367.92 − $7050 = $2317.92

- Add the total paid in monthly installments to the down payment to find the total sale price.

$9367.92 + $1400 = $10,767.92

Conclusion

The finance charge on Bud's loan will be $2317.92. The total sale price will be $10,767.92.

Related Problems

For each car financed, find the finance charge and the total sale price.

	Model	Total cost	Down payment	Amount financed	Monthly payment	Number of months	Total paid in monthly installments	Finance charge	Total sale price
						Installments			
	Compact	$8,450	$1400	$7050	$260.22	36	$9367.92	$2317.92	$10,767.92
1.	Compact	$7,740	$1740		$302.45	24			
2.	Full-sized	$9,204	$3450		$209.47	36			
3.	Station wagon	$9,848	$2995		$437.26	18			
4.	Subcompact	$6,732	$1235		$231.60	30			
5.	Mid-sized	$8,655	$2475		$572.48	12			
6.	Sports car	$13,147	$4350		$320.24	36			
7.	Full-sized	$9,918	$3065		$201.31	48			
8.	Compact	$7,960	$1975		$380.45	18			
9.	Mid-sized	$8,539	$3650		$247.64	24			
10.	Subcompact	$6,825	$1525		$490.96	12			

Harry Bretzlauf purchased a new compact car.

A summary of his purchase is shown at the right.

```
        S A L E   S U M M A R Y

Suggested Retail Price.....................$ 6775.40
    Optional equipment.......$  959.00
    Destination charge.......$  280.00
Sticker Price..............................$ 8014.40
    Price reduction..........$  750.00
Selling Price..............................$ 7264.40
    Sales tax ( 5 %)........$   363.22
    License-plate fee........$   30.00
    Title fee................$    4.50
    Other charges............$    N/A
Total Cost.................................$ 7662.12
    Trade-in allowance.......$ 1645.00
    Cash deposit.............$  817.12
Amount financed............................$ 5200.00
    Finance charge..........$ 1029.92
    ANNUAL PERCENTAGE RATE...    18%
    Number of payments.......     24
    Monthly payment.........$   259.58
    Total of payments.......$ 6229.92
Total Sale Price (deferred-payment price)...$ 8692.00
```

Use the strategies on pages 132–141 to fill in a sale summary for problems 11 and 12.

11. Bessie Papanos bought a new compact car with a suggested retail price of $6845. The optional equipment cost $739 and the destination charge was $260. She agreed to a price reduction of $500. The sales tax was 4% of the selling price. The title fee was $5 and the license-plate fee was $18. Bessie's cash deposit was $3060.76. The remaining cost was financed for 24 months. Her monthly payments are $231.89.

12. Ed Verenski bought a new mid-sized car with a sticker price of $9120. The dealer agreed to Ed's offer to pay 6% less than the sticker price. The sales tax was 5% of the selling price. The license-plate fee was $25 and the title fee was $6. Ed received a $2500 trade-in allowance and paid a $1032.44 cash deposit. He financed the remaining cost for 36 months. His monthly payments are $198.83.

CALCULATOR APPLICATIONS

Truth-in-Lending laws require the lender to show the finance charge and the annual percentage rate on an installment contract.

An approximation of the annual percentage rate can be found by using the following formula when the payments are made monthly.

$$\text{Approximate annual percentage rate} = \frac{24 \times \text{Finance charge}}{\text{Amount financed} \times (\text{Total number of payments} + 1)}$$

Mel Nelson is financing the cost of a car for 36 months. The finance charge is $1815.40. Find the approximate annual percentage rate.

$$\text{Approximate annual percentage rate} = \frac{24 \times \$1815.40}{\$5600 \times (36 + 1)}$$

≈ 0.2103 Round to the nearest ten-thousandth.

$= 21.03\%$ Write as a percent.

The approximate annual percentage rate is 21.03%.

Find the approximate annual percentage rate. Round to the nearest hundredth of a percent.

	Amount financed	Finance charge	Number of payments	Approximate annual percentage rate
1.	$4975	$731.33	18	
2.	$5590	$1693.77	36	
3.	$7250	$1959.50	30	
4.	$6435	$1312.74	24	
5.	$6435	$656.37	12	
6.	$6435	$1969.11	36	
7.	$8100	$1348.65	18	
8.	$4627	$971.67	24	

Automobile Salesperson

Career Cluster: Business Contact Beth Hall sells cars. For each car she sells, her commission is 25% of the dealer's profit. The profit is the difference between the selling price of the car and the amount the dealer paid for the car.

The dealer also has a bonus earnings plan. Each car is assigned from 1 to 5 points, depending on the model and how long it has been in stock. The amount of bonus earnings is determined by the number of points earned by the salesperson during the month. The dealer Beth works for uses this schedule.

Number of points per month	Bonus earnings
0–14	$0
15–20	$75
21–25	$350
26–29	$650
30–33	$800
34	$1200
35–39	$1400
40	$1500

Problem

During January, Beth earned 24 points for the sale of thirteen cars. The dealer's profit on the cars was $6500. What was Beth's gross pay for January?

Solution

Strategy

- Multiply by 25% to find the commission earnings.

  $0.25 \times \$6500 = \$1625$

- Read the table to find the amount of bonus earnings for 24 points.

  $350

- Add to find gross pay.

$1625	Commission earnings
+ 350	Bonus earnings
$1975	

Conclusion

Beth's gross pay for January was $1975.

Related Problems

Complete the table below to show Beth's total gross pay for the year.

	Month	Number of bonus points	Dealer's profit	Commission earnings	Bonus earnings	Gross pay
	January	24	$6500	$1625	$350	$1975
1.	February	33	$7254			
2.	March	30	$6820			
3.	April	33	$7010			
4.	May	37	$7416			
5.	June	39	$7936			
6.	July	28	$6413			
7.	August	20	$5400			
8.	September	32	$7212			
9.	October	22	$6135			
10.	November	19	$3700			
11.	December	13	$3610			
12.	Total	——	——			

13. Beth accumulated 33 bonus points in February. If she had received 1 more point, how much more gross pay would she have earned in February?

14. If Beth had received 1 less bonus point in March, how much less gross pay would she have earned that month?

For problems 15–17, assume that Beth sold one more car in August for a $375 dealer's profit and 3 bonus points.

15. What would Beth's commission earnings have been for August?

16. What would her bonus earnings have been for August?

17. What would her gross pay for August have been?

Skills Tune-Up

Subtracting whole numbers and decimals, pages 6–7

1. 98 − 64
2. 74 − 45
3. 32 − 8
4. 60 − 7
5. 83 − 16
6. 49 − 40
7. 85.6 − 64.5
8. 73.7 − 4.8
9. 43.36 − 25.16
10. 92.75 − 38.27
11. 53.47 − 32.5
12. 80.53 − 34.8
13. 6.041 − 2.26
14. 57.349 − 24.78
15. 87.103 − 65.831
16. 55.028 − 52.356
17. 0.37 − 0.007
18. 35.68 − 4.649
19. 73.6 − 72.7
20. 17.3 − 16.7
21. 23.789 − 18
22. 9.006 − 7
23. 58 − 31.4
24. 82 − 39.3
25. 5 − 3.04
26. 43 − 26.32
27. 95 − 47.496

Writing percents, decimals, and fractions, pages 32–33

Write as a decimal.

1. 29%
2. 5%
3. 9%
4. 16%
5. 82%
6. 2%
7. 73%
8. $3\frac{3}{4}$%
9. 18.42%
10. 6.3%
11. $67\frac{1}{2}$%
12. 4.5%
13. 8.25%
14. $10\frac{1}{2}$%
15. 18.4%
16. 7.5%
17. $8\frac{1}{4}$%
18. 525%
19. $20\frac{1}{2}$%
20. 115%
21. 405%
22. $5\frac{3}{8}$%
23. 250%
24. 400%

Write as a percent.

25. 0.56
26. 0.83
27. 0.03
28. 0.08
29. 0.5
30. 0.17
31. 0.49
32. 0.9
33. 0.053
34. 0.528
35. 0.339
36. 0.75
37. 0.906
38. 0.159
39. 0.0125
40. 0.8237
41. 0.3225
42. 0.0875
43. 0.9054
44. 3.87
45. 5.06
46. 2.48
47. 1.121
48. 8.675

Percent problems, pages 34–37

1. 14% of 35 is ____.
2. 65% of 30 is ____.
3. Find $3\frac{1}{4}$% of 1200.
4. Find 75% of 493.
5. What number is 5% of 4140?
6. What number is 4% of 425?
7. 13.2% of 50 is what number?
8. 27% of 32 is what number?
9. ____% of 56 is 7.
10. ____% of 80 is 12.
11. ____% of 210 is 6.3.
12. ____% of 78 is 62.4?
13. What percent of 75 is 24?
14. What percent of 150 is 144?
15. 77 is what percent of 175?
16. 336 is what percent of 1600?
17. 12% of ____ is 3.
18. 95% of ____ is 756.2.
19. 44% of ____ is 149.6.
20. $4\frac{1}{2}$% of ____ is 54.
21. 76% of what number is 2.28?
22. 85% of what number is 51?
23. 21 is 70% of what number?
24. 6.8 is 80% of what number?

146

Chapter 7 Review

New car sticker price, pages 132–133

1. The suggested retail price of a new mid-sized car is $7725. The destination charge is $265. Find the sticker price with these options.

Automatic transmission $370
Power steering $179
Air conditioner $625
AM-FM stereo radio $100

Making an offer for a car, page 134

2. Marcie selected a new subcompact car. The sticker price was $6790. Marcie offered the dealer 10% less than the sticker price. What was Marcie's offer for the car? Round the offer to the nearest hundred dollars.

Finding total cost of a car, pages 136–137

3. The price of a used subcompact car is $1975. The state sales tax is 5% of the price of the car. Find the amount of the state sales tax.

4. The price of a used compact car is $2895. The license-plate fee is $32 and the title fee is $6.50. The car needs repairs that will cost $47.35. The state sales tax is 4% of the price. Find the total cost of the car.

Shopping for a car, pages 138–139

5. The selling price of a new car is $9360. The dealer offered a trade-in allowance of $2685. Find the net price.

6. Which dealer offers the lowest net price?

Dealer	Selling price	Trade-in allowance
Sayo Imports	$9253	$1765
Crown Sales	$9408	$1810
Park Motors	$9317	$1795

Financing a car, pages 140–142

7. Greg is financing $7135 of the cost of his new sports car for 18 months. His monthly payment is $456.93. Find the finance charge.

8. The total cost of Sam's new car is $9745. He made a total down payment of $3700. Sam is financing the remaining cost for 24 months. His monthly payment is $304.72. Find the total sale price.

Automobile salesperson, pages 144–145

9. During the month of November, Weber Motors made a profit of $5415 on the cars sold by Sue Willis. Find Sue's commission earnings if she is paid 20% of the profit.

10. The dealer Joe works for follows the bonus earnings plan shown below.

Number of points per month	Bonus earnings
0–14	$0
15–20	$75
21–25	$350
26–29	$650
30–33	$800

Joe earned 27 bonus points for the sale of fifteen cars. The dealer's profit was $6220. Joe's commission earnings are 25% of the dealer's profit. Find Joe's gross pay.

Chapter 7 Test

1. The suggested retail price of a new compact car is $6844. The destination charge is $285. Find the sticker price of the car with these options.

   Automatic transmission $370
   Power front disc brakes $86
   Power steering $179
   Steel-belted, whitewall tires $110
   AM-FM radio $68

2. A new full-sized car has a sticker price of $9410. Mary offered the dealer 10% less than the sticker price. What was Mary's offer for the car? Round the offer to the nearest hundred dollars.

3. The price of a used mid-sized car is $4425. The state sales tax is 4% of the price of the car. Find the amount of the state sales tax.

4. The price of a used subcompact car is $2385. The sales tax is 5% of the price. The license-plate fee is $28 and the title fee is $7.50. The car needs repairs that will cost $63.45. Find the total cost of the car.

5. The selling price of a new car is $8850. The dealer offered a trade-in allowance of $2975. Find the net price.

6. Which dealer offers the lowest net price?

Dealer	Selling price	Trade-in allowance
Auer Auto	$8758	$2200
Ridge Motors	$8694	$2250
Perrini Imports	$8627	$2300

7. Justin is financing $8365 of the cost of his new luxury sedan for 24 months. His monthly payment is $417.58. Find the finance charge.

8. The total cost of Bill's new car is $7875. He made a total down payment of $1900. Bill is financing the remaining cost for 36 months. His monthly payment is $219.04. Find the total sale price.

9. During September, Fargo Motors made a profit of $4560 on the cars sold by Janice Whitecrow. Find Janice's commission earnings if she is paid 25% of the profit.

10. The dealer Lily works for follows the bonus earnings plan shown below.

Number of points per month	Bonus earnings
0–14	$0
15–20	$75
21–25	$350
26–29	$650
30–33	$800

    Lily earned 31 bonus points for the sale of twelve cars. The dealer's profit was $5310. Lily's commission earnings are 20% of the dealer's profit. Find Lily's gross pay.

Chapter 8   Automobile Operating Expenses

Finding Gasoline Costs

The cost of gasoline for a car depends partly on the car's **fuel economy rate.** Fuel economy rates can be expressed as the number of kilometers traveled on one liter of gasoline.

Monica Shang and her brother Vincent kept records of their gasoline purchases during October. Each started with a full tank of gasoline and filled the tank every time more was needed.

Problem

Monica drives a 6-cylinder mid-sized car. Her record for October is shown at the right. What was her car's fuel economy rate and her cost of gasoline per kilometer traveled during October?

Date	Odometer reading	Amount of gasoline	Cost
Oct. 1	15,302.5 km	full	—
16		46.4 L	$17.63
31	16,077.7 km	58.3 L	$22.15
		104.7 L	$39.78

Solution

Strategy

• Subtract to find the number of kilometers traveled in October.

Oct. 31 reading   Oct. 1 reading   Kilometers traveled

16,077.7 − 15,302.5 = 775.2

• Divide to find the car's fuel economy rate in kilometers per liter. Round to the nearest tenth.

Kilometers traveled   Liters of gas used   Kilometers per liter

775.2 ÷ 104.7 ≈ 7.4

• Divide to find the cost of gasoline for each kilometer traveled. Round to the nearest tenth of a cent.

Total cost   Kilometers traveled   Cost per kilometer

$39.78 ÷ 775.2 ≈ $0.051 or 5.1¢

Conclusion

Monica's car had a fuel economy rate of about 7.4 kilometers per liter. The cost of gasoline was about 5.1 cents per kilometer traveled during October.

Related Problems

Vincent Shang has an 8-cylinder full-sized car. He kept this record of gasoline purchases.

Date	Odometer reading	Amount of gasoline	Cost
Oct. 1	41,850.4 km	full	—
10		57.5 L	$21.85
21		43.9 L	$16.68
31	42,955.1 km	68.8 L	$26.14

1. How many kilometers did Vincent drive his car during the month?

2. How many liters of gasoline did he buy?

3. Find his car's fuel economy rate. Round the answer to the nearest tenth.

4. What was Vincent's total cost of gasoline for the month?

5. To the nearest tenth of a cent, find Vincent's cost of gasoline for each kilometer traveled.

6. Vincent drives his car about 10,000 km in a year. How much might he spend on gasoline in a year?

For each car, find the distance traveled and its fuel economy rate to the nearest tenth. Then find the cost of gasoline per kilometer. Round to the nearest tenth of a cent.

	Odometer reading (km)		Distance traveled (km)	Amount of gasoline	Fuel economy rate (km/L)	Total cost of gasoline	Cost per kilometer
	Oct. 1	Oct. 31					
7.	45,800.2	46,149.7		57.0 L		$21.66	
8.	62,521.3	63,343.3		68.5 L		$26.03	
9.	18,462.5	18,704.5		60.5 L		$22.99	
10.	13,520.9	13,976.9		48.0 L		$18.24	
11.	8,743.1	9,085.6		76.0 L		$28.88	
12.	38,465.0	38,883.0		41.8 L		$15.89	

Depreciation

The graph below shows how the trade-in value of a car decreases yearly. This loss in value is called **depreciation.** The percents given in the graph are based on the price of the car when it was new.

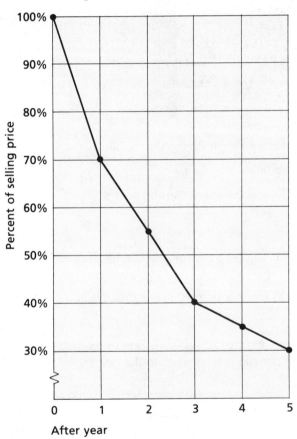

Average Trade-in Value

Percent of selling price

After year

1983   1984   198

Problem

Keith and Evelyn McLane bought a new car for $6300 two years ago. What is the approximate trade-in value of the car, and how much has the car depreciated?

Solution

Strategy

• Read the graph to find the average trade-in value after two years.

  55% of selling price

• Multiply the selling price by 55% to find the trade-in value.

  0.55 × $6300 = $3465

• Subtract to find the amount of depreciation.

$6300	Selling price
− 3465	Trade-in value
$2835	Depreciation

Conclusion

After two years the trade-in value of the McLanes' car is $3465. The car has depreciated $2835 in two years.

152

1986   1987   1988   1989   1990   1991

Related Problems

The selling prices of ten different cars are given. For each car, find its
trade-in value each year for 5 years. Use the graph on page 152 to help you.
Then subtract the trade-in value after 5 years from the selling price to find
the car's depreciation after 5 years.

	Selling price	Trade-in value after					Depreciation after 5 years
		1 year	2 years	3 years	4 years	5 years	
1.	$5800						
2.	$6000						
3.	$6200						
4.	$6600						
5.	$7100						
6.	$7700						
7.	$8500						
8.	$9000						
9.	$9700						
10.	$10,300						

Selling Price Based on Depreciation

A local rental agency is planning to sell some of its cars. The selling price of each car will depend partly upon how much the car has depreciated. The agency bases the amount of depreciation on the age of the car in months.

Age of car (months)	Monthly rate of depreciation
11 or less	2.7%
12 through 23	2.6%
24 through 35	2.5%

This rule is used for computing the amount of depreciation.

Monthly rate × Number of months × Original price = Total depreciation

Problem

The agency has a car that was purchased 1 year 4 months (16 months) ago for $6800. Find the total depreciation and the selling price based on depreciation.

Solution

Strategy
• Read the table to find the monthly rate of depreciation for 16 months.

2.6%

• Multiply to find the total depreciation. Round to the nearest dollar.

Monthly rate		Number of months		Original price		Total depreciation
0.026	×	16	×	$6800	≈	$2829

• Subtract from the original price to find the selling price based on depreciation.

$6800 − $2829 = $3971

Conclusion
The car depreciated $2829 in 16 months. The selling price based on depreciation is $3971.

Related Problems

Find the total depreciation for each car. Round each answer to the nearest dollar.

	Original price	Age of car
1.	$5720	21 months
2.	$5720	30 months
3.	$7500	9 months
4.	$6500	18 months
5.	$5200	24 months
6.	$6450	1 year 2 months
7.	$7325	1 year 7 months
8.	$6650	2 years 3 months
9.	$7000	1 year 11 months
10.	$7325	2 years 8 months
11.	$8500	1 year
12.	$9000	1 month

13–24. Find the selling price based on depreciation for each car in problems 1–12.

CALCULATOR APPLICATIONS

Fuel Economy

A car's fuel economy rate usually decreases if the car is driven at high speeds or if air conditioning is used. This table gives the fuel economy rates of five different cars driven at various speeds without air conditioning and with air conditioning.

Fuel Economy Rates

Car	Without air conditioning				With air conditioning			
	Speed in km/h				Speed in km/h			
	48	64	80	96	48	64	80	96
	Kilometers per liter				Kilometers per liter			
A	9.16	8.53	8.12	7.58	7.89	7.78	7.56	7.37
B	10.06	10.45	8.70	6.30	7.83	7.75	6.67	5.88
C	8.64	8.50	7.44	6.87	8.94	7.40	7.32	7.37
D	7.28	7.31	6.85	6.34	6.87	7.15	6.93	5.98
E	7.79	8.20	6.64	6.04	7.15	7.13	6.82	6.19

At each speed, find the average of the fuel economy rates for the five cars without air conditioning.

1. 48 km/h   **3.** 80 km/h

2. 64 km/h   **4.** 96 km/h

At each speed, find the average of the fuel economy rates for the five cars with air conditioning.

5. 48 km/h   **7.** 80 km/h

6. 64 km/h   **8.** 96 km/h

The table below shows that the fuel economy rate of car A without air conditioning is 4.81% less at 80 km/h than at 64 km/h. Complete the table to find the percent of decrease for the other cars without air conditioning. Round to the nearest hundredth of a percent.

Car	64 km/h rating (a)	80 km/h rating (b)	Change due to speed (c = a − b)	Percent decrease in fuel economy (d = c ÷ a)
A	8.53	8.12	0.41	4.81%
9. B				
10. C				
11. D				
12. E				

155

Automobile Mechanic

TUNE-UP

Career Cluster: Trades Russell Brandau is a mechanic at a gas station. Most of his work involves tuning engines and replacing parts that are worn out. Russell is paid 40% of the total charge for labor on each bill.

I HEREBY AUTHORIZE ALL REPAIR WORK AS DESCRIBED AND ALL NECESSARY REPLACEMENT OF PARTS.		CUSTOMER *Laura Red Eagle*		PHONE *555-0770*	OFFICE USE ONLY
X *Laura Red Eagle*		ADDRESS *8 Angeline Dr.*		CALL WHEN READY AM PM	
		MAKE	MODEL *6 cylinder*	ODOMETER *23,020*	
PARTS		TIME RECEIVED *8 AM*	TIME PROMISED *5 PM*	WRITTEN BY *Russ*	
1 oil filter	*$5.95*	LICENSE NO.	SERIAL NO.	DATE *11-27*	
1 fuel filter	*4.00*	JOB DESCRIPTION			LABOR
1 air filter	*6.25*	*20,000-km Inspection*			
8 spark plugs	*13.20*	*Engine tune-up*			*$55.00*
1 set points	*5.75*	*cln. battery, check PCV valve,*			
1 condenser	*2.50*	*new air filter, gap new plugs,*			
		check distributor cap and rotor,			
		replace and gap points, adjust			
		dwell, check timing & choke,			
		new fuel filter			
Total	*$37.65*	*Change oil, Lube chassis*			*4.50*
GAS, OIL, GREASE				TOTAL LABOR	*$59.50*
5 L oil @ 1.30	*$6.50*	CANFIELD SERVICE		TOTAL PARTS	*37.65*
Grease	*2.00*	4th St. & Highway A Canfield, Nebraska		GAS, OIL, GREASE	*8.50*
				OTHER	
Total	*$8.50*			TOTAL AMOUNT	*$105.65*

Problem

Laura Red Eagle brought in her car for a 20,000-kilometer inspection. What is the total amount of her bill? How much will Russell be paid for the work he did on the car?

Solution

Strategy

• Record the totals from the 3 sections of the bill.

• Add to find the total amount of the bill.
$59.50 + $37.65 + $8.50 = $105.65

• Multiply the total charge for labor by 40% to find the amount Russell will be paid for the work.
0.40 × $59.50 = $23.80

Conclusion

Laura's total bill is $105.65. Russell will be paid $23.80 for the work he did on the car.

Related Problems

Russell has completed the following work on Duane Beatty's car. Find the total for each section of the bill.

1.

JOB DESCRIPTION	LABOR
Tune - up	$55.00
Oil change, lube	4.50
Put on 2 snow tires	6.00

2.

PARTS	
Oil Filter	$4.95
Hose bracket	1.05

3.

GAS, OIL, GREASE	
4 L oil @ 1.30	$5.20
Grease	1.50

4. What is the total amount of Duane's bill?

5. How much will Russell be paid? (Find 40% of the total charge for labor.)

157

Find the total amount of each bill.

8. *Labor*
Replace muffler and tailpipe $32.75

Parts

Muffler	$45.15
Pipe	$14.90
Clamps	$2.60
Hanger	$11.53
Hanger	$3.36

9. *Labor*
Replace front and rear
shock absorbers $36.00

Parts
2 heavy-duty front
shocks with fittings $38.98
2 heavy-duty rear
shocks with fittings $38.98

Russell did the work listed on this bill.

JOB DESCRIPTION	LABOR
Aim headlights	$ 6.40
Adjust rear brakes	6.75
Check ignition timing	9.50

6. What is the total charge for labor?

7. How much will Russell be paid for this job?

Break Time

Do your skills go from A to Z?

Trace the letter A and cut it into 4 pieces that can be put together to form the letter Z. Try to do this without turning any piece over.

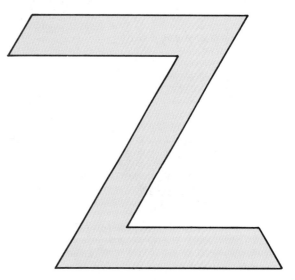

10. Find the total amount charged for labor in the two bills in problems 8 and 9.

11. How much will Russell be paid from these two bills?

Many people keep records of all of their bills during the year. How much did each of these people spend last year on automobile maintenance and repair?

12. Laura Red Eagle

Jan.	$26.25	June	$34.50
Mar.	$17.80	Aug.	$61.42
Apr.	$28.40	Nov.	$107.15

13. Duane Beatty

Feb.	$91.88	Aug.	$25.25
July	$45.20	Nov.	$74.15

Automobile Liability Insurance

Suppose you were a driver involved in an automobile accident in which someone was injured. If the court decided that you owed that person $35,000, could you pay? Most people could not, so they buy **liability insurance**. They pay **premiums** to an insurance company. The company then agrees to pay certain accident costs.

Liability insurance includes two types of coverage. **Bodily injury coverage** protects you financially if someone else is injured by your car. **Property damage coverage** protects you financially if someone's property is damaged by your car.

Some states require automobile owners to carry a minimum amount of liability insurance, such as 25/50/15 coverage. This means that in any one accident, the insurance company pays:

Bodily Injury
$25,000 maximum to each person you injure

Property Damage
$15,000 maximum to all persons whose property you damage

25/50/15

$50,000 maximum to all persons you injure

The premium you pay for liability insurance depends on the coverage you want, your age, where you live, how much you drive, and your driving record.

This table shows how annual premiums are figured by one company in a certain area. The base rates used here are for teen-aged drivers in the city. Rates vary greatly for different age groups and different localities.

BASE COVERAGE

25/50/15

BASE PREMIUMS

Teen male: $335.75
Teen female: $174.25

Premiums for Additional Coverage		
Type of coverage	Amount of coverage	Premium rate (Pay 100% of base plus:)
Bodily injury	50/100	9% of base
	100/300	20% of base
	250/500	33% of base
Property damage	25	2% of base
	50	5% of base
	100	8% of base

160

Problem

Gloria Stiller is 18. She bought liability insurance with 50/100/25 coverage. What is her annual premium? Remember, she must pay the base premium for a teen female, plus the premiums for additional coverage.

Solution

Strategy
• Use a percent to show the base premium rate.

100% of base

• Read the table to find the premium rate for bodily injury coverage of 50/100.

9% of base

• Read the table to find the premium rate for property damage coverage of 25.

2% of base

• Add to find the total premium rate for 50/100/25 coverage.

$$
\begin{array}{r}
100\% \text{ of base} \\
9\% \text{ of base} \\
+\ \underline{2\% \text{ of base}} \\
111\% \text{ of base}
\end{array}
$$

• Multiply the base premium by 111% to find the annual premium. Round to the nearest cent.

$1.11 \times \$174.25 \approx \$193.42$

Conclusion
Gloria's annual premium for liability insurance is $193.42.

Related Problems

If your liability insurance coverage is 250/500/100, what is the maximum amount the insurance company will pay

1. to each person you injure?

2. to all persons you injure?

3. to all persons whose property you damage?

Find the premium that Gloria Stiller would pay for each type of coverage.

4. 50/100/50

5. 100/300/50

6. 250/500/100

7. 100/300/100

8. 25/50/25

Gloria's brother Ray is 19. Find the annual premium he would pay for each type of coverage.

9. 25/50/25

10. 50/100/50

11. 100/300/100

12. 250/500/100

13. 50/100/25

14. Katy Olson is 17. Her liability insurance coverage is 50/100/25. She wants to change it to 100/300/25. How much will her annual premium increase?

Automobile Collision and Comprehensive Insurance

Liability insurance is only one part of a total automobile insurance program. Many automobile owners also buy insurance to protect themselves financially in case of damage to their own cars. This kind of coverage is usually required if you apply for an auto loan.

Collision insurance pays for the repair of damage on your car caused by an accident.

Comprehensive insurance pays for repair or replacement of your car in case of fire, theft, vandalism, or an act of nature, such as a flood.

To figure the premium for collision and comprehensive insurance, the insurance company classifies your car according to its age and the amount of extra equipment it has. Your premium will be less if your policy has a **deductible** feature. For example, with $100 deductible, you agree to pay the first $100 of any repair bill. Other deductibles are usually available.

This table shows one company's premium rates for Gloria Stiller's city.

Annual Premiums for Collision and Comprehensive Insurance					
		Collision premium for		Comprehensive premium for	
Car	Driver	$50 ded.	$100 ded.	No ded.	$50 ded.
Class B	Teen female	$338.66	$318.16	$69.20	$55.60
	Teen male	$652.54	$613.04	$69.20	$55.60
	Female, 25 and over	$181.72	$170.72	$69.20	$55.60
	Single male, 25–30	$264.32	$248.32	$69.20	$55.60
Class C	Teen female	$383.76	$359.16	$81.60	$64.80
	Teen male	$739.44	$692.04	$81.60	$64.80
	Female, 25 and over	$205.92	$192.72	$81.60	$64.80
	Single male, 25–30	$299.52	$280.32	$81.60	$64.80
Class F	Teen female	$402.62	$377.20	$89.60	$76.20
	Teen male	$775.78	$726.80	$89.60	$76.20
	Female, 25 and over	$216.04	$202.40	$89.60	$76.20
	Single male, 25–30	$314.24	$294.40	$89.60	$76.20

Problem

Gloria Stiller's car is rated as Class C. What would be her annual combined premium for collision insurance with $100 deductible and comprehensive insurance with no deductible?

Solution

Strategy
- Read the table to find Gloria's collision premium. Remember, she is 18, so find the heading "Teen female" in the Class C section.
  $359.16

- Read the table to find Gloria's comprehensive premium.
  $81.60

- Add to find the combined premium.
  $359.16 + $81.60 = $440.76

Conclusion
Gloria's combined premium for collision and comprehensive insurance is $440.76.

Related Problems

Use the rates shown in this lesson to complete the table.

	Driver	Class	Collision Deductible	Collision Premium	Comprehensive Deductible	Comprehensive Premium	Combined premium
	Teen female	C	$100	$359.16	None	$81.60	$440.76
1.	Teen male	C	$100		None		
2.	Female, 25 and over	C	$100		None		
3.	Single male, 25-30	C	$100		None		
4.	Teen female	B	$50		$50		
5.	Teen male	B	$50		$50		
6.	Female, 25 and over	B	$50		$50		
7.	Single male, 25-30	B	$50		$50		
8.	Teen female	F	$100		$50		
9.	Teen male	F	$100		$50		

10. Find Gloria Stiller's total annual premium for automobile insurance. Include liability, collision, and comprehensive insurance.

Annual Expenses

Gregory Brent, age 32, bought a new 6-cylinder mid-sized car 3 years ago. He financed the car with a two-year loan. This record shows his annual expenses.

	First year	Second year	Third year
Distance traveled	16,700 km	16,000 km	15,000 km
Depreciation	$1950.00	$975.00	$845.00
Fixed Costs			
Loan payments	$3250.00	$3250.00	——
Insurance	$458.49	$460.81	$423.13
License and fees	$49.00	$49.00	$49.00
Garage, tolls, parking	$275.00	$314.00	$256.00
Variable Costs			
Gas	$918.20	$902.00	$855.00
Repair, maintenance	$208.50	$245.39	$275.80
Radial tires	——	——	$144.70

Problem

During the first year that Greg owned his car, what was the cost per kilometer traveled?

Solution

Strategy

• Add to find the total fixed costs for the first year.

```
  $3250.00
    458.49
     49.00
+   275.00
  $4032.49
```

• Add to find the total variable costs.

```
  $918.20
+  208.50
 $1126.70
```

• Add to find the total cost for the year, including depreciation.

```
  $1950.00    Depreciation
   4032.49    Fixed costs
+  1126.70    Variable costs
  $7109.19
```

• Divide by the number of kilometers traveled to find the cost per kilometer. Round to the nearest tenth of a cent.

$7109.19 ÷ 16,700 ≈ $0.426 or 42.6¢

Conclusion

During the first year, Greg's car cost him about 42.6¢ per kilometer.

Related Problems

For problems 1-6, use Greg's records for the second year.

1. Find the total fixed costs.

2. Find the total variable costs.

3. Find the total cost for the year, including depreciation, fixed costs, and variable costs.

4. Find the cost per kilometer. Round the answer to the nearest tenth of a cent.

5. In the second year, which expenses decreased?

6. In the second year, which expenses increased?

For problems 7-11, use Greg's records for the third year.

7. Find the total fixed costs.

8. Find the total variable costs.

9. Find the total cost for the year, including depreciation, fixed costs, and variable costs.

10. Find the cost per kilometer. Round the answer to the nearest tenth of a cent.

11. What new expense did Greg have during the third year?

12. Why is the cost during the third year so much less than during the first or second year?

Alternatives to Owning a Car

Some people choose not to own a car because they can use **public transportation** such as buses, subways, trains, and taxicabs.

Problem

Ruth Steele lives 35 km from her place of work in the city. She takes a bus to and from the train station in her town for $0.60 each way. Ruth buys a monthly train ticket for $47.90. She walks to her office from the train station in the city. Find Ruth's monthly cost of traveling to and from work. Assume that each month has 20 working days.

Solution

Strategy

• Multiply to find the monthly cost of the bus.

Cost per trip		Trips per day		Days per month		Cost per month
$0.60	×	2	×	20	=	$24.00

• Add the cost of the train to the cost of the bus to find the total monthly cost.

$$
\begin{array}{ll}
\$24.00 & \text{Bus} \\
+ \ \ 47.90 & \text{Train} \\
\hline
\$71.90 &
\end{array}
$$

Conclusion

Ruth's monthly cost of traveling to and from work is $71.90.

Related Problems

For problems 1-6, find the monthly cost of traveling to and from work. Assume that each month has 20 working days.

1. $0.65 bus fare each way
   $45.60 monthly train ticket

2. $65.50 monthly train ticket
   $4.50 taxicab fare each way

3. $0.70 bus fare each way
   $0.20 bus transfer each way

4. $0.75 bus fare each way
   $0.45 subway transfer each way

5. $0.75 subway fare each way
   $0.30 subway transfer each way

6. $2.00 per week to neighbor for ride to and from bus stop
   $0.75 fare each way for express bus

7. Brett Bauman lives in one town and works in another. He takes two buses, one for $0.60 each way and the other for $0.75 each way. Find his monthly cost of traveling to and from work.

8. Find Brett's yearly cost of traveling to and from work.

9. Brett travels about 24,000 km to and from work each year. How much does he pay per kilometer?

10. Last year Brett drove his car to and from work. His annual expenses were about $2700 to drive the 24,000 km. How much did he pay per kilometer? Round the answer to the nearest tenth of a cent.

Another alternative to owning a car is **leasing** a car. A person pays a monthly fee to use a car. The car is returned at the end of the lease period. This table shows typical monthly leasing fees.

Monthly leasing fees				
Model	12 mo.	24 mo.	30 mo.	36 mo.
Compact	$195	$147	$138	$135
Mid-sized	$212	$158	$148	$145
Full-sized	$258	$189	$178	$175

Problem

Rick Velez leased a compact car for 24 months. What was his total cost for leasing the car?

Solution

Strategy
• Read the table to find the monthly fee. $147

• Multiply by 24 to find the total cost.   24 × $147 = $3528

Conclusion
Rick's total cost for leasing the car is $3528.

Related Problems

Find the total cost of leasing each car.

	Model	Number of months		Model	Number of months
11.	Mid-sized	24	16.	Compact	30
12.	Full-sized	24	17.	Mid-sized	30
13.	Compact	12	18.	Compact	36
14.	Mid-sized	12	19.	Mid-sized	36
15.	Full-sized	12	20.	Full-sized	36

Skills Tune-Up

Adding whole numbers and decimals, pages 6-7

1. $12 + 26 + 14$
2. $4 + 17 + 56$
3. $94 + 37 + 26$
4. $34 + 40 + 74$
5. $74 + 52 + 63$
6. $82 + 47 + 74$
7. $48 + 34 + 57 + 93$
8. $86 + 7 + 23 + 42$
9. $74 + 62 + 86 + 98$
10. $202 + 155 + 343$
11. $357 + 444 + 931$
12. $378 + 950 + 509$
13. $336 + 687 + 543$
14. $8.1 + 2.56$
15. $3.2 + 9.65$
16. $27.36 + 14.51$
17. $29.24 + 30.27$
18. $0.4 + 0.9 + 0.5$
19. $6.8 + 3.4 + 8.67$
20. $0.09 + 1.06 + 0.18$
21. $9.81 + 4.75 + 7.04$
22. $7.89 + 6.7 + 4.47$
23. $0.73 + 0.59 + 0.12$
24. $7.92 + 3.89 + 3.25$
25. $4.364 + 3.49 + 0.05$
26. $2.01 + 4.6 + 6.7 + 8.2$
27. $6.8 + 9.37 + 137.9$
28. $195.3 + 89.2 + 0.7$

Multiplying decimals, pages 10-11

1. 0.3×0.6
2. 0.4×0.5
3. 0.09×0.4
4. 0.07×0.3
5. 0.05×0.06
6. 0.11×0.04
7. 0.003×0.08
8. 0.06×0.011
9. 800×0.4
10. 600×0.7
11. 180×0.02
12. 0.09×500
13. 0.008×700
14. 400×0.001
15. 0.006×0.005
16. 0.003×0.009
17. 7000×0.0012
18. 3.4×4.2
19. 5.22×6.6
20. 5.2×8.23
21. 15.6×0.023
22. 8.367×9.72
23. 17.2×2.044
24. 4.17×0.3596
25. 16.76×0.374
26. 0.0027×5.46
27. 2.77×1.98
28. 38.09×0.006

Renaming fractions and mixed numbers, pages 14-15

Rename as a fraction.

1. $1\frac{3}{8}$
2. $3\frac{2}{3}$
3. $2\frac{5}{6}$
4. $7\frac{3}{4}$
5. $5\frac{1}{5}$
6. $2\frac{7}{8}$
7. $9\frac{1}{2}$
8. $6\frac{4}{5}$
9. $3\frac{5}{9}$
10. $12\frac{2}{3}$
11. $6\frac{3}{10}$
12. 5
13. 12
14. $4\frac{7}{12}$
15. $2\frac{3}{16}$
16. $8\frac{6}{7}$
17. $5\frac{9}{10}$
18. $7\frac{1}{12}$
19. $4\frac{8}{11}$
20. $3\frac{5}{16}$

Rename as a mixed number.

21. $\frac{9}{4}$
22. $\frac{17}{5}$
23. $\frac{3}{2}$
24. $\frac{23}{6}$
25. $\frac{13}{6}$
26. $\frac{10}{7}$
27. $\frac{14}{3}$
28. $\frac{11}{2}$
29. $\frac{65}{15}$
30. $\frac{45}{8}$
31. $\frac{21}{16}$
32. $\frac{36}{27}$
33. $\frac{19}{8}$
34. $\frac{48}{9}$
35. $\frac{36}{20}$
36. $\frac{37}{12}$
37. $\frac{67}{9}$
38. $\frac{48}{32}$

Chapter 8 Review

Finding gasoline costs, pages 150-151

1. Daniel drove 1482.4 km during August. He bought 218 liters of gasoline. Find his car's fuel economy rate.

Depreciation, pages 152-153

2. Estela bought a new $5600 car 3 years ago. How much has her car depreciated? Use the guideline that after 3 years the trade-in value is 40% of the price of the car when it was new.

Selling price based on depreciation, page 154

3. A rental agency is selling a car that was purchased 15 months ago for $6200. Find the total depreciation by multiplying the monthly rate times the number of months times the original price. Use this table.

Age of car (months)	Monthly rate of depreciation
11 or less	2.7%
12 through 23	2.6%
24 through 35	2.5%

Automobile mechanic, pages 156-159

Use this repair bill for problems 4 and 5.

TOTAL LABOR	$ 48.00
TOTAL PARTS	17.25
GAS, OIL, GREASE	6.50
OTHER	
TOTAL AMOUNT	

4. What is the total amount of this bill?

5. The mechanic is paid 40% of the labor charge for each job. How much will the mechanic be paid for this job?

Automobile liability insurance, pages 160-161

6. Gordon is 18. How much is his annual premium for liability coverage of 50/100/25? Use the table on page 160. Round the answer to the nearest cent.

Automobile collision and comprehensive insurance, pages 162-163

7. Marsha, age 17, has a Class C car. She is buying collision insurance with $50 deductible and comprehensive insurance with $50 deductible. How much is her annual combined premium? Use the table on page 162.

Annual expenses, pages 164-165

8. Kim Foss drove 15,000 km last year. She recorded these expenses for her car during the year:

Depreciation $1380.00
Fixed costs $2267.15
Variable costs $485.33

Find the cost per kilometer. Round the answer to the nearest tenth of a cent.

Alternatives to owning a car, pages 166-167

9. Harley takes the bus and the train to and from work. Bus fare is $0.60 each way. His monthly train ticket is $35.10. Find Harley's monthly cost of traveling to and from work. Assume that there are 20 working days in a month.

10. Glen leased a compact car for 12 months. Find his total cost for leasing the car. Use this table.

Monthly leasing fees				
Model	12 mo.	24 mo.	30 mo.	36 mo.
Compact	$195	$147	$138	$135
Mid-sized	$212	$158	$148	$145

Chapter 8 Test

1. Annette drove 1020.7 km during July. She bought 173 liters of gasoline. Find her car's fuel economy rate.

2. Howard Chinn bought a new $5900 car 5 years ago. How much has his car depreciated? Use the guideline that after 5 years the trade-in value is 30% of the price of the car when it was new.

3. A rental agency is selling a car that was purchased 30 months ago for $6500. Find the total depreciation by multiplying the monthly rate times the number of months times the original price. Use this table.

Age of car (months)	Monthly rate of depreciation
11 or less	2.7%
12 through 23	2.6%
24 through 35	2.5%

Use this repair bill for problems 4 and 5.

TOTAL LABOR	$ 68.40
TOTAL PARTS	15.50
GAS, OIL, GREASE	5.50
OTHER	
TOTAL AMOUNT	

4. What is the total amount of this bill?

5. A mechanic is paid 40% of the labor charge for each job. How much will the mechanic be paid for this job?

6. Elvina is 19. How much is her annual premium for liability coverage of 100/300/50? Use the table on page 160. Round the answer to the nearest cent.

7. Nick, age 17, has a Class B car. He is buying collision insurance with $100 deductible and comprehensive insurance with $50 deductible. How much is his annual combined premium? Use the table on page 162.

8. Hector Lopez drove 15,000 km last year. He recorded these expenses for his car during the year:

   Depreciation $975.00
   Fixed costs $1745.09
   Variable costs $792.73

   Find the cost per kilometer. Round the answer to the nearest tenth of a cent.

9. Lynn takes the bus and the train to and from work. Bus fare is $0.65 each way. Her monthly train ticket is $47.95. Find Lynn's monthly cost of traveling to and from work. Assume that there are 20 working days in a month.

10. Dick leased a full-sized car for 36 months. Find his total cost for leasing the car. Use this table.

Monthly leasing fees				
Model	12 mo.	24 mo.	30 mo.	36 mo.
Compact	$195	$147	$138	$135
Mid-sized	$212	$158	$148	$145
Full-sized	$258	$189	$178	$175

Chapter 9 Travel

Reading a Distance Chart

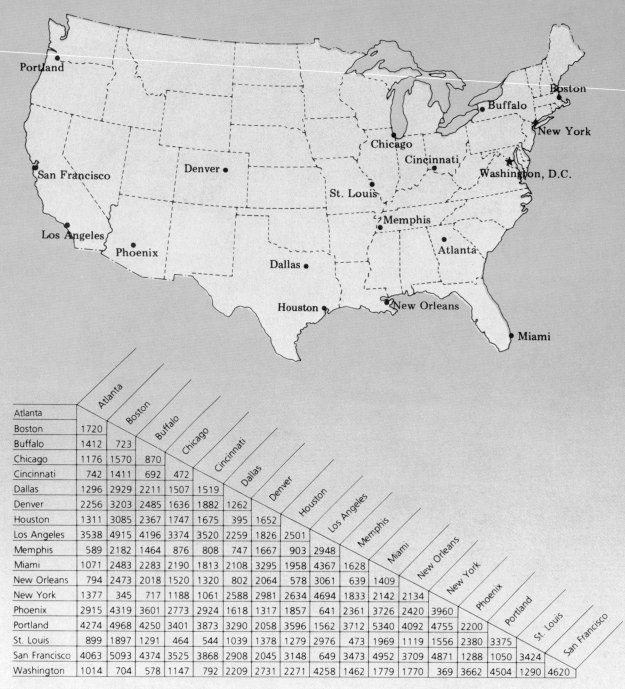

	Atlanta	Boston	Buffalo	Chicago	Cincinnati	Dallas	Denver	Houston	Los Angeles	Memphis	Miami	New Orleans	New York	Phoenix	Portland	St. Louis	San Francisco
Atlanta																	
Boston	1720																
Buffalo	1412	723															
Chicago	1176	1570	870														
Cincinnati	742	1411	692	472													
Dallas	1296	2929	2211	1507	1519												
Denver	2256	3203	2485	1636	1882	1262											
Houston	1311	3085	2367	1747	1675	395	1652										
Los Angeles	3538	4915	4196	3374	3520	2259	1826	2501									
Memphis	589	2182	1464	876	808	747	1667	903	2948								
Miami	1071	2483	2283	2190	1813	2108	3295	1958	4367	1628							
New Orleans	794	2473	2018	1520	1320	802	2064	578	3061	639	1409						
New York	1377	345	717	1188	1061	2588	2981	2634	4694	1833	2142	2134					
Phoenix	2915	4319	3601	2773	2924	1618	1317	1857	641	2361	3726	2420	3960				
Portland	4274	4968	4250	3401	3873	3290	2058	3596	1562	3712	5340	4092	4755	2200			
St. Louis	899	1897	1291	464	544	1039	1378	1279	2976	473	1969	1119	1556	2380	3375		
San Francisco	4063	5093	4374	3525	3868	2908	2045	3148	649	3473	4952	3709	4871	1288	1050	3424	
Washington	1014	704	578	1147	792	2209	2731	2271	4258	1462	1779	1770	369	3662	4504	1290	4620

Distances between cities in kilometers

Problem

Gene Papiri is driving from Boston to Dallas. He plans to stop in Memphis on his way to Dallas. How many kilometers will he travel?

Solution

Strategy

• Find Memphis on the chart and follow the chart across to the distance in kilometers listed under Boston.

2182

• Find Memphis on the chart and follow the chart across to the distance in kilometers listed under Dallas.

747

• Add to find the total distance.

2182 + 747 = 2929

Conclusion

Gene will travel about 2929 kilometers.

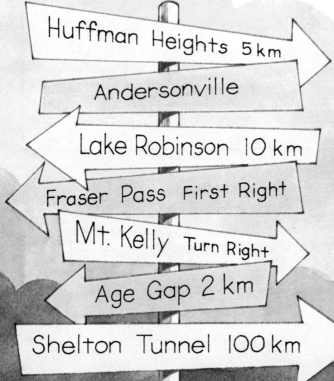

Related Problems

Find the distance along each route.

1. Washington to St. Louis to San Francisco

2. Miami to New Orleans to Phoenix

3. Cincinnati to Chicago to Denver

4. New York to Memphis to Los Angeles

5. Portland to St. Louis to Atlanta

6. Dallas to St. Louis to Buffalo

7. New Orleans to Los Angeles to Portland

8. Buffalo to Atlanta to Miami

9. Vancouver, British Columbia, is about 515 km north of Portland. Find the distance from New Orleans to Los Angeles to Portland to Vancouver.

10. Toronto, Ontario, is about 165 km north of Buffalo. Find the distance from Toronto to Buffalo to Atlanta to Miami.

11. How much farther is the distance from Houston to Washington by way of Cincinnati than by way of Atlanta?

12. How much farther is the distance from Phoenix to Chicago by way of Dallas than by way of Denver?

Lillian Barton is a regional sales manager. She is traveling from New York to Atlanta to Memphis to Cincinnati to Chicago to New York.

13. How far will Lillian travel?

14. If Lillian drives at an average rate of 80 kilometers per hour, about how many hours will she spend driving? Round your answer to the nearest hour.

Finding Distance and Travel Time

On this map of Wyoming, national interstate highways are shown in green, U.S. highways and state highways are in red, and other roads are in blue. Distances between dots are given in kilometers.

How to determine the scale

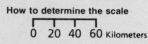

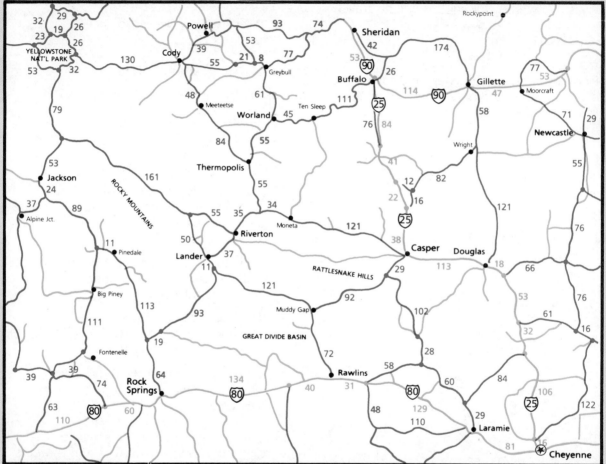

Problem

What is the distance from Sheridan to Casper? At a rate of 80 kilometers per hour (km/h), what is the travel time for this distance?

Solution

Strategy
- Add to find the total number of kilometers. $53 + 84 + 41 + 22 + 38 = 238$
- Divide to find the travel time. $238 \div 80 \approx 3$

Conclusion
The distance from Sheridan to Casper is about 238 km and the travel time is about 3 hours.

Related Problems

Find the distance along each route. Then find the travel time to the nearest hour. Use a rate of 80 km/h.

1. Sheridan to Powell

2. Gillette to Douglas

3. Rock Springs to Laramie

4. Rawlins to Cheyenne

5. Sheridan to Gillette by interstate

6. Sheridan to Gillette by U.S. highway

7. Casper to Douglas to Cheyenne

8. Casper to Laramie to Cheyenne

9. Jackson to Pinedale to Rock Springs

Problem

Julie Burdic plans to drive from Riverton to Casper on a local road. What is the measured distance from Riverton to Casper?

Solution

Strategy
• Using the scale of the map, mark off and label segments on a card.

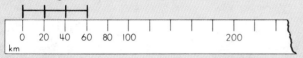

• Use the card to measure the most direct distance between Riverton and Casper.

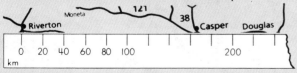

Conclusion
The measured distance from Riverton to Casper is about 170 km.

Related Problems

Measure to find the distance along each of these routes.

10. Ten Sleep to Moneta

11. Wright to Newcastle

12. Rockypoint to Gillette

13. Greybull to Meeteetse

14. Alpine Jct. to Big Piney

15. Fontenelle to Rock Springs

For each route, use the numbers on the map to compute the distance. Then measure to find the distance.

	Route	Computed distance	Measured distance
16.	Rock Springs to Rawlins		
17.	Lander to Muddy Gap		
18.	Pinedale to Rock Springs		
19.	Rawlins to Laramie		
20.	Muddy Gap to Casper		

For problems 21 and 22, use 40 km/h for the rate of travel on the roads shown in blue and 80 km/h for other roads.

21. To the nearest hour, what is the travel time from Riverton to Douglas?

22. Which route takes more time, Wright to Newcastle or Wright to Gillette to Moorcraft to Newcastle?

Expenses on the Road

Many people estimate their total expenses for a trip. The expenses might include costs for gasoline, food, and lodging.

Problem

Amy and Alex Thorson plan to drive the 1562 km from Los Angeles to Portland. They estimate that gas will cost $0.40 per liter and that their car's fuel economy rate will be about 7.8 km/L. They will spend 2 nights in motels for about $45 per night. They estimate that 12 meals (6 each for 2 people) will cost about $8 each. They are allowing $50 for other expenses. Find the total estimate for the cost of the trip.

Solution

Strategy

- Divide total distance by fuel economy rate to find the number of liters of gas needed to the nearest liter.

  $1562 \div 7.8 \approx 200$

- Multiply by $0.40 to find the cost of gas.

  $0.40 \times 200 = \$80$

- Multiply motel cost by 2 to find the cost of lodging.

  $2 \times \$45 = \$90$

- Multiply $8 by 12 to find the cost of meals.

  $12 \times \$8 = \$96$

- Add to find the total estimate, including $50 for other expenses.

  $\$80 + \$90 + \$96 + \$50 = \$316$

Conclusion

The total estimate for the cost of the trip is $316.

Related Problems

Find the total estimate for each trip. Round the amount of gasoline to the nearest liter. Assume gasoline costs $0.40 per liter.

1. Clifford White Feather plans to drive from Chicago to Minneapolis, a distance of 665 km. His car's fuel economy rate is about 8 km/L. He plans to have 2 meals for $6 each.

2. Lucinda Beran plans to drive 500 km from Pittsburgh to Philadelphia. Her car's fuel economy rate is about 9 km/L. She is allowing $10 for tolls and $5 for food. She plans to stay overnight in a motel for about $37.50.

3. Mr. and Mrs. Robb and their four sons are taking a 2300-km camping trip. They plan to spend $40 for campsites. The camper rental fee is $35 per day. While pulling a camper, their car has a fuel economy rate of 3 km/L. They estimate $30 per day for food for the 5-day trip.

4. Kristen and Jamie Cooper plan to drive 157 km to Houston to shop. The car's fuel economy rate is about 8.2 km/L. They are each allowing $7 for lunch and $200 for shopping. They expect to pay $6 for parking. They will return home that evening.

5. Ron Finkner is taking his two children to an amusement park. Tickets for the park cost $8 each. Ron expects to pay about $6 each for food. The park is 125 km from their home. The car's fuel economy rate is about 8.8 km/L. They will return home in the evening.

6. Six people are taking a van on a 400-km round trip to a football game. The van's fuel economy rate is about 5 km/L. Tickets to the game cost $12 each. Each person plans to spend $25 for food. Motel rooms cost $50 per room. Three rooms will be needed for one night. To the nearest cent, what is the estimated cost of the trip per person?

Break Time

Four jumbo jets and three super jets can carry as many passengers in five trips as three jumbo jets and five super jets can carry in four trips.

Which jet is bigger, jumbo or super?

Air Travel

For any given air trip, there are usually several different fares available. This summary lists types of service and the fares available for flights from Chicago to various other U.S. cities.

Fare code	Denver	Houston	Los Angeles	Miami	Minneapolis/ St. Paul	New Orleans	New York/ Newark
FARE SUMMARY from Chicago to							
One way							
F	$294	$223	$470	$226	$142	$198	$258
Y	$210	$185	$336	$219	$109	$165	$184
FN	$210	$185	$336	$219	$109	$165	$184
YN	$168	$148	$269	$175	$87	$132	$147
Round trip							
Ex	$289	$240	$520	$373	$186	$259	$316

Fares include Federal Transportation Tax. All fares and service are subject to change.

Explanation of codes
F—First class   FN—Night first class
Y—Coach   YN—Night coach
Children's fare (ages 2–11) for above: $\frac{3}{4}$ of adult fare

Ex—Excursion (round trip only)
Children's fare (ages 2–11) for above: One-way adult coach fare

Problem

Kathi Bishop and her children, ages 8 and 14, plan to fly from Chicago to Houston. What is the total fare if they fly night coach?

Solution

Strategy

- Read the table to find the night coach (YN) fare.
  $148

- Multiply by $\frac{3}{4}$ to find the child's fare.
  $\frac{3}{4} \times \$148 = \$111$

- Add two adult fares and one child's fare to find the total.
  $148 + $148 + $111 = $407

Conclusion

The total fare for Kathi and her children is $407.

Related Problems

Find the total one-way fare from Chicago.

1. One adult flying coach to New York

2. Four adults flying coach to New York

3. One adult and two children, ages 10 and 15, flying coach to Denver

4. Two adults and three children, ages 3, 5, and 8, flying first class to Los Angeles

5. Two adults and three children, ages 4, 7, and 10, flying night coach to Los Angeles

Find the total round-trip fare from Chicago.

6. One adult flying round trip night first class to Miami

7. One adult and one child, age 7, flying round trip first class to Minneapolis

8. Two adults and one child, age 3, flying excursion to New Orleans

9. One adult and three children, ages 4, 9, and 15, flying excursion to New York

10. If Kathi Bishop and her children fly round trip from Chicago to Houston, how much money could they save by flying excursion rather than by flying night coach?

Renting a Car

Dee and Stan Folsom rented a car during their vacation. The cost of car rental includes both a time charge and a distance charge. A chart listing the charges for various classes of cars is given below.

Class of car	Daily rate	Cost per kilometer
Compact	$19	$0.13
Mid-sized	$25	$0.15
Full-sized	$28	$0.16
Station wagon	$32	$0.20

Problem

The Folsoms rented a mid-sized car for 3 days and drove 401 km. What was their rental cost?

Solution

Strategy

• Read the chart to find the daily rate for a mid-sized car.
  $25

• Multiply by 3 to find the time charge.
  3 × $25 = $75

• Read the chart to find the cost per kilometer.
  $0.15

• Multiply by 401 to find the distance charge.
  401 × $0.15 = $60.15

• Add to find the total rental cost.
  $75 + $60.15 = $135.15

Conclusion

The Folsoms' rental cost was $135.15.

Related Problems

Use the rates in the table to find each rental cost.

1. Mid-sized car
   Rented 3 days
   Driven 500 km

2. Mid-sized car
   Rented 7 days
   Driven 975 km

3. Full-sized car
   Rented 2 days
   Driven 585 km

4. Full-sized car
   Rented 1 day
   Driven 42 km

5. Compact car
   Rented 6 days
   Driven 1137 km

6. Mid-sized car
   Rented 1 day
   Driven 217 km

7. Compact car
   Rented 4 days
   Driven 478 km

8. Station wagon
   Rented 2 days
   Driven 620 km

9. Full-sized car
   Rented 2 days
   Driven 974 km

10. If the distance driven is 850 km, how much less does it cost to rent a compact car than to rent a station wagon for 3 days?

CALCULATOR APPLICATIONS

Complete the table. Find the number of kilometers driven by subtracting the "start" reading from the "end" reading. Use the rental rates given on page 180.

	Class	Odometer		Distance driven	Distance charge	Number of days	Time charge	Rental cost
		Start	End					
1.	Mid-sized	6,285	7,113			7		
2.	Mid-sized	11,247	11,697			4		
3.	Full-sized	9,505	10,049			4		
4.	Full-sized	8,377	8,424			1		
5.	Station wagon	30,621	31,000			3		
6.	Station wagon	27,926	28,555			3		

The rental agency has this special rate.

COMPACT GETAWAY SPECIAL

7 days w/1600 km	$129
Each day over 7	$19
Each km over 1600	$0.20

For $129 a customer can rent a compact car for as long as 7 days and drive it as far as 1600 km.

However, if the car is kept longer and/or driven farther, there are extra charges. If a car is rented for 10 days and driven 2000 km, the extra charges are for 3 days (10 − 7) and for 400 km (2000 − 1600).

$129	Basic charge
57	Extra time (3 × $19)
+ 80	Extra distance (400 × $0.20)
$266	Rental cost

Find the rental cost using the *Compact Getaway Special* rate.

7. Rent for 10 days; drive 1700 km

8. Rent for 9 days; drive 2054 km

9. Rent for 10 days; drive 1200 km

10. Rent for 5 days; drive 1961 km

11. Rent for 3 days; drive 1400 km

12. Rent for 8 days; drive 737 km

13. Rent for 7 days; drive 2700 km

14. Using the rental rates on page 180, find the cost of renting a compact car for 7 days and driving 2700 km.

15. Use your answers to problems 13 and 14. Which rate costs less? How much less does the rate cost?

Travel Agent

Career Cluster: Business Contact Gordon Wickes is a travel agent at the Cross-Country Travel Agency. He points out to his customers the advantages of various methods of travel.

Gordon prepared this chart for a trip from Denver to San Francisco.

One-way costs, per person	Bus	Denver to San Francisco Train		Plane	
Adult fare	$115	Coach Single slumber Bedroom (2 people)	$142 $202 $519	F Y FN YN	$318 $204 $227 $182
Children's fare (ages 2–11)	$\frac{1}{2}$ adult fare	$\frac{1}{2}$ adult fare		$\frac{3}{4}$ adult fare	
Meals	About $20	About $35		No charge	
Transportation to center of city	None	None		$8–$20	

Problem

Harriet Kaplan and her daughter, age 10, asked Gordon for an estimate of the cost of taking a bus from Denver to San Francisco. What was Gordon's estimate of their travel expenses?

Solution

Strategy

- Read the table to find the adult fare. $115

- Multiply by $\frac{1}{2}$ to find a child's fare. $\frac{1}{2} \times \$115 = \$57.50$

- Multiply the meal cost by 2 to find the cost of food for two people. $2 \times \$20 = \$40$

- Add to find the total. $\$115 + \$57.50 + \$40 = \$212.50$

Conclusion

Gordon's estimate was $212.50.

Related Problems

Find the travel expenses for one adult going from Denver to San Francisco.

1. By bus

2. By train, single slumber

3. By plane, coach (Y). Allow $8 for bus to hotel.

4. By plane, first class (F). Allow $18 for taxi to hotel.

Find the travel expenses for two adults and one child, age 8, going from Denver to San Francisco.

5. By bus

6. By train, coach

7. By plane, coach (Y). Allow $8 each for bus to hotel.

8. By plane, first class (F). Allow $18 for a taxi for all three people.

9. Find the round-trip cost from Denver to San Francisco for four adults using two bedrooms on the train.

10. Which method costs less for four adults going round trip from Denver to San Francisco: by train, renting two bedrooms; or by plane, flying night coach (YN)? How much less?

Skills Tune-Up

Dividing decimals, pages 12–13

Find the quotient to the nearest hundredth.

1. $43.17 \div 4$
2. $53.56 \div 8$
3. $5.857 \div 77$
4. $0.0095 \div 0.14$
5. $8.71 \div 0.62$
6. $87.5 \div 6.2$
7. $5.4 \div 6.7$
8. $1.7 \div 3.24$
9. $32.1 \div 5.12$
10. $5.98 \div 5.06$
11. $71.9 \div 6.02$
12. $42.1 \div 6.92$

Find the quotient to the nearest whole number.

13. $28.7 \div 5$
14. $96.9 \div 8$
15. $21.41 \div 3.7$
16. $18.98 \div 9.3$
17. $15.09 \div 5.2$
18. $0.345 \div 0.06$
19. $0.561 \div 0.07$
20. $68 \div 0.4$
21. $64 \div 0.8$
22. $0.353 \div 0.174$
23. $0.7456 \div 0.023$
24. $0.3331 \div 0.042$

Adding fractions and mixed numbers, pages 18–19

1. $\frac{1}{3} + \frac{3}{4}$
2. $\frac{1}{14} + \frac{3}{7}$
3. $\frac{7}{12} + \frac{3}{4}$
4. $\frac{4}{7} + \frac{2}{21}$
5. $\frac{1}{2} + \frac{4}{7}$
6. $\frac{2}{15} + \frac{2}{3}$
7. $\frac{8}{9} + \frac{5}{12}$
8. $5\frac{1}{8} + \frac{11}{12}$
9. $\frac{1}{6} + 3\frac{9}{10}$
10. $4\frac{3}{4} + \frac{2}{9}$
11. $5\frac{3}{4} + 2\frac{7}{12}$
12. $7\frac{4}{5} + 8\frac{9}{20}$
13. $4\frac{7}{9} + 3\frac{1}{18}$
14. $3\frac{1}{4} + 1\frac{7}{8}$
15. $1\frac{1}{3} + 5\frac{3}{5}$
16. $2\frac{7}{10} + 8\frac{1}{6}$
17. $5\frac{9}{16} + 2\frac{5}{8}$
18. $3\frac{3}{8} + 5\frac{1}{5}$
19. $4\frac{9}{10} + 3\frac{1}{2} + 10\frac{3}{5}$
20. $13\frac{1}{3} + 4\frac{4}{5} + 6\frac{1}{2}$
21. $8\frac{1}{3} + 6\frac{3}{4} + 3\frac{5}{8}$

Subtracting fractions and mixed numbers, pages 18–19

1. $\frac{5}{6} - \frac{1}{3}$
2. $\frac{3}{4} - \frac{1}{2}$
3. $\frac{7}{8} - \frac{1}{2}$
4. $\frac{2}{3} - \frac{1}{5}$
5. $\frac{7}{8} - \frac{1}{6}$
6. $\frac{2}{3} - \frac{1}{2}$
7. $\frac{4}{7} - \frac{1}{2}$
8. $\frac{7}{10} - \frac{1}{4}$
9. $3 - \frac{5}{8}$
10. $12 - \frac{1}{5}$
11. $6\frac{1}{8} - 3\frac{5}{8}$
12. $9\frac{5}{8} - 3\frac{7}{8}$
13. $11 - 6\frac{2}{3}$
14. $6 - 5\frac{7}{10}$
15. $13\frac{7}{8} - 4\frac{5}{16}$
16. $16\frac{4}{5} - 9\frac{3}{4}$
17. $19\frac{3}{10} - 12\frac{5}{6}$
18. $8\frac{1}{3} - 4\frac{8}{15}$
19. $15\frac{5}{6} - 9\frac{1}{2}$
20. $16\frac{3}{10} - 7\frac{7}{15}$
21. $10\frac{1}{4} - 2\frac{5}{6}$

Chapter 9 Review

Reading a distance chart, pages 172–173

1. Use the chart below to find the distance from Atlanta to Cincinnati to Chicago.

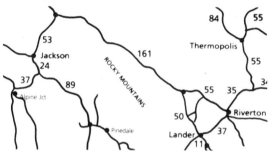

	Atlanta	Boston	Buffalo	Chicago	Cincinnati
Atlanta					
Boston	1720				
Buffalo	1412	723			
Chicago	1176	1570	870		
Cincinnati	742	1411	692	472	
Dallas	1296	2929	2211	1507	1519

Distances between cities in kilometers

Finding distance and travel time, pages 174–175

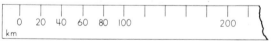

2. Distances on the map are given in kilometers. What is the distance from Jackson to Riverton?

3. Copy the card below to measure the distance between Jackson and Pinedale.

Expenses on the road, pages 176–177

4. Warren Crown has planned a 1260-km trip. His car's fuel economy rate is about 6.2 km/L. If gas costs $0.40 per liter, find the cost of gas for Warren's trip. (Round the amount of gas to the nearest liter.)

5. Linda Nelson has planned a trip. She is allowing $50 for gasoline, $20 for meals, and $3 for tolls. Find her total travel expense.

Air travel, pages 178–179

FARE SUMMARY from Chicago to			
Fare code	Denver	Houston	Los Angeles
One way			
F	$294	$223	$470
Y	$210	$185	$336

6. Find the total one-way fare for two adults and one child, age 6, flying coach (Y) from Chicago to Houston. A child's fare is $\frac{3}{4}$ of an adult fare.

7. Find the round-trip fare for two adults flying first class (F) from Chicago to Los Angeles.

Renting a car, page 180

8. Molly Little Horse rented a car for 4 days, driving it 673 km. She was charged $25 per day and $0.15 per kilometer driven. Find her rental cost.

Travel agent, pages 182–183

One-way costs	Denver to San Francisco			
		Train		Plane
Adult fare	Coach	$142	F	$318
	Single slumber	$202	Y	$204
	Bedroom (2 people)	$519	FN	$227
			YN	$182

9. Find the total travel expense for three adults going from Denver to San Francisco by train in 3 single slumbers.

10. Find the travel expense for three adults flying first class (F) from Denver to San Francisco and sharing a taxi for $15.

Chapter 9 Test

1. Use the chart below to find the distance from Dallas to Chicago to Boston.

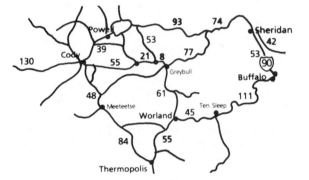

	Atlanta	Boston	Buffalo	Chicago	Cincinnati	Dallas
Atlanta						
Boston	1720					
Buffalo	1412	723				
Chicago	1176	1570	870			
Cincinnati	742	1411	692	472		
Dallas	1296	2929	2211	1507	1519	
Denver	2256	3203	2485	1636	1882	1262

Distances between cities in kilometers

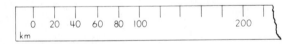

2. Distances on the map are given in kilometers. What is the distance from Cody to Greybull?

3. Copy the card below to measure the distance between Cody and Thermopolis.

```
0  20  40  60  80  100        200
km
```

4. Bill Binkoff has planned a 926-km trip. His car's fuel economy rate is about 7.2 km/L. If gas costs $0.40 per liter, find the cost of gas for Bill's trip. (Round the amount of gas to the nearest liter.)

5. Dave Olson has planned a trip. He is allowing $60 for gasoline, $35 for meals, and $90 for motels. Find Dave's total travel expense.

FARE SUMMARY from Chicago to			
Fare code	Denver	Houston	Los Angeles
One way			
F	$294	$223	$470
Y	$210	$185	$336

6. Find the total one-way fare for two adults and one child, age 4, flying first class (F) from Chicago to Denver. A child's fare is $\frac{3}{4}$ of an adult fare.

7. Find the round-trip fare for two adults flying coach (Y) from Chicago to Houston.

8. Lee Parks rented a car for 5 days, driving it 523 km. She was charged $28 per day and $0.16 per kilometer driven. Find her rental cost.

One-way costs Denver to San Francisco				
		Train		Plane
Adult fare	Coach	$142	F	$318
	Single slumber	$202	Y	$204
	Bedroom (2 people)	$519	FN	$227
			YN	$182

9. Find the travel expense for two adults going from Denver to San Francisco by train in 2 single slumbers.

10. Find the travel expense for two adults flying coach (Y) from Denver to San Francisco and sharing a taxi for $18.

Unit 3 Test

Choose the best answer.

1. The suggested retail price of a car is $5950. Find the sticker price with power steering ($185) and a radio ($58).

    A $243   **C** $5707

    B $6193   **D** $8135

2. Martha Long Bow offered a dealer 10% less than the $8929 sticker price for a new car. What was Martha's offer? Round to the nearest hundred dollars.

    A $900   **C** $8700

    B $9600   **D** $8000

3. A used car costs $2125 plus 5% sales tax. Find the sales tax.

    A $2231.25   **C** $106.25

    B $10.62   **D** $1062.50

4. The selling price of a car is $8930. Find the net price with a trade-in allowance of $1685.

    A $7300   **C** $7245

    B $10,615   **D** $7692

5. Ann made a down payment of $1200 on a $7695 car. She financed the balance for 36 months with monthly payments of $240.25. Find the finance charge.

    A $2154   **C** $7350

    B $6495   **D** $2450

6. For all cars he sells, Hal receives 25% of the dealer's profit. What does Hal receive on a dealer's profit of $9800?

    A $245   **C** $7350

    B $12,250   **D** $2450

7. Ben Valdez drove 528 km and used 85 L of gasoline. Find his car's fuel economy rate to the nearest tenth.

    A 6.3 km/L   **C** 44,880 km/L

    B 6.0 km/L   **D** 6.2 km/L

8. Chang bought a new car for $7500 five years ago. The trade-in value now is 30% of the original selling price. Find the trade-in value now.

    A $2250   **C** $5250

    B $9750   **D** $225

9. To find the total depreciation of a car, multiply the monthly depreciation rate times the number of months times the original price. The original price of a car was $8295. Find the total depreciation after 30 months at 2.5% per month. Round to the nearest dollar.

    A $2089   **C** $6200

    B $2074   **D** $6221

10. A mechanic is paid 40% of the labor charge on each job. What is the mechanic paid for a job in which the total charge for parts is $21.75 and the total labor charge is $65?

    A $8.70   **C** $86.75

    B $26   **D** $34.70

11. Joan pays a base premium of $174.25 for liability insurance. She also pays 20% of the base for increased bodily injury coverage and 8% of the base for increased property damage coverage. Find her annual premium.

    A $48.79   **C** $125.46

    B $209.10   **D** $223.04

12. Lucy, age 19, is buying collision and comprehensive insurance, both with $50 deductible. Find her combined premium.

Driver	Collision premium for $50 deductible	Comprehensive premium for $50 deductible
Teen female	$338.66	$55.60
Teen male	$652.54	$55.60

A $283.06   C $394.26

B $708.14   D $237.32

13. Sonia drove 14,000 km last year. Her total car expenses were $4920. To the nearest tenth of a cent, what was the cost per kilometer to operate her car?

A 40¢   C 30¢

B 35.2¢   D 35.1¢

14. Joy takes the train and bus to and from work each day. The train ticket is $55.85 a month and the bus fare is $0.75 each way. Find Joy's monthly travel cost based on 20 working days per month.

A $57.35   C $70.85

B $56.60   D $85.85

15. Use the chart to find the distance from Chicago to Buffalo to Atlanta. Distances between cities are given in kilometers.

Atlanta	Atlanta	Boston	Buffalo
Boston	1720		
Buffalo	1412	723	
Chicago	1176	1570	870

A 2282 km   C 2135 km

B 2746 km   D 3616 km

16. To the nearest hour, what is the travel time for 385 km at a rate of 80 km/h?

A 4 hours   C 5 hours

B 3 hours   D 6 hours

17. Stuart plans to drive 1350 km in a car with a fuel economy rate of 9 km/L. He estimates he will spend $0.40 per liter for gasoline, $30 for lodging, and $55 for meals. Estimate the total cost.

A $60   C $540

B $145   D $625

18. Find the total round-trip air fare for one adult and one 10-year-old child from New Orleans to Chicago. The one-way adult fare is $165. Children (ages 2–11) pay $\frac{3}{4}$ of the adult fare.

A $288.75   C $123.75

B $577.50   D $330

19. A car rents for $21 per day plus $0.14 per kilometer. Find the cost of renting the car for 2 days and driving 1000 km.

A $42   C $182

B $140   D $161

20. For an adult, the one-way bus fare from Denver to San Francisco is $115. Children (ages 2–11) pay $\frac{1}{2}$ of the adult fare. Find the total bus fare for one adult and two children, ages 5 and 9, for a one-way bus trip from Denver to San Francisco.

A $230   C $57.50

B $172.50   D $287.50

The scenic route through Great Mountain Park is 83 km long. The direct route is 59 km long. How much shorter is the direct route?

If the number that is subtracted is a multiple of 10, the subtraction is easier.

Find 83 − 59 mentally.

THINK

> Add 1 to 59 to get a multiple of 10.
> 59 + 1 = 60
>
> Add 1 to 83. 83 + 1 = 84
>
> Subtract 60 from 84. 84 − 60 = 24

The direct route is 24 km shorter.

Find 61 − 23 mentally.

THINK

> Subtract 3 from 23 to get a multiple of 10. 23 − 3 = 20
>
> Subtract 3 from 61. 61 − 3 = 58
>
> Subtract 20 from 58. 58 − 20 = 38

The answer is 38.

Use a *multiple-of-10* method to subtract mentally. Write only the answer.

1. 73 − 29	**15.** 63 − 26
2. 41 − 18	**16.** 69 − 48
3. 95 − 37	**17.** 87 − 22
4. 86 − 59	**18.** 51 − 14
5. 62 − 25	**19.** 87 − 29
6. 47 − 19	**20.** 99 − 52
7. 91 − 47	**21.** 126 − 19
8. 75 − 42	**22.** 153 − 28
9. 56 − 27	**23.** 283 − 48
10. 95 − 38	**24.** 394 − 87
11. 82 − 69	**25.** 275 − 56
12. 42 − 16	**26.** 118 − 59
13. 81 − 45	**27.** 204 − 76
14. 76 − 17	**28.** 263 − 89

COMPUTER APPLICATIONS

Steve Larson plans to buy a new car. He is comparing the cost of financing a loan at different lending institutions. Steve wrote the program shown to help him compare loans. He can try combinations of different interest rates and numbers of months to repay to calculate a monthly payment that will fit his budget.

Lines 30, 50, and 70 Only these values need to be entered to calculate the monthly payment.

Data required	Name
Amount to be financed	P
Annual rate of interest (%)	Y
Number of months to repay	N

Lines 20, 40, and 60 A PRINT statement before each INPUT statement shows what to enter.

Line 80 The annual interest rate is first divided by 100 so that it is in decimal form, and then it is divided by 12 fo find the rate per month.

Line 90 A formula is used to find the monthly payment (A). The symbol "$\wedge$" is used to raise a number to a power.

These are some examples of the computation the computer would perform for the symbol $\wedge$.

Part of statement	Computation
$5\wedge2$	5×5
$3\wedge4$	$3 \times 3 \times 3 \times 3$
$8\wedge N$ (6 is entered for N)	$8 \times 8 \times 8 \times 8 \times 8 \times 8$

The number following $\wedge$ indicates the number of times the number preceding $\wedge$ is used as a factor. In this program, the number N following $\wedge$ is entered in line 70 and can vary each time the program is run. The number preceding $\wedge$ depends upon the data entered in line 50 and the result of the computation in line 80. Without a computer, the computation in line 90 would be very complicated and tedious.

Line 100 The amount of the monthly payment is rounded to the nearest cent.

Lines 110–140 The given values are printed along with the monthly payment so that different financing plans can be compared.

Steve can borrow $5000 at 18% annual interest. By running the program, he found that the monthly payments for 24 months would be $249.62, and the monthly payments for 36 months would be $180.76.

```
10 REM   MONTHLY PAYMENT PROGRAM        90 LET A=P*((I*(1+I)^N)/((1+I)^N-1))
20 PRINT "AMOUNT TO FINANCE";          100 LET A=INT(A*100+.5)/100
30 INPUT P                             110 PRINT "AMOUNT TO FINANCE  $";P
40 PRINT "INTEREST RATE";              120 PRINT "ANNUAL INTEREST RATE";Y;"%"
50 INPUT Y                             130 PRINT "NUMBER OF MONTHS";N
60 PRINT "NUMBER OF MONTHS";           140 PRINT "MONTHLY PAYMENT  $";A
70 INPUT N                             150 END
80 LET I=(Y/100)/12
```

Give the output for the program above when

1. P is 2500, Y is 17, and N is 18.

2. P is 4800, Y is 18, and N is 30.

3. P is 5250, Y is 19, and N is 24.

4. P is 6400, Y is 18.5, and N is 36.

5. P is 7185, Y is 17.75, and N is 36.

6. $3850 is to be financed at 18% annually for 24 months.

7. $7210 is to be financed at 16.75% annually for 36 months.

8. $5500 is to be financed at 17% annually for 30 months.

9. $6820 is to be financed at 17.5% annually for 18 months.

10. $9000 is to be financed at 16.5% annually for 42 months.

For which finance plan is the monthly payment lower:

11. $3000 at 17.5% annually for 24 months, or $3500 at 18% annually for 30 months?

12. $6600 at 19% annually for 36 months, or $6250 at 17.5% annually for 30 months?

13. $4785 at 18.5% annually for 18 months, or $5000 at 17% annually for 24 months?

14. $7100 at 16.5% annually for 30 months, or $6800 at 18% annually for 30 months?

15. Modify the program so that the total cost of the car and the down payment are entered. Calculate the amount to be financed in the program.

16. Give the output when the total cost of the car is $7259, the down payment is $2000, the annual interest rate is 17%, and the number of monthly payments is 30.

17. For which finance plan is the monthly payment lower: financing a car with a total cost of $8745 and a $4000 down payment at 16.5% annually for 28 months, or financing a car with a total cost of $9282 and a $5000 down payment at 16.8% annually for 24 months?

18. Modify the program to include the cost of financing as part of the output.

19. Give the output when the total cost of the car is $8378, the down payment is $3500, the annual interest rate is 18.5%, and the number of monthly payments is 24.

20. Modify the program to include the total sale price as part of the output. Remember that the total sale price is the sum of the monthly payments and the down payment.

21. Give the output when the total cost of the car is $10,583, the down payment is $4000, the annual interest rate is 16.75%, and the number of monthly payments is 30.

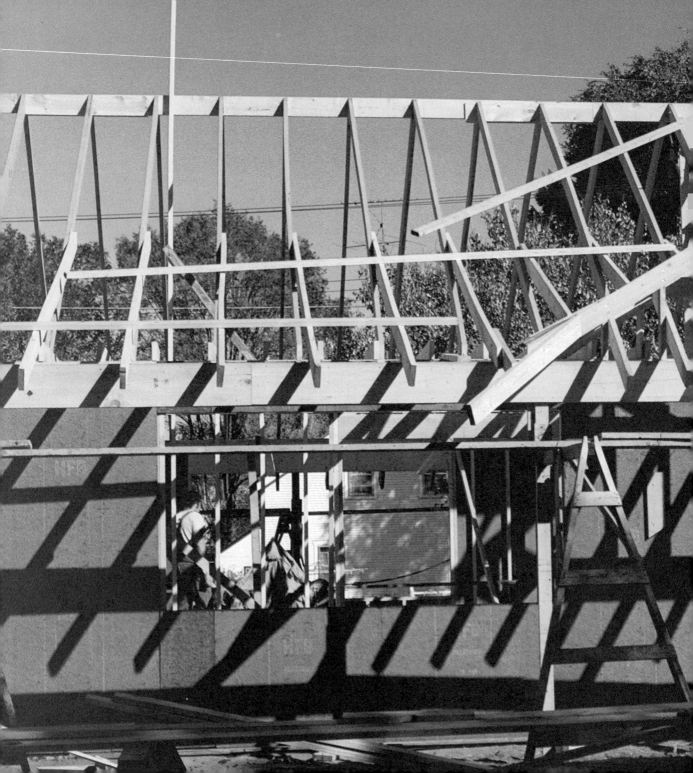

Unit 4 Housing

Chapter 10 Renting and Decorating a Home

Amount to Spend for Rent

Emily Coale and Paul Hines are trying to determine how much they can spend for rent when they get married. A common guideline is: *Do not spend more than one week's gross pay for shelter each month.*

Problem

Paul works 40 hours per week at $6.80 per hour. Emily is unemployed now. What is the most they can spend for rent?

Solution

Strategy
• Multiply hourly pay by 40 to find weekly pay. $40 \times \$6.80 = \$272$

Conclusion
Paul and Emily should not spend more than $272 per month for rent.

Related Problems

For each problem, use the given pay rate to find the maximum amount that should be spent for rent each month. Assume a 40-hour work week.

1. $6.30 per hour
2. $5.75 per hour
3. $8.60 per hour
4. $7.80 per hour

5. $7.25 per hour
6. $9.50 per hour
7. $12.50 per hour
8. $10.95 per hour

9. $10,816 per year
10. $11,180 per year
11. $15,600 per year
12. $19,500 per year

Emily and Paul read in a survey that families who rent spend about 28% of their annual net income on shelter. This amount includes utilities.

Problem

Paul's annual net income is $10,750. According to the survey, about how much will Paul and Emily probably spend for shelter each month?

Solution

Strategy

- Multiply annual net income by 0.28 to find expected annual amount for shelter.

$$0.28 \times \$10,750 = \$3010$$

- Divide by 12 to find monthly amount for shelter. Round to the nearest dollar.

$$\$3010 \div 12 \approx \$251$$

Conclusion

Paul and Emily will probably spend about $251 for shelter each month.

Related Problems

Using the 28% from the survey, find the expected monthly payment for shelter for the net incomes given. Round each answer to the nearest dollar.

13. $9802

14. $7633

15. $11,468

16. $10,575

17. $15,650

18. $18,000

19. $21,000

20. $12,042

21. Emily is looking for a full-time job. If she can earn at least $5 per hour for a 40-hour week, how much could she and Paul spend for rent each month? (Use the guideline on page 194.)

22. If Emily gets a job that gives her a net income of $7640 per year, about how much would she and Paul spend for shelter each month? Round your answer to the nearest dollar. (Use the survey.)

Selecting a Place to Rent

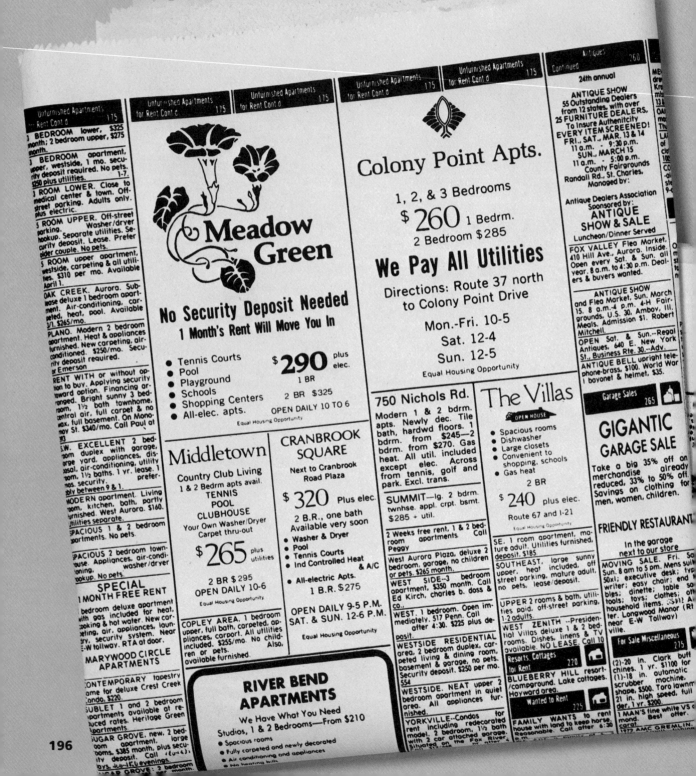

Mike and Jake Amano plan to rent one of the two-bedroom units
described in the ads on page 196. After investigating the cost
of utilities, they came to the following conclusions.

— "Plus utilities" means that the tenants pay gas heat and electricity.

— The cost of gas heat averages about $60 per month.

— The cost of electricity, without electric heat, averages about $25 per month.

— The cost of electricity for an all-electric apartment averages about $90 per month.

Problem

About how much will Mike and Jake pay for rent and utilities each
month if they rent a two-bedroom unit at Middletown Apartments?

Solution

Strategy

- Read the ad and the guidelines above to
  determine the rent and the utility costs.
  Then add to find the total.

$295	Rent
60	Gas
+ 25	Electricity
$380	

Conclusion

Mike and Jake will probably pay about $380 each month for
rent and utilities if they rent at Middletown Apartments.

Related Problems

Find the expected monthly total for rent and utilities
for a two-bedroom unit at each location.

1. Summit

2. 750 Nichols Road

3. Cranbrook Square

4. Meadow Green

5. Colony Point

6. The Villas

7. List in order all the two-bedroom units and their monthly totals
   for rent and utilities. Begin with the least expensive.

8. Find the difference in monthly totals between the least
   expensive and the most expensive two-bedroom units.

9. If Jake and Mike decide to split the rent and utility costs on a
   two-bedroom apartment at Cranbrook Square, about how much
   would each one pay every month?

Meter Reader

Career Cluster: Business Detail Rhonda Davis works for the electric company as a meter reader. From the readings Rhonda takes, the company can determine the number of kilowatt-hours of electricity that a customer uses during a specific period of time.

Problem

What is the reading on the dials of this electric meter?

Solution

Rhonda reads the dials from left to right. When the hand on any dial is between two numbers, she uses the smaller number. When the hand is between 9 and 0, as on the second dial, she thinks of the 0 as 10.

The reading is 29635.

Related Problems

Rhonda read the meter at the Radows' home every two months for a year. Give the reading for each date.

1. December 1, 1980

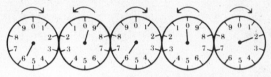

2. February 2, 1981

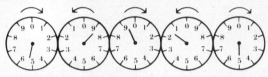

3. April 1, 1981

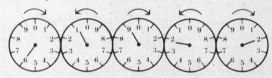

4. June 1, 1981

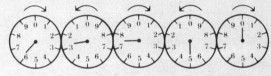

5. August 3, 1981

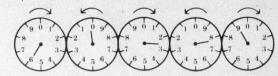

6. October 1, 1981

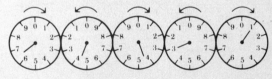

7. December 1, 1981

8. How many kilowatt-hours were used between December 1, 1980, and February 2, 1981? (Subtract the December reading from the February reading.)

9. Find the number of kilowatt-hours used during each of the other 2-month periods.

10. During which 2-month period was electric usage greatest?

CALCULATOR APPLICATIONS

The amount of electricity used to light a 100-watt light bulb for 10 hours is a **kilowatt-hour** (kW·h).

On the average, a freezer uses 1195 kW·h of electricity per year. Find the annual cost of electricity to operate the freezer when the rate is 4.973¢ per kilowatt-hour.

First, multiply the rate by 0.01 to change cents to dollars.

$4.973 \times 0.01 = 0.04973$ $4.973¢ = \$0.04973$

Then, multiply the annual usage by the rate to find the annual cost. Round the answer to the nearest cent.

$\$0.04973 \times 1195 \approx \$59.43$

The annual cost of electricity for the freezer is $59.43.

Find the annual cost of electricity for each appliance listed below. Use a rate of 4.973¢ per kilowatt-hour.

	Appliance	Average annual usage (kW·h)		Appliance	Average annual usage (kW·h)
1.	Hair dryer	18	**9.**	Clothes washer (automatic)	445
2.	Microwave oven	190	**10.**	Air conditioner (window)	1225
3.	Iron	144	**11.**	Vacuum cleaner	46
4.	Range with oven	1175	**12.**	Television (black and white)	262
5.	Dishwasher	363	**13.**	Television (color)	458
6.	Trash compactor	50	**14.**	Radio	86
7.	Toaster	39	**15.**	Stereo	109
8.	Clothes dryer	993	**16.**	Shaver	2

17. Find the annual cost of electricity for the appliances in the list. Use a rate of 5.017¢ per kilowatt-hour.

Break Time

The drawing below shows a perfect-squared rectangle. The rectangle is made up of squares A through J, all of different sizes. As shown, square E measures 7 cm on each side. Square F measures 12 cm on each side. Without measuring, find the dimensions of the other squares. What are the length and the width of the rectangle?

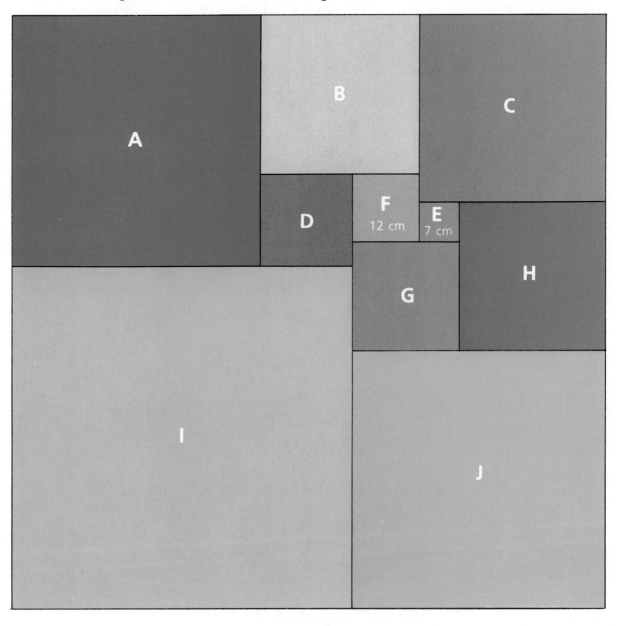

Interior Designer

Career Cluster: Arts Raul Cruz is an interior designer for Bentley's Furniture Store. He made a **scale drawing** of Arlene Novak's living room floor. Raul showed her possible arrangements for the furniture she plans to buy.

Problem

On his drawing, Raul used 1 cm to represent 0.2 m. Arlene's living room is 4.73 m long. To the nearest tenth of a centimeter, what is the scale length of the living room?

Solution

Strategy
• Write a proportion to find the scale length.

$$\frac{1}{0.2} = \frac{n}{4.73}$$ $\longleftarrow$ Scale length (cm)
$\longleftarrow$ Actual length (m)

• Write the cross-products and solve for n. Round your answer to the nearest tenth.

$$1 \times 4.73 = 0.2 \times n$$
$$4.73 = 0.2n$$
$$23.7 \approx n$$

Conclusion
To the nearest tenth of a centimeter, the scale length of the living room is 23.7 cm.

Related Problems

For problems 1–14, round your answers to the nearest tenth of a centimeter.

1. The living room is 3.40 m wide. What is the scale width of the room? Use a scale of 1 cm ⟶ 0.2 m.

Find the scale dimensions of each piece of furniture. Use a scale of 1 cm ⟶ 0.2 m.

2. Sofa: 2.10 m by 0.86 m

3. Love seat: 1.53 m by 0.86 m

4. Chair: 0.80 m by 0.86 m

5. Library table: 1.49 m by 0.58 m

6. End table: 0.65 m by 0.55 m

7. Antique desk: 1.28 m by 0.60 m

Raul made a scale drawing for another customer, using a scale of 1 cm ⟶ 0.25 m. Find the scale dimensions of the room and of each piece of furniture.

8. Bedroom: 3.60 m by 3.45 m

9. Bed: 1.95 m by 1.35 m

10. Night table: 0.57 m by 0.40 m

11. Chair: 0.65 m by 0.46 m

12. Bench: 1.08 m by 0.43 m

13. Triple dresser: 1.68 m by 0.48 m

14. Five-drawer chest: 0.90 m by 0.48 m

15. Use the scale dimensions in problem 8 to draw the outline of the bedroom on centimeter graph paper. Include a closet, a window, and a door.

16. Make scale drawings of the furniture for the bedroom (problems 9–14). Cut out the furniture and make an arrangement for the room.

Installing Floor Tiles

Lin Hong rents a house and wants to put floor tiles in the den.
His landlord will pay for the materials if Lin installs the tiles.
Each tile is a square 30 cm by 30 cm.

Problem

Lin's den measures 4.6 m by 3.9 m. How many tiles
are needed for the floor?

Solution

Strategy
- Change each dimension to centimeters. Length: 4.6 m = 460 cm
Width: 3.9 m = 390 cm

- Divide each dimension by 30 to find the number of   Length: $460 \div 30 \approx 16$
tiles needed. Round up to the next whole number.   Width: $390 \div 30 = 13$

- Multiply to find the total
number of tiles needed.

Number of tiles needed for length	Number of tiles needed for width	Total number of tiles needed
16 ×	13 =	208

Conclusion
Lin needs 208 tiles for the floor.

Related Problems

For each problem, find the number of tiles needed
for the length and the width. Then find the total
number of tiles needed for each room.

1. Bathroom: 2.4 m by 1.5 m

2. Bedroom: 4.2 m by 4.1 m

3. Dining room: 4.4 m by 3.9 m

4. Utility room: 3.8 m by 3.3 m

5. Recreation room: 6.3 m by 5.0 m

6. Kitchen: 4.4 m by 2.8 m

Problem

Lin wants to make a design with the tiles. He used graph paper to make the design shown below.

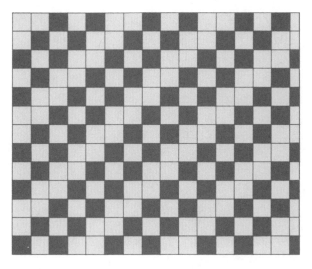

Find the cost of the brown tiles if a package of 5 tiles costs $6.50.

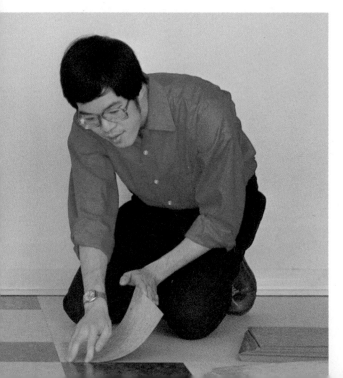

Solution

Strategy
• Count the number of brown tiles needed. Count each partial tile as a whole tile.

83

• Divide by 5 to find the number of packages needed. Round up to the next whole number.

$83 \div 5 \approx 17$

• Multiply $6.50 by 17 to find the total cost.

$17 \times \$6.50 = \$110.50$

Conclusion
The brown tiles will cost $110.50.

Related Problems

7. At $6.50 for a package of 5, find the cost of the beige tiles for Lin's den.

8. What is the cost of all the tiles for Lin's den?

9. Make a regular checkerboard pattern for Lin's recreation room on graph paper. (See problem 5.) He wants the design in green and blue, starting with a blue tile in the upper left-hand corner.

10. How many blue tiles are needed in the recreation room?

11. How many green tiles are needed in the recreation room?

12. At $6 for a package of 5 tiles, what is the cost of the blue tiles?

13. At the same price, what is the cost of the green tiles?

14. What is the total cost of the tiles for Lin's recreation room?

Painting an Apartment

Russell and Marie Atkin are planning to paint their apartment.
They know that one gallon of paint will cover about 400 sq. ft.

Problem

The Atkins' bedroom is 16 ft. by 14 ft. The walls are 8 ft. high. How many
gallons of paint will they need to paint the walls and the ceiling?

Solution

Strategy

• Draw a simple sketch of
  the room and a sketch
  showing the four walls
  placed end to end.

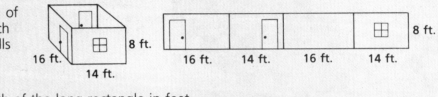

• Add to find the length of the long rectangle in feet.
  It is the same as the perimeter of the room. $16 + 14 + 16 + 14 = 60$

• Multiply total length by the wall height
  to find the area of the walls in square feet. $8 \times 60 = 480$

• Multiply length times width to find
  the area of the ceiling in square feet. $16 \times 14 = 224$

• Add to find the total area of walls
  and ceiling in square feet. $480 + 224 = 704$

• Divide by 400 to find the number of gallons
  needed. Round up to the next whole number. $704 \div 400 \approx 2$

Conclusion

Marie and Russell will need 2 gallons of paint.

Related Problems

Marie and Russell measured the other rooms to determine how much paint they would need. Then they made this chart.

Room	Room dimensions
Den	14 ft. by 11 ft.
Living room	18 ft. by 12 ft.
Entrance	6 ft. by 5 ft.
Dining room	12 ft. by 11 ft.
Hallway	25 ft. by 5 ft.

Complete the table below to find the number of gallons of paint needed for each room. Remember, the walls are 8 ft. high.

	Room	Wall area (square feet)	Ceiling area (square feet)	Total area to be painted (square feet)	Amount of paint needed (gallons)
	Bedroom	480	224	704	2
1.	Den				
2.	Living room				
3.	Entrance				
4.	Dining room				
5.	Hallway				

6. Paint is $10.49 per gallon. What will be the total bill for all the paint?

Ordering Wallpaper

Mary Grace Gettings plans to wallpaper her den. The clerk at the wallpaper store gave her these guidelines to help her decide how much paper to order.

— Find the total area of the walls, disregarding all openings.

— Divide the total area by 30. (Each roll of paper covers about 30 sq. ft.)

— Subtract $\frac{1}{2}$ roll for each window or single door and 1 roll for each picture window, double door, or other large opening.

Problem

A drawing of Mary Grace's den is shown below. How many rolls of wallpaper should she order?

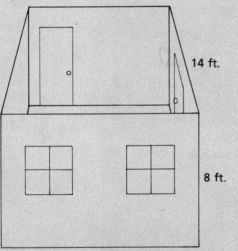

14 ft.

8 ft.

12 ft.

Solution

Strategy

• Add the lengths of the walls to find the perimeter of the room in feet.

$$12 + 14 + 12 + 14 = 52$$

• Multiply the total length by the wall height to find the total area of the walls in square feet.

$$8 \times 52 = 416$$

• Divide by 30 to find the total number of rolls needed, disregarding openings. Round up to the next whole number.

$$416 \div 30 \approx 14$$

• Subtract 2 rolls to allow for the 4 openings.
$(4 \times \frac{1}{2} = 2)$

$$14 - 2 = 12$$

Conclusion

Mary Grace should order 12 rolls of wallpaper.

Related Problems

Mary Grace wants to paper both her dining room and her living room. The walls in both rooms are 8 ft. high.

The dining room is 16 ft. long and 14 ft. wide. There are three windows, one door, and a large archway in the room.

1. Find the area of the walls, disregarding all openings.

2. Find the number of rolls of paper needed. (Disregard openings.)

3. Find the number of rolls that should be subtracted for the openings.

4. How many rolls of wallpaper should Mary Grace order?

5. Find the cost of the paper at $8.49 per roll.

Mary Grace's living room is 22 ft. long and 18 ft. wide. It has one window, one door, a large archway, and a picture window.

6. Find the area of the walls, disregarding all openings.

7. Find the number of rolls of paper needed. (Disregard openings.)

8. Find the number of rolls that should be subtracted for the openings.

9. How many rolls of wallpaper should Mary Grace order for the living room?

10. Mary Grace wants to paper the living room for $140. What is the most she can spend per roll? Round your answer to the nearest cent.

11. Mary Grace plans to cover the bathroom walls with vinyl covering. The room is 9 ft. long and 6 ft. wide. The height of the wall area to be covered is 4 ft. The room has one window and one door. How many rolls of vinyl are needed?

12. The vinyl covering is $14.75 per roll. Find the cost of covering the walls.

Personal Property Insurance

Jeff Scott carries renter's insurance. This type of insurance covers losses or damage to personal property caused by misfortunes such as fire or theft. Jeff's insurance agent gave him the information shown here. To determine the amount of depreciation, Jeff needs to know the age and the replacement cost of any article lost or destroyed.

Item	Average useful years	Annual rate of depreciation
Athletic equipment	5	20%
Barbecue	8	12%
Bicycle	5	20%
Clock—Electric	15	7%
—Grandfather	30	3%
Furniture—Card tables, chairs	10	10%
—Children's	5	20%
—Desks, tables	20	5%
—Lamps	20	5%
—Wood-frame (example: sofa)	10	10%
Golf clubs	8	12%
Stereo	12	8%
Television	8	12%
Tools	20	5%
Typewriter—Home	20	5%
—Office	5	20%

Problem

Jeff's apartment was burglarized and his typewriter was taken. The typewriter is 3 years old and will cost $175 to replace. Jeff has a $50-deductible insurance policy. How much can Jeff expect to receive from the insurance company?

Solution

Strategy

- Read the list to find the annual rate of depreciation for the typewriter.   5% per year

- Multiply the replacement cost by the rate of depreciation. $0.05 \times \$175 = \$8.75$

- Multiply to find the depreciation for 3 years. $3 \times \$8.75 = \$26.25$

- Subtract to find the present value. $\$175 - \$26.25 = \$148.75$

- Subtract the deductible amount from the present value to find the insurance benefit. $\$148.75 - \$50 = \$98.75$

Conclusion

Jeff can expect to receive $98.75 from the insurance company.

Related Problems

The storage area in Tom Smith's apartment building was damaged by water. The items he lost are listed below. Find the value for each item after depreciation.

Item	Replacement cost	Age in years
1. Bicycle	$150	2
2. Golf clubs	$175	5
3. Barbecue	$65	1
4. Electric clock	$75	3
5. Circular saw	$110	4
6. Camping equipment	$355	2
7. Desk	$175	5

8. Tom has a $50-deductible policy. How much will he receive from the insurance company?

Donna Littlebird had a fire in her apartment. The following items were destroyed. Find the value for each item after depreciation.

Item	Replacement cost	Age in years
9. Sofa	$580	3
10. Chair	$225	2
11. Chair	$185	3
12. End table	$120	2
13. Stereo	$325	2
14. Television	$535	1
15. Lamp	$60	3

16. Donna has a $100-deductible policy. How much will she receive from the insurance company?

Skills Tune-Up

Dividing whole numbers,
pages 12–13

1. 3577 ÷ 7

2. 2336 ÷ 8

3. 1948 ÷ 6

4. 7448 ÷ 8

5. 18,968 ÷ 4

6. 5812 ÷ 6

7. 6832 ÷ 54

8. 8189 ÷ 27

9. 5745 ÷ 53

10. 4275 ÷ 19

11. 8154 ÷ 67

12. 2235 ÷ 65

13. 2112 ÷ 48

14. 3366 ÷ 30

15. 7038 ÷ 34

16. 2449 ÷ 71

17. 3792 ÷ 47

18. 69,184 ÷ 46

19. 63,762 ÷ 53

20. 62,043 ÷ 82

21. 140,668 ÷ 18

22. 110,653 ÷ 58

23. 377,166 ÷ 88

24. 595,038 ÷ 714

25. 188,496 ÷ 924

26. 452,953 ÷ 806

27. 648,713 ÷ 394

Multiplying fractions and
mixed numbers, pages 14–15

1. $\frac{5}{6} \times \frac{1}{4}$

2. $\frac{3}{4} \times \frac{1}{6}$

3. $\frac{4}{5} \times \frac{5}{14}$

4. $\frac{4}{5} \times \frac{3}{8}$

5. $\frac{3}{8} \times \frac{2}{9}$

6. $\frac{9}{14} \times 7$

7. $8 \times \frac{7}{16}$

8. $8\frac{1}{3} \times \frac{3}{5}$

9. $2\frac{3}{5} \times \frac{6}{13}$

10. $\frac{4}{15} \times 3\frac{3}{4}$

11. $5\frac{5}{6} \times \frac{3}{14}$

12. $3\frac{5}{9} \times 1\frac{3}{8}$

13. $5\frac{5}{8} \times 4\frac{4}{5}$

14. $4\frac{1}{4} \times 2\frac{2}{3}$

15. $1\frac{5}{7} \times 5\frac{1}{4}$

16. $7 \times 2\frac{1}{4}$

17. $12\frac{1}{5} \times 2$

18. $\frac{7}{10} \times \frac{5}{8} \times \frac{1}{7}$

19. $5\frac{2}{5} \times 3\frac{1}{2} \times \frac{5}{9}$

20. $7 \times 1\frac{3}{8} \times 2\frac{6}{7}$

Ratio and proportion,
pages 30–31

Find the cross-products.
Tell whether the ratios are
equal.

1. $\frac{3}{14}$ $\frac{2}{8}$

2. $\frac{18}{21}$ $\frac{6}{7}$

3. $\frac{15}{20}$ $\frac{64}{80}$

4. $\frac{75}{1.5}$ $\frac{300}{6}$

5. $\frac{6}{8}$ $\frac{18}{19.6}$

6. $\frac{99}{5}$ $\frac{2.97}{0.15}$

Solve and check.

7. $\frac{6}{7} = \frac{a}{35}$

8. $\frac{n}{28} = \frac{15}{7}$

9. $\frac{56}{7} = \frac{24}{c}$

10. $\frac{8}{x} = \frac{16}{9}$

11. $\frac{26.5}{12} = \frac{n}{2.4}$

12. $\frac{0.9}{d} = \frac{0.4}{4.8}$

13. $\frac{0.9}{7.2} = \frac{50}{n}$

14. $\frac{x}{17} = \frac{10.4}{68}$

Chapter 10 Review

Amount to spend for rent, pages 194–195

1. Linda earns $7.85 per hour in a 40-hour work week. If she uses the "week's gross pay" guideline (do not spend more than one week's gross pay for shelter each month), what is the most she can spend for rent each month?

2. A survey states that people who rent spend about 28% of their annual net income on shelter. If Fred's net income is $10,200 per year, about how much will he probably spend on shelter each month?

Selecting a place to rent, pages 196–197

3. Sam estimates that his electric bill will be about $40 per month and that his gas bill will be about $55 per month. If the rent for his apartment is $275, what will be the monthly total for rent and utilities?

Meter reader, pages 198–199

4. Give the reading for this electric meter.

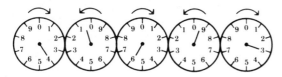

Interior designer, pages 202–203

5. Using a scale of 1 cm ⟶ 0.2 m, find the scale length of a room 4.40 m long.

Installing floor tiles, pages 204–205

6. How many floor tiles will be needed to cover a floor 5.6 m by 4.5 m? Each tile is a square 30 cm by 30 cm.

7. The tiles Cathy wants for her bathroom floor cost $6.50 for a package of 5 tiles. Find the total cost if she needs 48 tiles.

Painting an apartment, pages 206–207

8. Eleanor plans to paint the walls and the ceiling of her den. The room measures 12 ft. by 12 ft., and the walls are 8 ft. high. If one gallon of paint covers about 400 sq. ft., how much paint will Eleanor need?

Ordering wallpaper, pages 208–209

9. Jack wants to wallpaper his study. The room measures 15 ft. by 16 ft., and the walls are 8 ft. high. The room has 3 windows and 1 door. Find the number of rolls of wallpaper Jack should order. (Each roll of paper covers about 30 sq. ft. Subtract $\frac{1}{2}$ roll for each window or door.)

Personal property insurance, pages 210–211

10. Juanita's renter's insurance is a $100-deductible policy. Her television set was stolen, and it will cost $365 to replace. The set was 2 years old. If the annual rate of depreciation is 12%, how much will she receive from the insurance company?

Chapter 10 Test

1. Duane earns $8.95 per hour in a 40-hour work week. If he uses the "week's gross pay" guideline (do not spend more than one week's gross pay for shelter each month), what is the most he can spend for rent each month?

2. A survey states that people who rent spend about 28% of their annual net income on shelter. If Jane's net income is $11,400 per year, about how much will she probably spend on shelter each month?

3. Margo is interested in renting an apartment for $325 per month. She estimates that her electric bill will be about $35 per month and that her gas bill will be about $50 per month. What will be the monthly total for rent and utilities?

4. Give the reading for this electric meter.

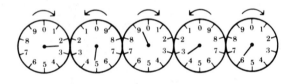

5. Using a scale of 1 cm ⟶ 0.25 m, find the scale length of a sofa that is 2.75 m long.

6. How many tiles will be needed to cover a floor 5.2 m by 3.6 m? Each tile is a square 30 cm by 30 cm.

7. The tiles Ned wants for his den floor cost $6 for a package of 5 tiles. Find the total cost if he needs 72 tiles.

8. Marty plans to paint the walls and the ceiling of his living room. The room measures 18 ft. by 12 ft., and the walls are 8 ft. high. If one gallon of paint covers about 400 sq. ft., how much paint will Marty need?

9. Anna is going to wallpaper her dining room. The room measures 16 ft. by 14 ft., and the walls are 8 ft. high. The room has 2 doors and 2 windows. Find the number of rolls of wallpaper Anna should order. (Each roll of paper covers about 30 sq. ft. Subtract $\frac{1}{2}$ roll for each window or door.)

10. Beverly's renter's insurance is a $50-deductible policy. Her stereo was destroyed in a fire, and it will cost $285 to replace. The stereo was 3 years old. If the annual rate of depreciation is 8%, how much will she receive from the insurance company?

Chapter 11 Buying a Home

Amount to Borrow for a Home

Edward and Marta Rivera are thinking of buying their own home. They will need to borrow most of the money to pay for it. To help them decide how much they can afford to borrow, their banker gave this advice: *Do not consider borrowing more than 2 times your annual gross income.*

Problem

Edward earns $6.50 per hour working 40 hours a week. Marta earns $1150 per month. How much can they consider borrowing?

Solution

Strategy

- Multiply Edward's hourly income by 40 to find his weekly income.

  $40 \times \$6.50 = \$260$

- Multiply by 52 to find Edward's annual income.

  $52 \times \$260 = \$13,520$

- Multiply Marta's monthly income by 12 to find her annual income.

  $12 \times \$1150 = \$13,800$

- Add to find the Riveras' annual gross income.

  $\$13,520 + \$13,800 = \$27,320$

- Multiply by 2 to find the greatest amount they can consider borrowing.

  $2 \times \$27,320 = \$54,640$

Conclusion

The Riveras can consider borrowing $54,640.

Related Problems

Use the general guideline to determine the greatest amount a person earning each salary could consider borrowing for a home while earning the given income. Assume a 40-hour work week.

1. $18,000 per year

2. $31,400 per year

3. $780 per month

4. $1150 per month

5. $280 per week

6. $455 per week

7. $6.80 per hour

8. $13.50 per hour

9. $5.50 per hour

10. $12.50 per hour

For problems 11–13, assume a 40-hour work week.

11. Richard earns $9.50 per hour. Maria earns $625 per month. Can they consider a $58,000 loan?

12. Lenny earns $6.50 per hour. Helene earns $375 per week. Can they consider a $60,500 loan?

13. Ann earns $175 per week. Harvey earns $5.75 per hour. Can they consider a $40,000 loan?

14. Barbara earns $4.25 per hour in a 20-hour work week. Frank earns $21,500 per year. Can they consider a $68,000 loan?

Down Payment and Monthly Payment

Most people do not pay for a house with cash. At the time of purchase, they pay part of the price with a down payment. They borrow the rest of the money from a lending institution. This **mortgage loan** is paid back in equal monthly payments. An **amortization table** is used to find the amount of each monthly payment.

Problem

Paula Jeffers is interested in buying a condominium for $48,000. At the savings and loan company, she was told she needs 20% of $48,000 for the down payment. She can borrow the rest of the money at 12.5% annual interest, to be paid back over 25 years. How much does Paula need for the down payment? What will her monthly payment be?

Solution

Strategy
- Multiply by 20% to find the amount of the down payment.

  $0.20 \times \$48,000 = \$9600$

- Subtract to find the amount of the loan.

  $\$48,000 - \$9600 = \$38,400$

- Read the table to find the monthly payment for $1000 for 25 years at 12.5% interest.

  $10.90

- Multiply to find the monthly payment. Think of 38,400 as 38.4 thousands.

  $38.4 \times \$10.90 = \$418.56$

Conclusion
Paula's down payment is $9600. Her monthly payment will be $418.56.

Amortization of a $1000 Loan

Interest rate	Monthly payment		
	20-year loan	25-year loan	30-year loan
10.0%	$9.66	$9.09	$8.78
10.5%	$9.99	$9.45	$9.15
11.0%	$10.33	$9.81	$9.53
11.5%	$10.66	$10.16	$9.90
12.0%	$11.01	$10.53	$10.29
12.5%	$11.36	$10.90	$10.67
13.0%	$11.72	$11.28	$11.06
13.5%	$12.07	$11.66	$11.45
14.0%	$12.44	$12.04	$11.85
14.5%	$12.80	$12.42	$12.25
15.0%	$13.17	$12.81	$12.64
15.5%	$13.54	$13.20	$13.05
16.0%	$13.92	$13.59	$13.45
16.5%	$14.29	$13.99	$13.86
17.0%	$14.67	$14.38	$14.26
17.5%	$15.05	$14.78	$14.67
18.0%	$15.44	$15.18	$15.08

Related Problems

Complete the table. Round the amount of the monthly payment to the nearest cent.

	Purchase price	Down payment	Amount of down payment	Amount of loan	Interest rate	Time (years)	Monthly payment
	$48,000	20%	$9600	$38,400	12.5%	25	$418.56
1.	$50,000	20%			13.5%	30	
2.	$50,000	10%			13.5%	20	
3.	$75,000	20%			12.5%	30	
4.	$75,000	30%			12.0%	25	
5.	$60,000	25%			13.0%	30	
6.	$82,000	30%			14.5%	30	
7.	$105,000	20%			11.5%	20	
8.	$94,000	25%			15.0%	25	

9. Find the difference in the amounts of the down payments for the two homes that cost $50,000. (Use the table above.)

10. Find the difference in the amounts of the down payments for the two homes that cost $75,000. (Use the table above.)

11. Find the difference in the monthly payments for these loans.

$32,500 at 14% interest for 20 years
$32,500 at 14% interest for 25 years

12. Find the difference in the monthly payments for these loans.

$48,000 at 12% interest for 25 years
$48,000 at 12.5% interest for 25 years

The purchase price of a certain home is $72,000.

13. Find the amount of the loan with a 25% down payment.

14. Find the amount of the loan with a 20% down payment.

15. Find the difference in the monthly payments for the loans in problems 13 and 14 at 14.5% interest for 30 years.

Interest on a Mortgage Loan

On many home loans, people actually pay back three or four times the amount they borrow.

Problem

How much interest will be paid on a loan of $40,000 for 30 years if the annual interest rate is 13.5%?

Solution

Strategy
- Use the strategy on page 218 to find the monthly payment. $458

- Multiply the number of years by 12 to find the total number of payments. $12 \times 30 = 360$

- Multiply to find the total amount repaid. $360 \times \$458 = \$164,880$

- Subtract the amount borrowed to find the amount of interest. $\$164,880 - \$40,000 = \$124,880$

Conclusion
$124,880 interest will be paid.

Related Problems

Complete this table. Use the amortization table on page 218 for problems 5–7.

	Amount borrowed	Interest rate	Time (years)	Monthly payment	Total payments	Amount repaid	Amount of interest
	$40,000	13.5%	30	$458.00	360	$164,880	$124,880
1.	$40,000	13.5%	25	$466.40			
2.	$40,000	14%	30	$474.00			
3.	$40,000	14%	25	$481.60			
4.	$40,000	14%	20	$497.60			
5.	$35,500	13%	20				
6.	$55,500	10%	30				
7.	$55,500	18%	30				

Use the answers you found for the table to help you with the following problems.

8. Find the difference in the amounts of interest paid on these loans.

$40,000 at 14% interest for 30 years
$40,000 at 14% interest for 25 years

9. Find the difference in the amounts of interest paid on these loans.

$40,000 at 14% interest for 30 years
$40,000 at 14% interest for 20 years

10. Find the difference in the amounts of interest paid on these loans.

$40,000 at 13.5% interest for 25 years
$40,000 at 14% interest for 25 years

11. Find the difference in the amounts of interest paid on these loans.

$55,500 at 10% interest for 30 years
$55,500 at 18% interest for 30 years
(Notice that these are the lowest and highest interest rates on page 218.)

12. In problem 1, the amount repaid is about how many times as great as the amount borrowed? (Round your answer to the nearest tenth.)

13. In problem 2, the amount repaid is about how many times as great as the amount borrowed? (Round your answer to the nearest tenth.)

Principal and Interest in a Monthly Payment

Part of each monthly payment on a mortgage loan is the interest for that month. The rest of the payment is used to reduce the principal.

Problem

The Hermans are borrowing $54,000 at 14% annual interest to be repaid over 30 years. Their monthly payment will be $639.90. How much of their first monthly payment will go toward the principal and how much will be interest? What is the "new" principal (the amount still owed after the first month)?

Solution

Strategy

• Use the simple interest formula to find the interest for the first month. (1 month is $\frac{1}{12}$ of a year.)

$I = P \times R \times T$

$I = \$54,000 \times 14\% \times \frac{1}{12}$

$I = \$54,000 \times \frac{14}{100} \times \frac{1}{12}$

$I = \$630$

• Subtract to find the amount paid on the principal the first month.
$639.90 - \$630 = \$9.90$

• Subtract to find the new principal.
$54,000 - \$9.90 = \$53,990.10$

Conclusion

Of the Hermans' first monthly payment, $9.90 will go toward the principal and $630 will be interest. The new principal is $53,990.10.

Related Problems

Use the given information about the Hermans' loan to solve these problems. Round interest amounts to the nearest cent.

1. Find the amount of interest for the second month. Use the new principal, $53,990.10.

2. Find the amount paid on the principal the second month.

3. Find the new principal at the end of the second month.

4. Find the amount of interest for the third month. Use the new principal from problem 3.

5. Find the amount paid on the principal the third month.

6. Find the new principal at the end of the third month.

7. Find the amount of interest for the fourth month.

8. Find the amount paid on the principal the fourth month.

9. Find the new principal at the end of the fourth month.

CALCULATOR APPLICATIONS

Many lending agencies provide their customers with an amortization table that shows how each monthly payment is divided between interest and principal. Scott Lynch is borrowing $40,000 at 13.5% annual interest for 25 years. His monthly payment will be $466.40. Use your calculator and the strategy on page 222 to complete these sections of Scott's amortization table.

	Payment number	Principal	Amount of interest	Amount paid on principal	New principal
	1	$40,000.00	$450.00	$16.40	$39,983.60
1.	2	$39,983.60			
2.	3				
3.	4				
4.	5				
5.	6				
6.	7				
7.	8				
8.	9				
9.	10				
10.	11				
11.	12				
	236	$21,253.33	$239.10	$227.30	$21,026.03
12.	237	$21,026.03			
13.	238				
14.	239				
15.	240 (20 yr.)				

16. Beginning with which payment will the amount paid on the principal be greater than the amount of interest?

17. After 20 years, what percent of the principal will be yet unpaid? Round to the nearest percent.

Homeowner's Insurance

Carl Meil has a mortgage loan to pay for his house. The lender requires Carl to have homeowner's insurance.

The insurance company charges a basic annual premium to insure the house and its contents. The amount of this premium is based on many things including the type of materials used to build the house, the location of the house, and the amount for which the house is insured.

In addition to the basic insurance to cover the house and its contents, Carl wants coverage on several valuable articles. His insurance agent gave him the following table to determine the cost of insuring these items.

Personal property	One-year rate per $100 of value*
Jewelry	$1.40
Furs and garments trimmed with fur	$0.41
Fine art	$0.28
Cameras, projectors, etc.	$1.65
Musical instruments—amateur	$0.69
Musical instruments—professional and organs	$2.85
Silverware, silver-plated items, etc.	$0.50
Stamp collections	$0.90
Coin collections	$1.95

*Available only in multiples of $100.

Problem

Carl's basic premium for his homeowner's insurance is $165. He has a gold ring worth $700 and a camera worth $225 that he wants to insure separately. What is the total premium for his insurance?

Solution

Strategy
• Read the table to find the rate for each item.

Jewelry: $1.40   Camera: $1.65

• Multiply the rate by the number of hundreds of dollars each item is worth. (Round all values up to the next $100.)

Ring: 7 × $1.40 = $9.80

Camera: 3 × $1.65 = $4.95

• Add to find the total premium.

$165 + $9.80 + $4.95 = $179.75

Conclusion
Carl's total insurance premium is $179.75.

Related Problems

Find the annual premium for each item. Then find each total premium.

Teresa Granados' basic premium is $175.

1. $600 ring

2. $350 gold chain

3. $300 flute (amateur)

4. $450 painting

5. Teresa's total premium

Lawrence Hetter's basic premium is $165.

6. $1250 organ

7. $325 violin (amateur)

8. $250 watch

9. $800 coin collection

10. Lawrence's total premium

Sam and Polly Pfaff's basic premium is $140.

11. $325 camera

12. $2500 in silverware

13. $2300 stamp collection

14. $425 coat with fur collar

15. The Pfaffs' total premium

Steve Davids is in a rock band that plays professionally. He insures his equipment as part of his homeowner's policy. Steve's basic premium is $130.

16. $325 drums

17. $150 bass guitar

18. $240 amplifier

19. $435 ring

20. Steve's total premium

Many lending agencies require borrowers to pay $\frac{1}{12}$ of their annual homeowner's insurance premium every month. Find the amount each person listed below would pay for insurance each month. (Round each answer up to the next cent.)

21. Teresa Granados

22. Lawrence Hetter

23. Steve Davids

Real Estate Taxes

In most areas, the local government's chief source of income is the **real estate tax.** This is an annual tax based on the value of each taxpayer's property.

The local government taxes the property at a certain percentage of the current **market value.** This percentage is known as the **rate of assessment.** The market value multiplied by this rate gives the **assessed valuation** of the property.

A **tax rate** is used to determine the amount of the real estate tax. This rate is often expressed in terms of an amount per $100 of the assessed valuation of the property.

Problem

The market value of Peggy and Ed Wilson's condominium is $58,000. The rate of assessment in their area is 60% of the market value. The tax rate is $3.87 per $100 of assessed valuation. What is the amount of real estate tax on the Wilsons' condominium?

Solution

Strategy
• Multiply by 60% to find the assessed valuation.

0.60 × $58,000 = $34,800

• Multiply by the tax rate per hundred to find the amount of real estate tax. Think of 34,800 as 348 hundreds.

$3.87 × 348 = $1346.76

Conclusion
The real estate tax on the Wilsons' condominium is $1346.76.

Related Problems

Complete the table. Round each answer to the nearest cent.

	Market value	Rate of assessment	Assessed valuation	Tax rate per $100	Real estate tax
	$58,000	60%	$34,800	$3.87	$1346.76
1.	$52,000	50%		$2.75	
2.	$49,000	60%		$3.50	
3.	$68,000	50%		$2.95	
4.	$78,000	60%		$3.12	
5.	$60,000	60%		$4.14	
6.	$83,500	50%		$3.70	
7.	$105,000	30%		$5.21	
8.	$92,000	25%		$7.05	
9.	$64,500	30%		$7.576	
10.	$73,750	35%		$5.321	

11. The Wilsons pay $\frac{1}{12}$ of their annual real estate tax every month to the bank which holds their mortgage loan. This is to assure the payment of these taxes each year. How much do the Wilsons pay for real estate tax each month?

Closing Costs

At the time of signing the necessary papers for the purchase of a home, the buyer must pay a number of fees known as **closing costs.** The actual fees vary in different areas. Sometimes the fees involving the title are split with the seller, or fully paid by the seller. William and Angela Head were given the following information to help them determine their closing costs.

Lawyer's fee: _____ *0.3% of purchase price*
for writing and reviewing
documents of the sale

Loan costs: _____ *2% of loan*
for the loan application,
house appraisal, and a
credit report on the buyer

Title examination fee: _____ *$300, buyer pays half*
for tracing the records
of previous ownership of
the property, to assure
rightful ownership

Title transfer tax: _____ *0.1% of purchase price*
for change in ownership

Recording fee: _____ *$25*
for keeping of records at
government offices

Real estate taxes: _____ *$795*

Problem

The purchase price of the Heads' home is $63,700. The amount of their loan is $50,000. What is the total of their closing costs?

Solution

Strategy

• Multiply the purchase price by 0.3% to find the lawyer's fee.

$0.003 \times \$63,700 = \$191.10$

• Multiply the amount of the loan by 2% to find the loan costs.

$0.02 \times \$50,000 = \$1000$

• Multiply the title examination fee by $\frac{1}{2}$ to find the Heads' share.

$\frac{1}{2} \times \$300 = \$150$

• Multiply the purchase price by 0.1% to find the title transfer tax.

$0.001 \times \$63,700 = \$63.70$

• Add to find total closing costs including recording fee and real estate taxes.

```
$  191.10
   1000.00
    150.00
     63.70
     25.00
 +  795.00
  $2224.80
```

Conclusion

The total of the Heads' closing costs is $2224.80.

Related Problems

For each buyer, find the amount of each fee listed. Then find total closing costs.

The Zobels: $58,000 purchase price
$45,000 loan

1. Lawyer: 0.2% of purchase price

2. Loan costs: 1.5% of loan

3. Title examination: $180, pay half

4. Title transfer: 0.1% of purchase price

5. The Zobels' total closing costs, including $575 for real estate taxes and $20 for recording fee

June Kowalski: $52,000 purchase price
$40,000 loan

6. Loan costs: 2% of loan

7. Title transfer: 2% of purchase price, pay half

8. Recording: 0.05% of purchase price

9. June's total closing costs including $663.50 for real estate taxes and $200 for lawyer's fee

The Corrins: $75,000 purchase price
$60,500 loan

10. Lawyer: 0.5% of purchase price

11. Loan costs: 1% of loan

12. Title examination: $235, pay half

13. Title transfer: 0.5% of purchase price, pay half

14. Recording: 0.1% of purchase price

15. The Corrins' total closing costs, including $425 for real estate taxes

Real Estate Agent

Career Cluster: Business Contact Sarah Currier is a real estate agent. Her job involves bringing together people who want to sell property with those who want to buy property.

Problem

The agency Sarah works for charges a commission of 7% for selling a house. James and Lucille Whitewolf want to receive at least $62,000 on the sale of their home. For what price should Sarah list the Whitewolfs' home?

Solution

Strategy

- Show the commission as 7% of the list price. Let L represent the list price.

- Write an equation relating the list price, commission, and amount desired by the seller.

- Solve the equation. Remember, $L = 1L$. Round the answer up to the next hundred dollars.

$$\text{Commission} = 0.07 \times L$$

List price	Commission		Amount desired
L	$-$ 0.07L	$=$	$62,000
1L	$-$ 0.07L	$=$	$62,000
	0.93L	$=$	$62,000
	$\dfrac{0.93L}{0.93}$	$=$	$\dfrac{\$62,000}{0.93}$
	L	$\approx$	$66,700

Conclusion

Sarah should list the Whitewolfs' home for $66,700.

Related Problems

For what price should each house be listed? Use the commision rate given. Round each answer up to the next hundred dollars.

	Amount desired by seller	Commission
1.	$65,000	6%
2.	$83,500	7%
3.	$73,800	8%
4.	$58,800	7%
5.	$97,900	8%
6.	$105,300	7%

7. Suppose Sarah's agency changes the commission rate to 8%. For what amount should Sarah then list the Whitewolfs' house?

8. For the Whitewolfs' house, find the difference between the list prices with a 7% commission and an 8% commission.

9. Suppose Sarah earns 3% on any house she sells. What would her earnings be on a $37,500 sale?

10. Sarah sold the Guytons' house for $51,000, the Wheatleys' house for $81,500, and the Garcias' house for $64,200 during a three-month period. At a 3.5% commission, how much did Sarah earn for that period?

11. The Walker Real Estate Agency sold Myoshi Tamura's house for $88,500. After the 7% commission was deducted, how much did Myoshi receive from the sale of her house?

Some of Sarah's clients need information about home loans in various parts of the United States. To help them, Sarah uses a table prepared by the Federal Home Loan Bank Board.

Problem

Dave Peters is being transferred to Dallas. What can he expect to pay as a down payment on a $94,000 house?

Solution

Strategy

• Read the table to find the average down payment percent in Dallas.

  22.5%

• Multiply the cost of the house by 22.5% to find the amount of the down payment.

  0.225 × $94,000 = $21,150

Conclusion

Dave can expect to pay $21,150 as a down payment.

Home Loans   March, 1981

Metropolitan area	Average interest rate	Average purchase price	Average down payment
Atlanta	14.09%	$92,100	24.2%
Baltimore	13.67%	$89,100	26.6%
Boston	14.94%	$76,100	28.6%
Chicago-Northwestern Indiana	13.58%	$93,300	27.7%
Cleveland	13.57%	$70,600	26.6%
Dallas	13.45%	$93,700	22.5%
Denver	13.21%	$84,400	26.0%
Detroit	14.41%	$69,900	26.5%
Houston	13.79%	$92,200	19.7%
Los Angeles-Long Beach	14.46%	$110,100	24.4%
Miami	15.01%	$87,600	27.8%
Minneapolis-St. Paul	14.18%	$80,200	39.8%
New York-Northeastern New Jersey	14.91%	$88,900	34.5%
Philadelphia	14.10%	$65,100	29.5%
St. Louis	14.00%	$52,000	22.6%
San Francisco-Oakland	14.00%	$126,200	24.4%
Seattle-Tacoma	13.58%	$87,300	20.5%
Washington, D.C., Maryland, Virginia	14.21%	$101,200	23.6%

Related Problems

12. Eleanor Hesen is moving to Boston. She expects to buy a home for $75,000. What can Eleanor expect to pay for her down payment?

13. Grace and Oliver Matthews are moving to Seattle. They plan to spend $85,000 on a house. What can they expect to pay for a down payment?

Of the metropolitan areas listed in the table on page 232, which area has

14. the lowest average purchase price?

15. the highest average purchase price?

16. the lowest average interest rate?

17. the highest average interest rate?

Rosalee and Grayson Woodbury want to move to a warm climate. They are considering Atlanta, Houston, Los Angeles, and Miami.

18. How much greater is the average purchase price of a house in Los Angeles than in Miami?

19. How much less could the Woodburys expect to pay as a down payment on a $90,000 house in Houston than in Miami?

20. Of the four areas the Woodburys are considering, which has the lowest average interest rate?

Break Time

Suppose you were given 1 billion dollars and were told to spend the money at the rate of 1 dollar per second. How long would it take you to spend the 1 billion dollars? Give your answer in years, days, hours, minutes, and seconds. (Use 365 days for 1 year.)

Skills Tune-Up

Multiplying whole numbers, pages 8–9

1. 40×80
2. 60×90
3. 100×30
4. 200×500
5. 700×400
6. 7000×30
7. 90×5000
8. 600×8000
9. 32×553
10. 784×292
11. 60×53
12. 76×2384
13. 800×4300
14. 66×3
15. 51×16
16. 350×500
17. 679×3
18. 603×4
19. 7000×1200
20. 564×37
21. 536×404
22. 800×460
23. 5268×70
24. 2400×300
25. 943×1363
26. 5932×889
27. 209×3467
28. 7406×503

Renaming fractions and mixed numbers, pages 14–15

Rename in lowest terms.

1. $\frac{2}{8}$
2. $\frac{9}{15}$
3. $\frac{3}{6}$
4. $\frac{3}{9}$
5. $\frac{9}{12}$
6. $\frac{6}{9}$
7. $\frac{11}{22}$
8. $\frac{6}{18}$
9. $\frac{28}{32}$
10. $\frac{4}{16}$
11. $\frac{20}{24}$
12. $\frac{8}{32}$
13. $\frac{35}{50}$
14. $\frac{35}{56}$
15. $\frac{42}{56}$
16. $\frac{20}{25}$
17. $\frac{4}{42}$
18. $\frac{36}{48}$
19. $\frac{11}{33}$
20. $\frac{76}{100}$

Rename as a fraction.

21. $2\frac{2}{5}$
22. $10\frac{1}{8}$
23. $2\frac{3}{10}$
24. $5\frac{1}{4}$
25. $1\frac{4}{5}$
26. $2\frac{1}{3}$
27. $3\frac{1}{5}$
28. $4\frac{2}{3}$
29. $6\frac{5}{8}$
30. $8\frac{9}{10}$
31. $3\frac{3}{4}$
32. $12\frac{1}{2}$
33. $4\frac{3}{8}$
34. $5\frac{5}{6}$
35. $1\frac{1}{10}$
36. $3\frac{7}{8}$
37. $2\frac{5}{12}$
38. $6\frac{7}{10}$

Dividing fractions and mixed numbers, pages 16–17

1. $\frac{3}{8} \div \frac{1}{4}$
2. $\frac{1}{4} \div \frac{2}{3}$
3. $\frac{3}{8} \div \frac{1}{3}$
4. $\frac{9}{20} \div \frac{3}{8}$
5. $\frac{3}{7} \div \frac{5}{8}$
6. $\frac{7}{15} \div \frac{4}{9}$
7. $3 \div \frac{2}{5}$
8. $\frac{1}{3} \div 2$
9. $10 \div \frac{5}{8}$
10. $\frac{2}{5} \div 6$
11. $4\frac{1}{6} \div \frac{2}{3}$
12. $\frac{2}{3} \div 1\frac{1}{2}$
13. $5\frac{1}{3} \div 3$
14. $9 \div 1\frac{1}{2}$
15. $5\frac{3}{4} \div 3\frac{3}{4}$
16. $7\frac{2}{5} \div 2\frac{1}{5}$
17. $3\frac{1}{8} \div 4\frac{1}{4}$
18. $6\frac{3}{5} \div 1\frac{4}{7}$
19. $4\frac{3}{4} \div 6\frac{1}{3}$
20. $6\frac{2}{9} \div 2\frac{2}{3}$
21. $3\frac{3}{8} \div 1\frac{4}{5}$

Chapter 11 Review

Amount to borrow for a home, pages 216–217

1. Dawn Kenoi earns $7.45 per hour working 40 hours per week. What is the greatest amount she should borrow for a home? (Use the general guideline of 2 times annual income.)

Down payment and monthly payment, pages 218–219

2. Cecilia Diaz is buying a condominium for $58,500. She must make a 20% down payment. What is the amount of the loan after the down payment?

3. What is the monthly payment on a loan of $46,500 for 25 years if the annual interest rate is 12.5%? (Use the table on page 218.)

Interest on a mortgage loan, pages 220–221

4. What is the total amount of interest that will be paid on a loan of $45,000 for 30 years if the monthly payment is $463.05?

Principal and interest in a monthly payment, page 222

5. Bill Dunkle borrowed $37,000 at 13.5% annual interest. What is the amount of interest he will pay the first month?

Homeowner's insurance, pages 224–225

6. Walter's basic premium for his homeowner's insurance is $130. He has a stamp collection worth $2100 that he wants to insure separately. What is the total premium for his insurance? (Use the table on page 224.)

Real estate taxes, pages 226–227

7. The Lees' property has a market value of $78,500. The rate of assessment in the area is 60%. The tax rate is $3.23 per $100 of assessed valuation. What is the Lees' real estate tax?

Closing costs, pages 228–229

8. The Condiffs paid a lawyer's fee of 0.5% of the purchase price of their home. What was the fee if the house cost $82,500?

Real estate agent, pages 230–231

9. Hal Parsons is a real estate agent. For what amount should he list a house so that the seller will receive at least $72,000? The commission is 7%. (Round the answer up to the next hundred dollars.)

10. The Days are moving to Denver. What can they expect to pay as a down payment on a $90,000 house? (Use the table on page 232.)

Chapter 11 Test

1. Paul Labe earns $10.50 per hour working 40 hours per week. What is the greatest amount he should borrow for a home? (Use the general guideline of 2 times annual income.)

2. Elizabeth Markley is buying a home that costs $53,000. She made a 20% down payment. What is the amount of the loan after the down payment?

3. What is the monthly payment on a loan of $37,000 for 30 years if the annual interest rate is 12.5%? (Use this table.)

Monthly Payments for $1000 Loan

Interest rate	20-year loan	25-year loan	30-year loan
10.0%	$9.66	$9.09	$8.78
10.5%	$9.99	$9.45	$9.15
11.0%	$10.33	$9.81	$9.53
11.5%	$10.66	$10.16	$9.90
12.0%	$11.01	$10.53	$10.29
12.5%	$11.36	$10.90	$10.67
13.0%	$11.72	$11.28	$11.06

4. What is the total amount of interest that will be paid on a loan of $42,500 for 25 years if the monthly payment is $495.55?

5. Machiko Ohira borrowed $38,000 at 15% annual interest. What is the amount of interest she will pay the first month?

6. Joyce's basic premium for her homeowner's insurance is $125. She wants to insure a watch worth $200 separately. What is the total premium for her insurance? (Use this table.)

Personal property	One-year rate per $100 of value
Jewelry	$1.40
Furs and garments trimmed with fur	$0.41

7. The Waltons' property has a market value of $62,800. The rate of assessment in the area is 50%. The tax rate is $3.71 per $100 of assessed valuation. What is the Waltons' real estate tax?

8. In one area the recording fee is 0.1% of the purchase price of the home. What is the fee if a house costs $56,200?

9. Tracy Johnson sells real estate. For what amount should she list a home if the sellers hope to get at least $84,000? The real estate commission is 7%. (Round the answer up to the next hundred dollars.)

10. Dan Meza is moving to Baltimore. What can he expect to pay as a down payment on a $95,000 house? (Use this table.)

Home Loans   March, 1981

Metropolitan area	Average interest rate	Average purchase price	Average down payment
Atlanta	14.09%	$92,100	24.2%
Baltimore	13.67%	$89,100	26.6%

Chapter 12　Building a Home

Surveyor

Career Cluster: Technology Rita Lawsen is a surveyor. She is often hired to make a land survey and a scale drawing of a piece of property.

To make a land survey, Rita determines the **bearings**, or direction, of each side of the property. She uses this information to make a scale drawing. In the diagram below, side XY has bearings N 81° E (81° east of north).

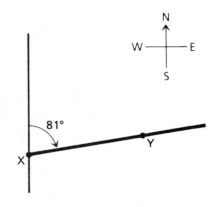

Problem

Make a scale drawing using this information from Rita's land survey. Use the scale of 1 cm → 10 m.

Side AB: N 11° W, 39 m
Side BC: S 85° E, 41 m
Side CD: S 8° W, 40 m
Side DA: N 80° W, 29 m

Solution

Strategy

• Select a starting point A. Draw a north-south line through A.

• Draw a line through A with bearings N 11° W. Use a protractor to draw the 11° angle.

• Use a proportion to find the scale length of side AB.

$$\frac{1}{10} = \frac{x}{39}$$ ← Scale length (cm)
← Actual length (m)

$x = 3.9$

• Measure 3.9 cm from point A and label point B.

• Draw a north-south line through point B. Then draw a line through B with bearings S 85° E (85° east of south).

• Use a proportion to find that the scale length of side BC is 4.1 cm. Measure 4.1 cm from point B and label point C.

• Draw a north-south line through point C. Repeat the process and draw side CD.

• Draw side DA. If the drawing is correct, side DA is 2.9 cm long with bearings N 80° W (80° west of a north-south line through point D). Label each side with the bearings and the actual length.

Conclusion

This is the scale drawing of the lot.

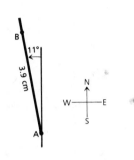

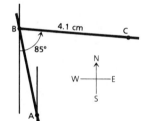

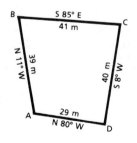

Related Problems

For each problem, draw the side of a lot with the given bearings and length. Use the scale of 1 cm → 10 m.

1. N 15° W, 20 m

2. N 87° W, 40 m

3. N 76° E, 38 m

4. N 32° E, 22 m

5. S 18° E, 54 m

6. S 65° E, 42 m

7. S 21° W, 35 m

8. S 9° W, 28 m

For problems 9-12, make a drawing of each lot using the given bearings and lengths. Use the scale of 1 cm → 10 m.

9. Side AB: N 10° W, 45 m
Side BC: S 80° E, 40 m
Side CD: S 5° W, 44 m
Side DA: N 77° W, 27 m

10. Side KL: N 20° W, 50 m
Side LM: N 75° E, 53 m
Side MN: S 6° W, 64 m
Side NK: N 84° W, 27 m

11. Side WX: N 12° E, 42 m
Side XY: N 72° E, 38 m
Side YZ: S 16° E, 65 m
Side ZW: N 81° W, 64 m

12. Side QR: N 7° E, 54 m
Side RS: S 73° E, 43 m
Side ST: S 17° W, 36 m
Side TQ: S 81° W, 38 m

Cost of Building a House

Diana and Miguel Vasquez want to build a house. The cost will depend on the size and style of the house, the location, and the kind of building materials used.

Problem

Miguel and Diana have decided to build a one-story house with a brick exterior. The contractor told them that the house will cost $43 per square foot to build. The garage will cost $13.50 per square foot. What will be the total cost of building the house and garage?

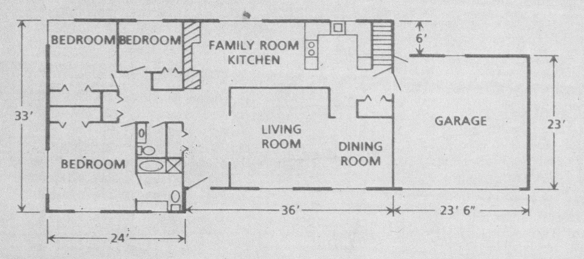

Solution

Strategy

- Multiply to find the area in square feet of each rectangular section of the house (excluding the garage). Then add to find the total area.

Area of left side: $24 \times 33 = 792$
Area of right side: $36 \times 29 = 1044$
Total area: $792 + 1044 = 1836$

- Multiply to find the cost of building the house.

$1836 \times \$43 = \$78{,}948$

- Multiply to find the area of the garage. Round up to the next square foot. Remember, $23'6'' = 23\frac{1}{2}'$.

$23\frac{1}{2} \times 23 \approx 541$

- Multiply to find the cost of building the garage.

$541 \times \$13.50 = \$7303.50$

- Add to find the total cost.

$\$78{,}948 + \$7303.50 = \$86{,}251.50$

Conclusion

The total cost of building the house and garage will be $86,251.50.

Related Problems

The two-story house below will cost about $38 per square foot to build, and the garage will cost about $13 per square foot.

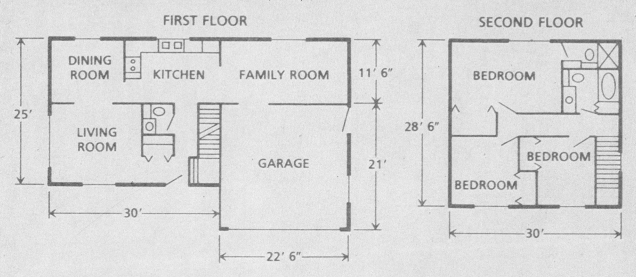

FIRST FLOOR

DINING ROOM   KITCHEN   FAMILY ROOM   11' 6"

25'

LIVING ROOM   GARAGE   21'

30'

22' 6"

SECOND FLOOR

BEDROOM   28' 6"

BEDROOM

BEDROOM

30'

1. Find the area of the left side of the first floor.

2. Find the area of the right side of the first floor (excluding the garage).

3. Find the area of the second floor.

4. Find the total area of the house. Round up to the next square foot.

5. Find the cost of building the house.

6. Find the area of the garage. Round up to the next square foot.

7. Find the cost of building the garage.

8. Find the total cost of building the house and garage.

The split-level house below costs $40 per square foot to
build. The garage costs $11.50 per square foot.

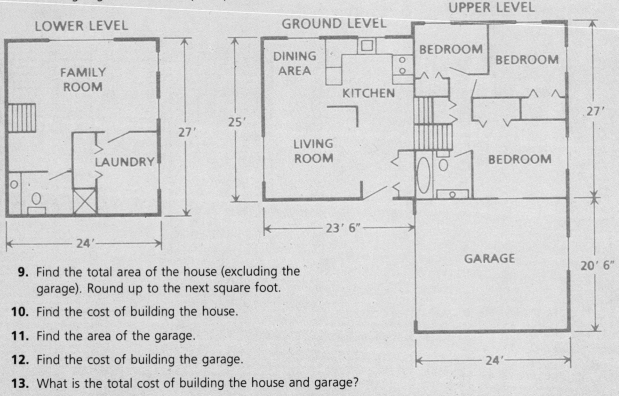

LOWER LEVEL

FAMILY
ROOM

LAUNDRY

27'

24'

GROUND LEVEL

DINING
AREA

KITCHEN

LIVING
ROOM

25'

23' 6"

UPPER LEVEL

BEDROOM

BEDROOM

BEDROOM

27'

GARAGE

20' 6"

24'

9. Find the total area of the house (excluding the
   garage). Round up to the next square foot.

10. Find the cost of building the house.

11. Find the area of the garage.

12. Find the cost of building the garage.

13. What is the total cost of building the house and garage?

Break Time

Separate this lot into four smaller lots,
each with the same shape as the larger lot.
Each of the smaller lots should have the
same area.

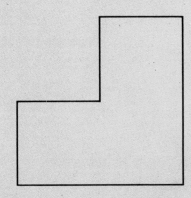

CALCULATOR APPLICATIONS

Building Costs

A builder is quoting the following prices for new homes.
Complete the table and determine each total estimate.

	Style	Cost per square foot		Area (sq. ft.)				Cost		
		House	Garage	First level	Second level	Third level	Garage	House	Garage	Total
	Homes built with aluminum-siding exterior									
1.	One-story	$36.50	$12.00	1750	——	——	625			
2.	Two-story	$32.50	$12.00	1000	950	——	450			
3.	Split-level	$34.00	$11.50	570	580	725	425			
	Homes built with brick exterior									
4.	One-story	$41.50	$13.50	1685	——	——	340			
5.	Two-story	$37.00	$13.00	950	1065	——	615			
6.	Split-level	$39.50	$13.00	615	700	775	625			
	Homes built with stone exterior									
7.	One-story	$45.00	$15.00	1925	——	——	585			
8.	Two-story	$40.50	$14.50	875	925	——	585			
9.	Split-level	$42.50	$14.50	430	490	675	585			
	Homes built with wood exterior									
10.	One-story	$35.00	$11.50	1875	——	——	500			
11.	Two-story	$31.50	$11.50	1050	1100	——	585			
12.	Split-level	$33.00	$11.00	650	670	580	550			

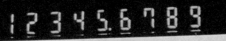

Cost of Installing a Driveway

Peter Dubois is going to have a driveway installed. This will involve excavating the area, spreading and rolling gravel, and finally applying asphalt.

Problem

Peter drew this diagram of the driveway he wants installed. The contractor told him that the driveway will cost $1.35 per square foot. What will be the cost of installing the driveway?

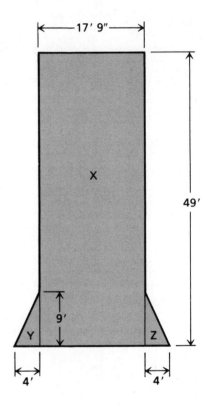

Solution

Strategy
- Multiply the length times the width to find the area in square feet of rectangular section X.
  Remember, $17'9'' = 17\frac{3}{4}'$.
  $49 \times 17\frac{3}{4} = 869\frac{3}{4}$

- For triangular sections Y and Z, multiply $\frac{1}{2}$ times the base times the height to find the area in square feet.
  Area of Y: $\frac{1}{2} \times 4 \times 9 = 18$
  Area of Z: $\frac{1}{2} \times 4 \times 9 = 18$

- Add to find the total area of the driveway. Round up to the next square foot.
  $869\frac{3}{4} + 18 + 18 \approx 906$

- Multiply by $1.35 to find the cost of installing the driveway.
  $\$1.35 \times 906 = \$1223.10$

Conclusion
The cost of installing the driveway will be $1223.10.

Related Problems

Use the sketch of the driveway shown below for problems 1-10.

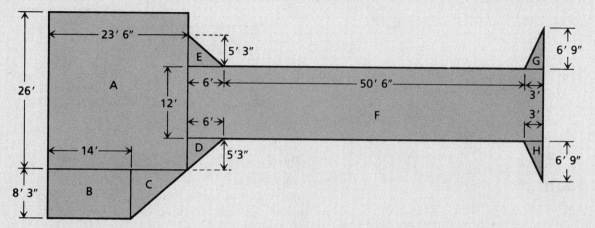

Find the area of each of the following sections of the driveway.

1. Section A   5. Section E

2. Section B   6. Section F

3. Section C   7. Section G

4. Section D   8. Section H

9. Find the total area of the driveway. Round up to the next square foot.

10. Find the cost of installing the driveway at $1.35 per square foot.

Bricklayer

Career Cluster: Trades Bill Sewell is a bricklayer. He determines the number of bricks and the amount of mortar he needs for a job by first finding the number of square feet to be covered.

Problem
Bill is going to brick the front of the garage shown at the right. The door is 18 ft. by 6 ft. 6 in., and the window is 3 ft. by 4 ft. Find the number of square feet to be covered with bricks.

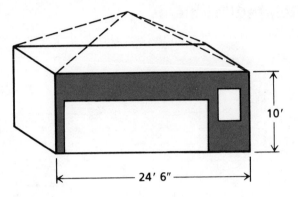

Solution

Strategy
• Multiply to find the area in square feet of the front of the garage.

$24\frac{1}{2} \times 10 = 245$

• Multiply to find the area of each opening.

Door: $18 \times 6\frac{1}{2} = 117$

Window: $3 \times 4 = 12$

• Add to find the total area of the openings.

$117 + 12 = 129$

• Subtract to find the number of square feet to be covered with bricks.

$245 - 129 = 116$

Conclusion
116 sq. ft. will be covered with bricks.

Problem
Bill estimates it will take 7 bricks to cover each square foot of surface. He uses 3 bags of cement and 9 cubic feet of sand to make enough mortar to cover 100 sq. ft. How many bricks, how much cement, and how much sand does he need for the front of the garage (116 sq. ft. of surface)?

Solution

Strategy
• Multiply the area to be covered by 7 to find the number of bricks needed.

$7 \times 116 = 812$

• Use proportions to find the amount of cement and sand needed. Round up to the next whole number.

$\dfrac{3}{100} = \dfrac{n}{116}$ ⟵ Number of bags of cement
⟵ Square feet of surface to be covered

$n \approx 4$

$\dfrac{9}{100} = \dfrac{n}{116}$ ⟵ Cubic feet of sand
⟵ Square feet of surface to be covered

$n \approx 11$

Conclusion
Bill needs 812 bricks, 4 bags of cement, and 11 cu. ft. of sand.

Related Problems

All four sides of the house shown at the right will be covered with bricks.

1. Find the area of the front of the house.

2. Find the area of the left side of the house.

3. Find the total area of all four sides. The back is the same size as the front, and the right side is the same size as the left side.

4. Each front window is 12 ft. by 5 ft. Find the total area of these two openings.

5. There are eight windows, each 2 ft. 6 in. by 5 ft. Find the total area of these eight openings.

6. There are two doors, each 3 ft. 6 in. by 7 ft. Find the total area of these two openings.

7. Find the total area of the twelve openings.

8. Find the number of square feet that will be covered with bricks.

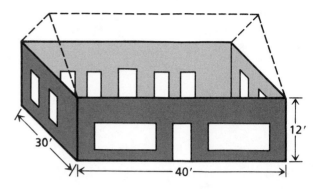

9. Find the number of bricks needed for the house.

10. Find the number of bags of cement needed to make mortar for the house. Round up to the next whole number.

11. Find the number of cubic feet of sand needed to make the mortar. Round up to the next whole number.

Skills Tune-Up

Multiplying fractions and mixed numbers, pages 16-17

1. $\frac{5}{8} \times \frac{7}{10}$
2. $\frac{5}{8} \times \frac{6}{7}$
3. $\frac{4}{9} \times \frac{9}{10}$
4. $\frac{7}{8} \times \frac{4}{7}$
5. $\frac{13}{28} \times \frac{21}{26}$
6. $9 \times \frac{1}{12}$
7. $\frac{2}{9} \times 36$
8. $\frac{1}{3} \times 14$
9. $2\frac{1}{2} \times \frac{1}{4}$
10. $6\frac{1}{4} \times \frac{5}{8}$
11. $1\frac{3}{5} \times 1\frac{1}{2}$
12. $3\frac{4}{7} \times 3\frac{1}{2}$
13. $4\frac{3}{5} \times 8\frac{1}{3}$
14. $2\frac{1}{12} \times 3\frac{9}{10}$
15. $3\frac{3}{7} \times 5\frac{1}{2}$
16. $8 \times 6\frac{5}{8}$
17. $7\frac{5}{12} \times 3$
18. $\frac{1}{7} \times \frac{7}{8} \times \frac{3}{5}$
19. $\frac{1}{4} \times 8\frac{2}{3} \times \frac{9}{13}$
20. $2\frac{1}{10} \times 1\frac{2}{3} \times \frac{2}{3}$

Adding fractions and mixed numbers, pages 18-19

1. $\frac{1}{3} + \frac{5}{12}$
2. $\frac{2}{15} + \frac{2}{5}$
3. $\frac{11}{12} + \frac{1}{2}$
4. $\frac{5}{12} + \frac{1}{4}$
5. $\frac{1}{6} + \frac{7}{9}$
6. $\frac{11}{12} + \frac{2}{3}$
7. $\frac{7}{10} + \frac{1}{2}$
8. $\frac{3}{8} + \frac{9}{16}$
9. $\frac{1}{4} + 2\frac{1}{3}$
10. $4\frac{1}{6} + \frac{1}{8}$
11. $2\frac{1}{5} + 1\frac{3}{10}$
12. $3\frac{3}{5} + 5\frac{3}{20}$
13. $6\frac{3}{8} + 2\frac{5}{6}$
14. $1\frac{3}{4} + 2\frac{7}{12}$
15. $8\frac{7}{15} + 5\frac{2}{5}$
16. $1\frac{1}{8} + 6\frac{2}{3}$
17. $2\frac{7}{30} + 7\frac{9}{10}$
18. $5\frac{7}{24} + 4\frac{5}{8}$
19. $1\frac{1}{3} + 2\frac{1}{4} + 3\frac{5}{12}$
20. $12\frac{4}{5} + 5\frac{11}{15} + 9\frac{2}{3}$

Subtracting fractions and mixed numbers, pages 18-19

1. $\frac{11}{18} - \frac{1}{9}$
2. $\frac{13}{14} - \frac{3}{7}$
3. $\frac{3}{5} - \frac{1}{2}$
4. $\frac{17}{24} - \frac{1}{4}$
5. $\frac{7}{9} - \frac{11}{18}$
6. $\frac{17}{20} - \frac{1}{10}$
7. $\frac{13}{16} - \frac{5}{8}$
8. $\frac{3}{5} - \frac{13}{30}$
9. $10\frac{1}{3} - 1\frac{2}{3}$
10. $20\frac{1}{7} - 2\frac{5}{7}$
11. $3 - \frac{1}{3}$
12. $9 - \frac{1}{5}$
13. $6\frac{3}{8} - 4\frac{1}{4}$
14. $17\frac{3}{5} - 2\frac{9}{10}$
15. $6\frac{5}{6} - 3\frac{2}{9}$
16. $13\frac{3}{7} - 4\frac{13}{14}$
17. $5\frac{7}{9} - 2\frac{5}{6}$
18. $13\frac{1}{3} - 6\frac{4}{5}$
19. $7\frac{1}{4} - 5\frac{5}{12}$
20. $15\frac{2}{3} - 4\frac{7}{9}$

Chapter 12 Review

Surveyor, pages 238-239

1. Draw the side of a lot with bearings and length S 76° W, 42 m. Use the scale of 1 cm → 10 m.

Cost of building a house, pages 240-242

2. Find the total area of the house shown below. Round up to the next square foot.

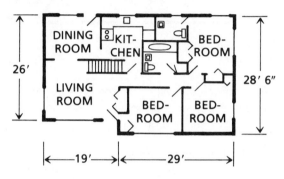

3. A builder will build this house for $39 per square foot. Find the cost of building this house.

4. Find the cost of building the garage shown below at $12.50 per square foot.

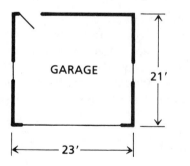

5. What will be the total cost of building the house and garage?

Cost of installing a driveway, pages 244-245

6. Find the total area of the driveway shown below. Round up to the next square foot.

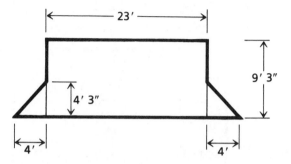

7. A contractor will install the driveway for $1.15 per square foot. What will be the cost of installing the driveway?

Bricklayer, pages 246-247

8. The front of a garage 24 ft. 6 in. long and 10 ft. high is going to be covered with bricks. There is a garage door 17 ft. 6 in. by 8 ft. and a window 2 ft. by 3 ft. Find the number of square feet to be covered with bricks.

9. Seven bricks will cover one square foot of surface. How many bricks will be needed for 195 sq. ft. of surface?

10. Nine cubic feet of sand are used to make enough mortar to cover 100 sq. ft. of surface. If 275 sq. ft. of surface is to be covered with bricks, how much sand is needed to make enough mortar for the job? Round up to the next whole number.

Chapter 12 Test

1. Draw the side of a lot with bearings and length N 84° E, 47 m. Use the scale of 1 cm ⟶ 10 m.

2. Find the total area of the house shown below. Round up to the next square foot.

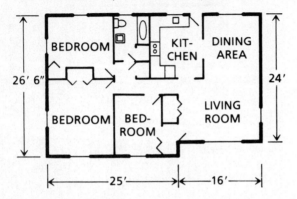

3. A builder will build this house for $41 per square foot. Find the cost of building this house.

4. Find the cost of building the garage shown below at $14.50 per square foot.

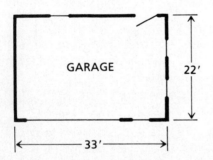

5. What will be the total cost of building the house and garage?

6. Find the total area of the driveway shown below. Round up to the next square foot.

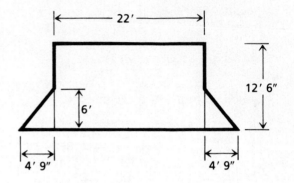

7. A contractor will install the driveway for $1.25 per square foot. What will be the cost of installing the driveway?

8. The front of a store 30 ft. long and 9 ft. 6 in. high is going to be covered with bricks. There is a window 15 ft. by 6 ft. and a door 4 ft. by 7 ft. 6 in. Find the number of square feet to be covered with bricks.

9. Seven bricks will cover one square foot of surface. How many bricks will be needed for 286 sq. ft. of surface?

10. Three bags of cement are used to make enough mortar to cover 100 sq. ft. If 325 sq. ft. of surface is to be covered with bricks, how many bags of cement are needed to make enough mortar for the job? Round up to the next whole number.

Unit 4 Test

Choose the best answer.

1. Mario earns $7.50 per hour in a 40-hour work week. What is the most he should spend for rent each month? (Use the guideline of not spending more than one week's gross pay for shelter each month.)

A $47.50   **C** $1200

B $300   **D** $290

2. Shelley Big Eagle rented an apartment for $255 per month plus utilities. Electricity costs will average $25 per month and heating costs will average $35 per month. How much will Shelley pay for rent and utilities each month?

A $315   **C** $195

B $290   **D** $340

3. Give the reading for this electric meter.

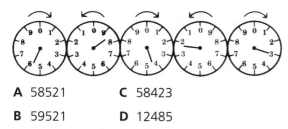

A 58521   **C** 58423

B 59521   **D** 12485

4. To the nearest tenth, what is the scale length of a table that is 1.5 m long? Use the scale of 1 cm ⟶ 0.2 m.

A 3.0 cm   **C** 0.75 cm

B 0.3 cm   **D** 7.5 cm

5. How many tiles will be needed to cover a floor 4.5 m by 3.0 m? Each tile is a square 30 cm by 30 cm.

A 900 tiles   **C** 14 tiles

B 25 tiles   **D** 150 tiles

6. A gallon of paint covers 400 sq. ft. About how much paint will be needed to paint the walls of a basement 35 ft. by 22 ft.? The walls are 7 ft. high.

A 1 gallon   **C** 3 gallons

B 2 gallons   **D** 13.5 gallons

7. A roll of wallpaper covers 30 sq. ft. How many rolls are needed for a room 15 ft. by 12 ft. with walls 8 ft. high? Subtract $\frac{1}{2}$ roll for each of the 2 windows and 2 doors.

A 13 rolls   **C** 15 rolls

B 11 rolls   **D** 46 rolls

8. Koyi has a $100-deductible insurance policy. His 5-year-old TV was stolen and will cost $800 to replace. If the annual rate of depreciation is 12%, how much will the insurance company pay?

A $96   **C** $220

B $320   **D** $380

9. Ruth earns $18,500 per year. What is the greatest amount she should borrow to buy a home? (Use the general guideline of 2 times annual income.)

A $37,000   **C** $9250

B $36,000   **D** $55,500

10. An amortization table shows that the monthly payment for a $1000 loan for 30 years at 12% interest is $10.29. Find the monthly payment on a 30-year home loan of $50,000 at 12% per year.

A $5145   **C** $514.50

B $308.70   **D** $600

11. How much interest will Lucita pay on a loan of $30,000 for 25 years if the monthly payments are $361.20?

A $20,970   **C** $277.87

B $78,360   **D** $108,360

12. Maude borrowed $48,000 at an annual interest rate of 14%. How much interest will she pay the first month?

A $6720   **C** $286

B $5600   **D** $560

13. Drew's basic premium for homeowner's insurance is $195. He has a $600 camera and a $300 guitar he wants to insure separately. Use the table below and find the total premium for his insurance.

Personal property	One-year rate per $100 of value
Cameras, projectors, etc.	$1.65
Musical instruments—amateur	$0.69

A $206.97   **C** $183.03

B $1392   **D** $11.97

14. Find the assessed valuation of a home with a market value of $74,000. The rate of assessment is 60% of market value.

A $118,400   **C** $44,400

B $29,600   **D** $103,600

15. The recording fee is 0.1% of the purchase price of a home. What is the recording fee on a $94,000 home?

A $846   **C** $9400

B $94   **D** $940

16. A real estate salesperson's commission is 7% of the selling price of a home. For what amount should a house be listed if the seller wants at least $75,000? Round up to the next hundred dollars.

A $80,300   **C** $5300

B $80,700   **D** $525,000

17. Give the bearings of side XY.

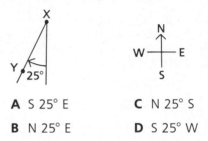

A S 25° E   **C** N 25° S

B N 25° E   **D** S 25° W

18. A builder charges $42 per square foot to build a one-story house. Find the cost of building a house 35 feet wide and 50 feet long.

A $73,500   **C** $35,700

B $72,500   **D** $71,400

19. A contractor will install a driveway for $1.15 per square foot. What is the cost of a driveway 16 ft. 6 in. wide and 20 ft. long?

A $330   **C** $83.95

B $381.80   **D** $379.50

20. A store front is 30 ft. long and 10 ft. high. It contains one opening 8 ft. by 7 ft. If a bricklayer uses 7 bricks per square foot of surface covered, about how many bricks will be needed for the store front?

A 350 bricks   **C** 1708 bricks

B 2100 bricks   **D** 35 bricks

Break Time

Many items sold in stores have prices close to a multiple-of-10 amount or an even-dollar amount. For example, 89¢ is close to 90¢, and $7.98 is close to $8. Multiplying mentally to find total costs is easy with numbers like 90 and 8.

Blank cassette tapes cost 89¢ each. How much would 5 tapes cost?

THINK

> 89 cents is 1 cent less than 90 cents.
>
> 5 × 90 cents = 450 cents
>
> 5 × 1 cent = 5 cents
>
> 450 cents − 5 cents = 445 cents, or $4.45

The 5 tapes would cost $4.45.

Stereo tapes cost $7.98 each. How much would 4 stereo tapes cost?

THINK

> $7.98 is 2 cents less than 8 dollars.
>
> 4 × 8 dollars = 32 dollars
>
> 4 × 2 cents = 8 cents
>
> 32 dollars − 8 cents = $31.92

The 4 stereo tapes would cost $31.92.

Find these products mentally. Write only the answer.

1. 4 × 79¢
2. 6 × 99¢
3. 8 × 59¢
4. 2 × 88¢
5. 7 × 48¢
6. 5 × 35¢
7. 9 × 39¢
8. 15 × 19¢

9. 4 × $1.99
10. 3 × $3.98
11. 6 × $1.97
12. 2 × $4.99
13. 5 × $2.95
14. 8 × $2.99
15. 4 × $5.98
16. 12 × $1.99

Now try these. A hint is given for exercise 17.

17. 3 × $2.09

THINK

> $2.09 is 9 cents more than 2 dollars.
>
> 3 × 2 dollars = 6 dollars
>
> 3 × 9 cents = 27 cents
>
> 6 dollars + 27 cents = ▓▓

18. 6 × $1.05
19. 4 × $6.08
20. 7 × $2.10
21. 5 × $4.03

22. 5 × 81¢
23. 8 × 32¢
24. 9 × 12¢
25. 6 × 73¢

COMPUTER APPLICATIONS

Amortization Tables

Betty Johnson is a loan officer at a savings and loan association. She uses the program shown to print amortization tables for mortgage loans.

Lines 40, 60, and 80 These values must be entered.

Data required	Name
Amount financed	P
Annual interest rate (%)	Y
Number of years to repay	N

Line 20 Each calculation in this program must be rounded, or error will compound. The DEF function can be used when rounding must be done many times. To define a function to round to the nearest cent, first use DEF, then a name of three letters beginning with FN, and then another name of one letter in parentheses.

Line 90 The number of years is multiplied by 12 to change it to the number of monthly payments.

Line 110 The monthly payment (A) is calculated.

Line 120 The monthly payment is rounded up to the next higher cent.

Lines 130 and 140 PRINT statements are used to print headings for the table.

Lines 160 and 240 A FOR–NEXT loop is used to calculate and print each payment of the amortization table. The calculations and PRINT statements go between lines 160 and 240. M counts the number of months.

Line 170 The interest (I) is calculated and rounded.

Line 180 The interest is subtracted from the payment to find the amount (P1) that is applied to the principal.

Line 190 As long as the amount applied to the principal doesn't exceed the principal, line 200 is skipped.

Line 200 On the last payment, the amount paid to the principal often exceeds the amount of principal left to be paid. In this case, P1 is changed so that only P is paid.

Line 210 The amount applied to the principal in line 180 is subtracted from the principal to find the new principal (P2).

Line 220 Each payment of the table is printed.

Line 230 The rounded new principal becomes the principal for the next time the loop is executed.

```
10 REM   MORTGAGE AMORTIZATION TABLE
20 DEF FNR(Z)=INT(Z*100+.5)/100
30 PRINT "AMOUNT FINANCED";
40 INPUT P
50 PRINT "INTEREST RATE";
60 INPUT Y
70 PRINT "NUMBER OF YEARS";
80 INPUT N
90 LET N=N*12
100 LET R=Y/100/12
110 LET A=P*((R*(1+R)^N)/((1+R)^N-1))
120 LET A=INT(A*100+.999)/100
130 PRINT "PAYMENT";TAB(23);"AMOUNT OF";
TAB(35);"AMOUNT PAID";TAB(50);"/NEW/"
140 PRINT "NUMBER";TAB(11);"PRINCIPAL";
TAB(23);"INTEREST";TAB(35);"ON
PRINCIPAL";TAB(50);"PRINCIPAL"
150 PRINT
160 FOR M=1 TO N
170 LET I=FNR(P*R)
180 LET P1=FNR(A-I)
190 IF P1<=P THEN 210
200 LET P1=FNR(P)
210 LET P2=FNR(P-P1)
220 PRINT TAB(2);M;TAB(11);P;TAB(24);I;
TAB(38);P1;TAB(50);P2
230 LET P=FNR(P2)
240 NEXT M
250 END
```

Give the output for the program above when

1. P is 2000, Y is 16, and N is 3.

2. P is 6500, Y is 14.5, and N is 2.5.

3. P is 4475, Y is 15.25, and N is 2.75.

4. P is 8000, Y is 17, and N is 2.25.

5. the principal is $5000, the annual interest rate is 15%, and the number of years is 2.

6. the principal is $7865, the annual interest rate is 16.5%, and the number of years is 2.75.

7. the principal is $3600, the annual interest rate is 14.75%, and the number of years is 2.5.

8. the principal is $2200, the annual interest rate is 17.5%, and the number of years is 1.5.

9. $4000 is financed at 16.75% annually for 2.25 years.

10. $1600 is financed at 18% annually for 0.75 years.

11. $9500 is financed at 14% annually for 3 years.

12. $6195 is financed at 16.5% annually for 2.5 years.

13. Modify the program so that a title, the principal, the annual rate of interest, the number of months, and the monthly payment are printed before the table. Only PRINT statements need to be added.

14. Give the output when the principal is $3000, the annual interest rate is 14.75%, and the number of years is 2.

15. Modify the program so that the total paid to interest and the total paid to principal are printed after the table. Use LET statements before the FOR–NEXT loop to make T1 and T2 equal to zero. Then use T1 and T2 inside the loop to keep running totals.

16. Give the output when the principal is $3785, the annual interest rate is 15.5%, and the number of years is 2.5.

17. Give the output when the principal is $2755, the annual interest rate is 17.5%, and the number of years is 0.5.

Unit 5 Taxes, Insurance, and Investments

Chapter 13   Income Tax

Who Must File a Tax Return

1 Control number	22222			

2 Employer's name, address, and ZIP code	3 Employer's identification number	4 Employer's State number
Valley Supermarket 2307 Lake Street Spring Valley, MI 49100	5 Stat. em- ☐ De- ceased ☐ Pension plan ☐ Legal rep. ☐ 942 emp. ☐ Sub- total ☐ Cor- rection ☐ Void ☐ 6	7 Advance EIC payment

8 Employee's social security number	9 Federal income tax withheld	10 Wages, tips, other compensation	11 FICA tax withheld
999-32-5110	$105.77	$1,511.72	$100.53

12 Employee's name, address, and ZIP code	13 FICA wages	14 FICA tips
Bert Steiger 562 Chestnut Street Spring Valley, MI 49100	$1,511.72	
	16 Employer's use	

17 State income tax	18 State wages, tips, etc.	19 Name of State
$68.43	$1,511.72	MI
20 Local income tax	21 Local wages, tips, etc.	22 Name of locality

Form **W-2 Wage and Tax Statement 1980** Copy B To be **filed with employee's FEDERAL tax return**
This information is being furnished to the Internal Revenue Service. Department of the Treasury
Internal Revenue Service

At the end of each year, employers provide a **wage and tax statement**, Form W-2, to each person they have employed during the year. This form indicates the income earned and taxes withheld during the year. A copy of the W-2 form must accompany the person's **income tax return** when it is filed with the Internal Revenue Service (IRS).

The W-2 form shown above indicates that Bert Steiger earned $1511.72 at Valley Supermarket. It also shows that $105.77 was withheld for federal income tax, $100.53 was withheld for FICA (social security), and $68.43 was withheld for state income tax.

Two factors, **gross income** and **filing status**, are used to determine who must file a tax return. Gross income is total annual income that is taxed, such as income from wages, tips, interest, dividends, and self-employment. Filing status depends on marital status.

A person may not be required by law to file a tax return; but if he or she is entitled to a tax refund, a tax return must be filed in order to receive the refund.

General Instructions

Who Must File

Your income and your filing status generally determine whether or not you must file a tax return.

You must file a return for 1980, even if you owe no tax:	And your income was at least:
If you were single (this also means legally separated, divorced, or married with a dependent child and living apart from your spouse for all of 1980) and:	
Under 65	$3,300
65 or over	4,300
If you were married filing a joint return and were living with your spouse at the end of 1980 (or on the date your spouse died), and:	
Both were under 65	5,400
One was 65 or over	6,400
Both were 65 or over	7,400
If you were married filing a	

Problem

Bert Steiger is a single 18-year-old student. Last year he worked for both the Valley Supermarket, where he earned $1511.72, and the Ace Construction Company, where he earned $1396.26. What was his gross income for the year? Is he required to file a tax return?

Solution

Strategy
• Add to find the gross income.
  $1511.72 + $1396.26 = $2907.98

• Find the minimum income for a single person under 65 for which a tax return must be filed.
  $3300

• Compare Bert's income with the minimum income.
  $2907.98 < $3300

Conclusion
Bert's gross income was $2907.98. Bert is not required to file a tax return.

Related Problems

For problems 1-8, find the gross income. Then write *yes* if a tax return is required or *no* if it is not required.

1. Louette Romas
Single (age 18)
Income: $2235.80 and $1310.75

2. Patti and Greg Talman
Married filing joint return (ages 64 and 67)
Income: $4420.88 and $2132.18

3. Martin and Sandra Weiler
Married filing joint return (both age 72)
Income: $3395.27, $2537.18, and $988.25

4. Norman Demato
Single (age 80)
Income: $3211.75, $1067.95, and $210.50

5. Kevin and Bea Orzel
Married filing joint return (ages 68 and 70)
Income: $5100, $1273.14, $557.20, and $214.25

6. Clarence and Anne Friedman
Married filing joint return (both age 60)
Income: $2967.20, $1582.13, $456.63, and $272.95

7. Ruth Lampert
Single (age 66)
Income: $2116.25, $1349.31, and $714.30

8. Luke Kaywaykla
Single (age 21)
Income: $2182.50, $586.17, $436.15, and $118.23

9. Samuel Taylor is single and 67 years old. He has earned $2875 so far this year. How much more can he earn and still remain under the minimum income for filing a tax return?

10. Marie and Tom Hannah are both 69 years old and will file a joint return. They have earned $5580 so far this year. How much more can they earn and still remain under the minimum income for filing a tax return?

Adjusted Gross Income and Tax Credit

By April 15 of each year, taxpayers should file an income tax return with the IRS. Most taxpayers complete either the **short form**, Form 1040A, or the **long form**, Form 1040.

The IRS allows taxpayers to round amounts to the nearest dollar on tax returns. The amounts shown on this tax return have been rounded to the nearest dollar.

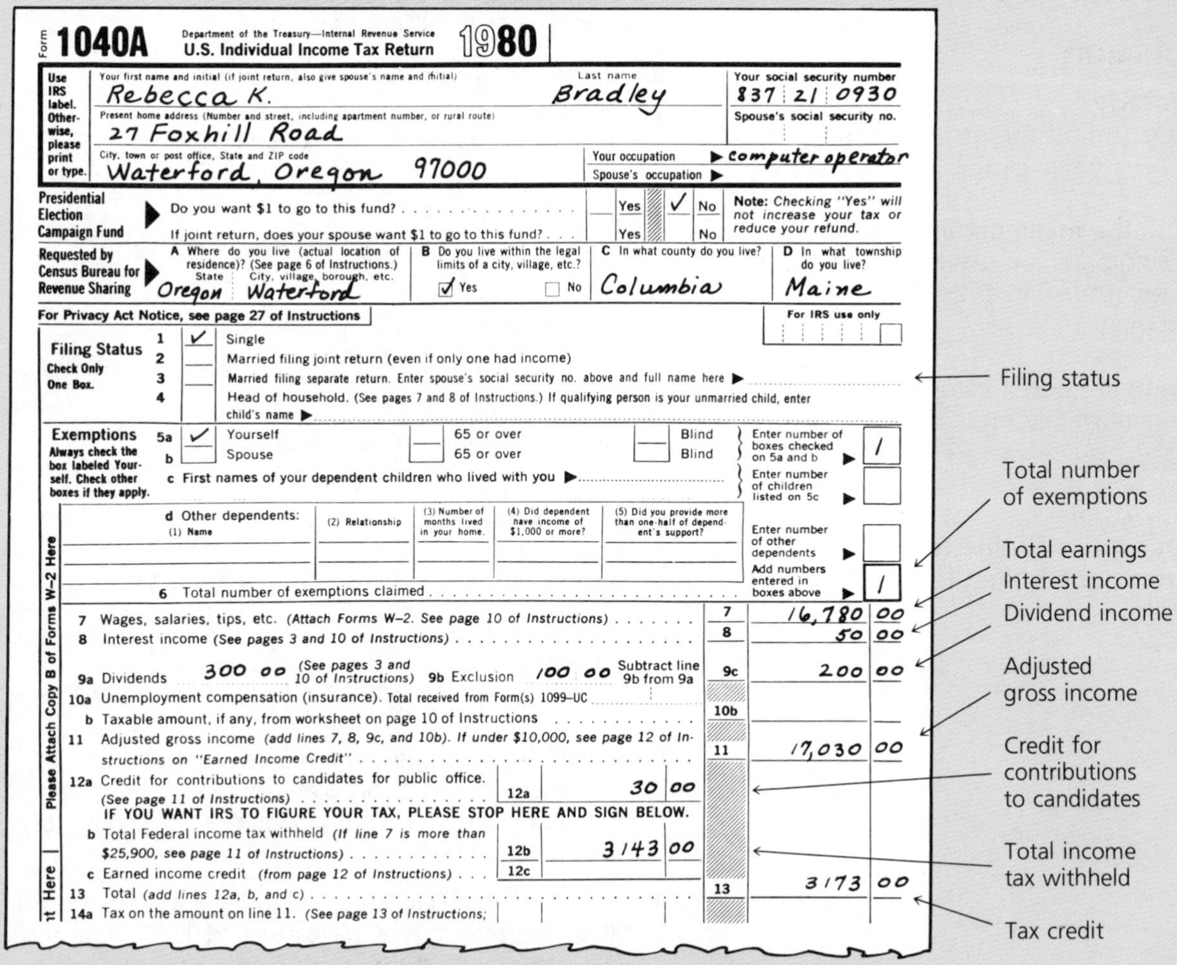

Form 1040A Department of the Treasury—Internal Revenue Service **1980**
U.S. Individual Income Tax Return

Use IRS label. Other-wise, please print or type.

Your first name and initial (if joint return, also give spouse's name and initial): Rebecca K.
Last name: Bradley
Your social security number: 837 21 0930

Present home address (Number and street, including apartment number, or rural route): 27 Foxhill Road
Spouse's social security no.

City, town or post office, State and ZIP code: Waterford, Oregon 97000
Your occupation ▶ computer operator
Spouse's occupation ▶

Presidential Election Campaign Fund
Do you want $1 to go to this fund? . . . . Yes [ ] No [✓]
If joint return, does your spouse want $1 to go to this fund? . . . Yes [ ] No [ ]
Note: Checking "Yes" will not increase your tax or reduce your refund.

Requested by Census Bureau for Revenue Sharing
A Where do you live (actual location of residence)? (See page 6 of Instructions.)
State: Oregon City, village, borough, etc.: Waterford
B Do you live within the legal limits of a city, village, etc.? Yes [✓] No [ ]
C In what county do you live? Columbia
D In what township do you live? Maine

For Privacy Act Notice, see page 27 of Instructions

For IRS use only

Filing Status Check Only One Box.
1 [✓] Single
2 [ ] Married filing joint return (even if only one had income)
3 [ ] Married filing separate return. Enter spouse's social security no. above and full name here ▶
4 [ ] Head of household. (See pages 7 and 8 of Instructions.) If qualifying person is your unmarried child, enter child's name ▶

Exemptions Always check the box labeled Yourself. Check other boxes if they apply.
5a [✓] Yourself [ ] 65 or over [ ] Blind
b Spouse [ ] 65 or over [ ] Blind
Enter number of boxes checked on 5a and b ▶ 1
c First names of your dependent children who lived with you ▶ . . . .
Enter number of children listed on 5c ▶

d Other dependents:
(1) Name	(2) Relationship	(3) Number of months lived in your home.	(4) Did dependent have income of $1,000 or more?	(5) Did you provide more than one-half of dependent's support?

Enter number of other dependents ▶

6 Total number of exemptions claimed . . . .
Add numbers entered in boxes above ▶ 1

7 Wages, salaries, tips, etc. (Attach Forms W–2. See page 10 of Instructions) . . . . | 7 | 16,780 00
8 Interest income (See pages 3 and 10 of Instructions) . . . . | 8 | 50 00
9a Dividends 300 00 (See pages 3 and 10 of Instructions) 9b Exclusion 100 00 Subtract line 9b from 9a | 9c | 200 00
10a Unemployment compensation (insurance). Total received from Form(s) 1099–UC
b Taxable amount, if any, from worksheet on page 10 of Instructions . . . . | 10b |
11 Adjusted gross income (add lines 7, 8, 9c, and 10b). If under $10,000, see page 12 of Instructions on "Earned Income Credit". | 11 | 17,030 00
12a Credit for contributions to candidates for public office. (See page 11 of Instructions) | 12a | 30 00
IF YOU WANT IRS TO FIGURE YOUR TAX, PLEASE STOP HERE AND SIGN BELOW.
b Total Federal income tax withheld (If line 7 is more than $25,900, see page 11 of Instructions) . . . . | 12b | 3143 00
c Earned income credit (from page 12 of Instructions) . . . | 12c |
13 Total (add lines 12a, b, and c) . . . . | 13 | 3173 00
14a Tax on the amount on line 11. (See page 13 of Instructions)

Please Attach Copy B of Forms W–2 Here
Attach W–2 Here

Labels on right:
— Filing status
— Total number of exemptions
— Total earnings
— Interest income
— Dividend income
— Adjusted gross income
— Credit for contributions to candidates
— Total income tax withheld
— Tax credit

The following is the information needed for filling out lines 7-13 of Form 1040A.

Line 7 is the total of all earnings for the year shown on W-2 forms.

Line 8 is all interest income for the year.

Line 9a is all dividend income. The exclusion on line 9b is determined as follows:

Single or Married Filing Separate Return: $100 exclusion

Married Filing Joint Return: $200 exclusion for stock owned jointly

Line 9c is the taxable dividend income.

Line 11 is the **adjusted gross income**.

Line 12a is credit for contributions to candidates running for public office. The credit is determined as follows:

Single or Married Filing Separate Return: One half of the contribution up to $50 maximum credit

Married Filing Joint Return: One half of the contribution up to $100 maximum credit

Line 12b is the total federal income tax withheld for the year as shown on W-2 forms.

Line 13 is the **tax credit**. This is the total amount of credits and taxes withheld.

Problem

Rebecca Bradley's tax return is shown on page 260. She contributed $60 to a candidate running for public office. What are her adjusted gross income and tax credit?

Solution

Strategy

• Fill in total earnings (line 7), interest income (line 8), and dividend income (line 9a).

• Determine exclusion (line 9b) for dividend income.

• Subtract the dividend exclusion (line 9b) from the dividends (line 9a) to find the dividend income that is taxed (line 9c).

• Determine if one half of the contribution to a candidate running for public office is less than the maximum allowed. Fill in the credit for contributions to candidates (line 12a).

$$\tfrac{1}{2} \times \$60 = \$30$$ $30 is less than $50 maximum for a single person filing a separate return.

• Fill in income tax withheld (line 12b), and add to find the tax credit (line 13).

Conclusion

Rebecca's adjusted gross income is $17,030 (line 11). Her tax credit is $3173 (line 13).

Related Problems

Find the adjusted gross income and the tax credit.

1. Doug Erickson, Single
   Salary: $12,436
   Interest income: $47
   Dividend income: $378
   Contribution to candidates: $30
   Federal tax withheld: $1947

2. Viola Jackson, Single
   Salary: $14,682
   Interest income: $250
   Dividend income: $45
   Federal tax withheld: $2534

3. Margo Vitero
   Married filing separate return
   Salary: $18,200
   Interest income: $90
   Dividend income: $175
   Contribution to candidates: $100
   Federal tax withheld: $2554

4. Lisa and Joseph Rojas
   Married filing joint return
   Salary: $27,120
   Interest income: $175
   Contribution to candidates: $40
   Federal tax withheld: $4673

5. Gene and Kim Quan
   Married filing joint return
   Salaries: $15,800 and $10,300
   Interest income: $325
   Dividend income: $316
   Federal tax withheld: $1485 and $1060

6. Al and Kay McCarthy
   Married filing joint return
   Salaries: $10,995 and $4765
   Interest income: $95
   Dividend income: $160
   Contribution to candidates: $150
   Federal tax withheld: $1371 and $214

Break Time

The spoon weighs 22 grams. What is the total weight of a fork, knife, spoon, and plate?

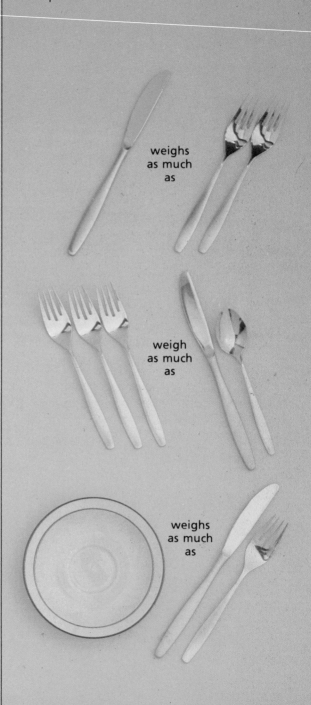

weighs as much as

weigh as much as

weighs as much as

Tax Liability

The federal income tax is based on a graduated system in which the tax rate increases as income increases. Most people can use a tax table to find their **tax liability**. The table the taxpayer uses depends on his or her filing status. Parts of three of these tables are shown on pages 406-408.

Table A/Single
Table B/Married Filing Joint Return
Table C/Married Filing Separate Return

The following section is from Table A.

1980 Tax Table A/Single				
If line 11, Form 1040A, or line 34, Form 1040, is—		And the total number of exemptions claimed on line 6 is—		
		1	**2**	**3**
Over	**But not over**	Your tax Is—		
16,900	16,950	2,883	2,586	2,326
16,950	17,000	2,898	2,599	2,339
17,000	17,050	2,913	2,613	2,352
17,050	17,100	2,928	2,628	2,365

Problem

Rebecca Bradley is single claiming 1 exemption. She has an adjusted gross income of $17,030. What is her tax liability?

Solution

Strategy
• Find the line in Tax Table A/Single for an adjusted gross income (line 11, Form 1040A) over $17,000 but not over $17,050.

• Read the tax liability for 1 exemption.
  $2913

Conclusion
Rebecca's tax liability is $2913.

Related Problems

Find the tax liability. Use the tax tables on pages 406-408.

1. Fred Livingston
   Single, 1 exemption
   Adjusted gross income: $11,543

2. Harold and Yvonne Rader
   Married filing joint return, 3 exemptions
   Adjusted gross income: $19,775

3. Nancy Madden
   Married filing separate return, 1 exemption
   Adjusted gross income: $14,029

4. Robert and Karen Kato
   Married filing joint return, 4 exemptions
   Adjusted gross income: $25,725

5. Shannon McGill
   Single, 2 exemptions
   Adjusted gross income: $19,820

6. Charles Krueger
   Single, 1 exemption
   Adjusted gross income: $16,239

7. Isabel and Jose Gomez
   Married filing joint return, 5 exemptions
   Adjusted gross income: $28,525

8. Mary and Donald Hughes
   Married filing joint return, 7 exemptions
   Adjusted gross income: $19,160

9. Gerald Ledder
   Married filing separate return, 3 exemptions
   Adjusted gross income: $18,725

Find the tax liability on an adjusted gross income of $18,560 for a person with 2 exemptions whose filing status is

10. single.

11. married filing joint return.

12. married filing separate return.

Tax Refund or Balance Due

The final step in completing an income tax return is comparing the tax liability with the tax credit.

If the tax credit is greater, find the **refund** due the taxpayer:

Tax credit − Tax liability = Refund

If the tax liability is greater, find the **balance due** the IRS:

Tax liability − Tax credit = Balance due

Problem

Rebecca Bradley wrote her tax liability on lines 14a and 15 of her tax return. What is her refund or balance due?

Solution

Strategy
- Compare the tax credit (line 13) and the tax liability (line 15). The tax credit is greater.
- Subtract to find the refund (line 16).

Conclusion
Rebecca will receive a refund of $260.

6	Total number of exemptions claimed . . . . Boxes above ▶		
7	Wages, salaries, tips, etc. *(Attach Forms W–2. See page 10 of Instructions)*	7	16,780 00
8	Interest income *(See pages 3 and 10 of Instructions)*	8	50 00
9a	Dividends 300 00 *(See pages 3 and 10 of Instructions)* 9b Exclusion 100 00 Subtract line 9b from 9a	9c	200 00
10a	Unemployment compensation (insurance). Total received from Form(s) 1099–UC		
b	Taxable amount, if any, from worksheet on page 10 of Instructions	10b	
11	Adjusted gross income (add lines 7, 8, 9c, and 10b). If under $10,000, see page 12 of Instructions on "Earned Income Credit"	11	17,030 00
12a	Credit for contributions to candidates for public office. *(See page 11 of Instructions)*	12a	30 00
	IF YOU WANT IRS TO FIGURE YOUR TAX, PLEASE STOP HERE AND SIGN BELOW.		
b	Total Federal income tax withheld *(If line 7 is more than $25,900, see page 11 of Instructions)*	12b	3143 00
c	Earned income credit *(from page 12 of Instructions)* . . .	12c	
13	Total *(add lines 12a, b, and c)*	13	3173 00
14a	Tax on the amount on line 11. *(See page 13 of Instructions; then find your tax in the Tax Tables on pages 15–26)*	14a	2913 00
b	Advance earned income credit (EIC) *(from Form W–2)* . . .	14b	
15	Total *(add lines 14a and 14b)*	15	2913 00
16	If line 13 is larger than line 15, enter amount to be **REFUNDED TO YOU** . . . . ▶	16	260 00
17	If line 15 is larger than line 13, enter **BALANCE DUE.** Attach check or money order for full amount payable to "Internal Revenue Service." Write your social security number on check or money order . ▶	17	

Adjusted gross income ◀ (line 11)

Tax credit ◀ (line 13)

Tax liability ◀ (line 15)
Refund ◀ (line 16)

Balance due ◀ (line 17)

Please Sign Here: Under penalties of perjury, I declare that I have examined this return, including accompanying schedules and statements, and to the best of my knowledge and belief, it is true, correct, and complete. Declaration of preparer (other than taxpayer) is based on all information of which preparer has any knowledge.

Rebecca K. Bradley 2/19/81
Your signature   Date   Spouse's signature (if filing jointly, BOTH must sign even if only one had income)

Paid Preparer's Use Only
Preparer's signature and date ▶
Firm's name (or yours, if self-employed) and address ▶
Check if self-employed ▶ ☐
Preparer's social security no.
E.I. No. ▶
ZIP code ▶

☆ U.S. GOVERNMENT PRINTING OFFICE 1980–O–313–447 04–1213190   Form **1040A** (1980)

Related Problems

Find the refund or balance due. Then write *refund* or *balance due*.

1. Brad and Joyce Levy
   Tax liability: $2213
   Tax credit: $2314

2. Hank and Beth McGovern
   Tax liability: $1529
   Tax credit: $1456

3. Emmett Lentz
   Tax liability: $950
   Tax credit: $1079

4. Grace and Wilson Hardy
   Tax liability: $1619
   Tax credit: $1702

5. Joe and Rita Blackfoot
   Tax liability: $2167
   Tax credit: $2118

6. Olivia and Kurt Alvarez
   Tax liability: $2847
   Tax credit: $3085

7. Flora Westerfield
   Tax liability: $4064
   Tax credit: $3822

8. Vernon Gracy
   Tax liability: $3303
   Tax credit: $3521

9. Juan and Ana Cabellon
   Tax liability: $1450
   Tax credit: $1325

10. Sue and Tim Kennedy
    Tax liability: $2105
    Tax credit: $1936

11. Hazel Widenaur
    Tax liability: $3705
    Tax credit: $3822

12. Dave and Kris Stewart
    Tax liability: $8153
    Tax credit: $7215

Completing Form 1040A

Form **1040A**	Department of the Treasury—Internal Revenue Service U.S. Individual Income Tax Return	19**80**

Use IRS label. Other-wise, please print or type.	Your first name and initial (if joint return, also give spouse's name and initial) Albert R. and Ethel M.	Last name Riley	Your social security number 800 22 4116
	Present home address (Number and street, including apartment number, or rural route) 3871 Ninth Street		Spouse's social security no. 800 28 0917
	City, town or post office, State and ZIP code Middlefield, Texas 77200	Your occupation ▶ Carpenter Spouse's occupation ▶	

Presidential Election Campaign Fund	▶ Do you want $1 to go to this fund?	✓ Yes / No	Note: Checking "Yes" will not increase your tax or reduce your refund.
	If joint return, does your spouse want $1 to go to this fund? . . .	✓ Yes / No	

Requested by Census Bureau for Revenue Sharing	**A** Where do you live (actual location of residence)? (See page 6 of Instructions.) State — City, village, borough, etc. TX Middlefield	**B** Do you live within the legal limits of a city, village, etc.? ✓ Yes ☐ No	**C** In what county do you live? Richmond	**D** In what township do you live? Clay

For Privacy Act Notice, see page 27 of Instructions | For IRS use only

Filing Status Check Only One Box.	1		Single
	2	✓	Married filing joint return (even if only one had income)
	3		Married filing separate return. Enter spouse's social security no. above and full name here ▶
	4		Head of household. (See pages 7 and 8 of Instructions.) If qualifying person is your unmarried child, enter child's name ▶

Exemptions Always check the box labeled Your-self. Check oth. boxes if they apply.	5a	✓	Yourself		65 or over		Blind		Enter number of boxes checked on 5a and b ▶	2
	b	✓	Spouse		65 or over		Blind			
	c First names of your dependent children who lived with you ▶ Susan, Jeffrey								Enter number of children listed on 5c ▶	2

	d Other dependents:		(3) Number of months lived in your home.	(4) Did dependent have income of $1,000 or more?	(5) Did you provide more than one-half of dependent's support?	Enter number of other dependents ▶	
	(1) Name	(2) Relationship					

	6 Total number of exemptions claimed	Add numbers entered in boxes above ▶	4

7	Wages, salaries, tips, etc. (Attach Forms W-2. See page 10 of Instructions)	7	25,482	00
8	Interest income (See pages 3 and 10 of Instructions)	8	80	00
9a	Dividends 390 00 (See pages 3 and 10 of Instructions) 9b Exclusion 200 00 Subtract line 9b from 9a	9c	190	00
10a	Unemployment compensation (insurance). Total received from Form(s) 1099-UC			
b	Taxable amount, if any, from worksheet on page 10 of Instructions	10b		
11	Adjusted gross income (add lines 7, 8, 9c, and 10b). If under $10,000, see page 12 of Instructions on "Earned Income Credit"	11	25,752	00
12a	Credit for contributions to candidates for public office. (See page 11 of Instructions) . . . . 12a 100 00 **IF YOU WANT IRS TO FIGURE YOUR TAX, PLEASE STOP HERE AND SIGN BELOW.**			
b	Total Federal income tax withheld (If line 7 is more than $25,900, see page 11 of Instructions) 12b 3515 00			
c	Earned income credit (from page 12 of Instructions) . . . 12c			
13	Total (add lines 12a, b, and c)	13	3615	00
14a	Tax on the amount on line 11. (See page 13 of Instructions; then find your tax in the Tax Tables on pages 15–26) 14a 3714 00			
b	Advance earned income credit (EIC) (from Form W-2) . . . 14b			
15	Total (add lines 14a and 14b)	15	3714	00
16	If line 13 is larger than line 15, enter amount to be **REFUNDED TO YOU** . . . . ▶	16		
17	If line 15 is larger than line 13, enter **BALANCE DUE.** Attach check or money order for full amount payable to "Internal Revenue Service." Write your social security number on check or money order . ▶	17	99	00

Please Sign Here	Under penalties of perjury, I declare that I have examined this return, including accompanying schedules and statements, and to the best of my knowledge and belief, it is true, correct, and complete. Declaration of preparer (other than taxpayer) is based on all information of which preparer has any knowledge.
	▶ Albert R. Riley 2/15/81 ▶ Ethel M. Riley
	Your signature	Date	Spouse's signature (if filing jointly, BOTH must sign even if only one had income)

Paid Preparer's Use Only	Preparer's signature and date ▶	Check if self-em-ployed ▶ ☐	Preparer's social security no.
	Firm's name (or yours, if self-employed) and address ▶		E.I. No. ▶ ZIP code ▶

☆ U.S. GOVERNMENT PRINTING OFFICE 1980—O—313-447 04—1213190 | Form **1040A** (1980)

Problem

Albert and Ethel Riley are married, file a joint return, and claim 4 exemptions. Their completed Form 1040A is shown on page 266. Last year they earned $25,482 in wages, $80 in interest, and $390 from dividends. They contributed $250 to a political candidate, and they had $3515 withheld for federal tax. What are their adjusted gross income, tax credit, tax liability, and refund or balance due?

Solution

Strategy

- Compute the adjusted gross income (line 11).
- Compute the tax credit (line 13).
- Use Table B on page 407 to find the tax liability (lines 14a and 15).
- Compute the refund (line 16) or balance due (line 17).

Conclusion

The Rileys' adjusted gross income is $25,752, their tax credit is $3615, their tax liability is $3714, and their balance due is $99.

Related Problems

For each problem, find the adjusted gross income, tax credit, and tax liability. Then find the refund or balance due and write *refund* or *balance due*. Use the tax tables on pages 406-408.

1. Francis Turner
Single, 2 exemptions
Salary: $14,780
Interest income: $235
Federal tax withheld: $2500

2. Donald and Theresa Moore
Married, joint return, 4 exemptions
Salary: $18,568
Dividend income: $250
Federal tax withheld: $1695

3. Patsy Dotterweich
Single, 1 exemption
Salary: $17,763
Dividend income: $173
Contribution to candidates: $50
Federal tax withheld: $3225

4. Kate Watkins
Married, separate return, 2 exemptions
Salary: $17,565
Interest income: $21
Dividend income: $176
Contribution to candidates: $10
Federal tax withheld: $3547

5. Gary and Rose Masani
Married, joint return, 5 exemptions
Salary: $26,175
Interest income: $140
Dividend income: $310
Contribution to candidates: $350
Federal tax withheld: $3448

Tax Consultant

Career Cluster: Social Service Meyer Wolman is a tax consultant. Since income tax laws are complicated and always changing, taxpayers often come to him for advice. He finds that some of his clients cannot use Form 1040A because they have income that cannot be reported on the form, or because they claim more exemptions than are shown on the tax tables. These taxpayers must use Form 1040. Mr. Wolman also has clients who could use Form 1040A, but would pay less tax if they used Form 1040.

The government allows taxpayers a minimum deduction, or **zero bracket amount**. This amount is built into the tax tables.

Filing Status	Zero Bracket Amount
Single	$2300
Married Filing Joint Return	$3400
Married Filing Separate Return	$1700

A taxpayer's deductions may be greater than the zero bracket amount because of such things as medical and dental bills, interest expenses on mortgages and loans, state and local taxes, contributions to charities, casualty or theft losses, and other miscellaneous expenses. Such taxpayers should itemize deductions and use Form 1040.

Problem

Mr. Wolman has advised Anita and Jerry Prado to itemize deductions. Anita and Jerry file a joint return and claim 3 exemptions. They have an adjusted gross income of $21,175 and a tax credit of $2262. Their allowable itemized deductions are as follows:

Medical and dental expenses: $165
State and local taxes: $2255
Interest expenses: $2565
Contributions to charity: $947
Casualty loss: $120

What is the Prados' tax liability? What is their refund or balance due?

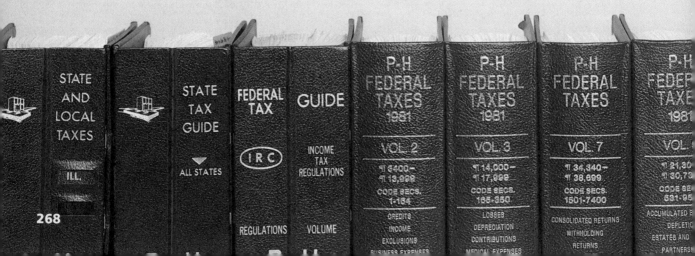

Solution

Strategy

• Add to find the total itemized deductions.
$165 + $2255 + $2565 + $947 + $120 = $6052

• Compare this total with the zero bracket amount for married filing joint return.
$6052 > $3400

• Subtract to find the excess over the zero bracket amount.
$6052 − $3400 = $2652

• Subtract from the adjusted gross income to find the amount to look for in the tax table (line 34, Form 1040).
$21,175 − $2652 = $18,523

• Use Table B on page 407 to find the tax liability for $18,523.
$2165

• Compare the tax liability with the tax credit.
$2165 < $2262

• Subtract to find the amount of the refund.
$2262 − $2165 = $97

Conclusion

The Prados' tax liability is $2165. They will receive a refund of $97.

Related Problems

For each problem, find the tax liability. Then find the refund or balance due and write *refund* or *balance due*. Itemize deductions and use the zero bracket amounts on page 268. Use the tax tables on pages 406-408.

1. Jake and Mildred Bartlett
Married, joint return, 3 exemptions
Adjusted gross income: $29,895
Tax credit: $3886
Allowable itemized deductions
  Medical and dental expenses: $250
  State and local taxes: $2135
  Interest expenses: $3200
  Contributions to charity: $790
  Miscellaneous: $240

2. Willard Jones
Married, separate return, 3 exemptions
Adjusted gross income: $18,950
Tax credit: $3325
Allowable itemized deductions
  State and local taxes: $2377
  Interest expenses: $1750
  Contributions to charity: $800
  Theft losses: $395
  Miscellaneous: $240

3. Paula Swanson
Single, 1 exemption
Adjusted gross income: $18,380
Tax credit: $3150
Allowable itemized deductions
  State and local taxes: $1745
  Interest expenses: $495
  Contributions to charity: $650
  Miscellaneous: $350

4. Suppose Paula used Form 1040A and did not itemize deductions. Find her tax liability on $18,380. How much does she save by itemizing deductions?

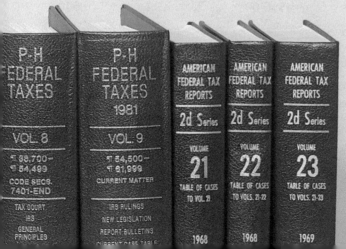

Some of Mr. Wolman's clients cannot use the tax tables because the amount on line 34, Form 1040, exceeds the maximum listed on the tables. In these cases, they use Schedule TC and compute their tax using Schedule X, Y, or Z. Schedules X and Y are shown on page 409. The tax is based on **taxable income** (Schedule TC, Part 1, line 3), which is the income after all allowable deductions are made.

Part of Schedule Y for married couples filing a joint return is shown here.

If the amount on Schedule TC, Part I, line 3, is:		Enter on Schedule TC, Part I, line 4:	
Not over $3,400		—0—	
Over—	But not over—		of the amount over—
$3,400	$5,500	14%	$3,400
$5,500	$7,600	$294 + 16%	$5,500
$35,200	$45,800	$8,162 + 43%	$35,200
$45,800	$60,000	$12,720 + 49%	$45,800
$60,000	$85,600	$19,678 + 54%	$60,000

Problem

Mr. Wolman has determined that Alice and Ronald Winkner must use Schedule TC and Schedule Y. Alice and Ronald have a taxable income of $54,869, and they are filing a joint return. What is their tax liability?

Solution

Strategy
- Use Schedule Y. Read the tax information on the line for taxable income over $45,800 but not over $60,000.

  $12,720 + 49% of the amount over $45,800

- Subtract to find the taxable income over $45,800.

  $54,869 − $45,800 = $9069

- Find 49% of $9069. Round to the nearest dollar.

  $0.49 \times \$9069 \approx \$4444$

- Add to find the tax liability.

  $12,720 + $4444 = $17,164

Conclusion
The Winkners' tax liability is $17,164.

Related Problems

Compute the tax liability. Use Schedule X or Y on page 409. Round to the nearest dollar.

5. Gina Simpson
Single
Taxable income: $50,000

6. Harry and May Thomas
Married, joint return
Taxable income: $116,500

7. Brian Anderson
Married, separate return
Taxable income: $53,460

8. William Fresco
Single
Taxable income: $79,600

9. Amanda and Peter Stein
Married, joint return
Taxable income: $172,750

10. Ed and Ida Ross
Married, joint return
Taxable income: $250,000

CALCULATOR APPLICATIONS

Self-employed people must estimate their income tax and pay it in four partial payments on or before these dates: April 15, June 15, September 15, and January 15. These payments must total at least 80% of the tax liability for the year. If they do not, there is a penalty charge on each underpayment based on an annual rate of 12%. For each underpayment the approximate rate of the penalty charge is shown below.

1st underpayment (1 year delinquent):   12% of underpayment

2nd underpayment ($\frac{5}{6}$ year delinquent):   10% of underpayment

3rd underpayment ($\frac{7}{12}$ year delinquent):   7% of underpayment

4th underpayment ($\frac{1}{4}$ year delinquent):   3% of underpayment

Last year, Gail Shaffer estimated her income tax at $3000. She paid this amount in four equal payments on the dates required. When she filed her tax return she had a tax liability of $5000. What is her penalty charge?

a. Estimated tax — $3000

b. Tax liability — $5000

c. 80% of tax liability — $0.80 \times \$5000 = \$4000$

d. Required partial payment (line c divided by 4) — $\$4000 \div 4 = \$1000$

e. Actual partial payment (line a divided by 4) — $\$3000 \div 4 = \$750$

f. Each underpayment (line d minus line e) — $\$1000 - \$750 = \$250$

g. 1st penalty charge (12% of line f) — $0.12 \times \$250 =$ **$30.00**

h. 2nd penalty charge (10% of line f) — $0.10 \times \$250 =$ **$25.00**

i. 3rd penalty charge (7% of line f) — $0.07 \times \$250 =$ **$17.50**

j. 4th penalty charge (3% of line f) — $0.03 \times \$250 =$ **$7.50**

k. Total penalty charge (sum of lines g–h) — **$80.00**

For each problem, use steps a–k to find the total penalty charge to the nearest cent. Assume that the estimated tax was paid in four equal payments on the dates required.

	Estimated tax	Tax liability		Estimated tax	Tax liability
1.	$6000	$9000	**4.**	$16,500	$25,225
2.	$7500	$10,000	**5.**	$25,000	$33,728
3.	$1650	$4389	**6.**	$0	$3890

271

State Income Tax

Many states and some cities have income taxes that are similar to federal income tax. Different states include different items as income and allow varying amounts for deductions. Methods for determining the amount of tax in various states are shown below.

California

If taxable income is—		YOUR TAX IS—
OVER	BUT NOT OVER	
12,950	13,050	245
13,050	13,150	248
13,150	13,250	251
13,250	13,350	255
13,350	13,450	259
27,450	27,550	1,015
27,550	27,650	1,022
27,650	27,750	1,029
27,750	27,850	1,036
27,850	27,950	1,043
59,450	59,550	4,236
59,550	59,650	4,247
59,650	59,750	4,258
59,750	59,850	4,269
59,850	59,950	4,280
59,950	60,000	4,288
over 60,000		4,291 plus 11% of the amount over $60,000

Maryland

Maryland Income Tax		
Taxable income		
over	but not over	Amount of tax
$ 0	$1000	2% of taxable income
1000	2000	$20 plus 3% of amount over $1000
2000	3000	$50 plus 4% of amount over $2000
3000	—	$90 plus 5% of amount over $3000

Illinois

Amount of tax is 2.5% of the taxable income.

Michigan

Amount of tax is 4.6% of the taxable income.

Mississippi

Amount of tax is 3% of the first $5000 of taxable income plus 4% of the taxable income over $5000.

Problem

Ted Marten lives in Maryland. What is his state income tax on taxable income of $14,800?

Solution

Strategy
- Use the tax information for Maryland. $14,800 is greater than $3000. Subtract to find the amount over $3000.

  $14,800 − $3000 = $11,800

- Find 5% of the amount over $3000.

  $0.05 × $11,800 = $590

- Add to $90 to find the total tax.

  $90 + $590 = $680

Conclusion
Ted's state income tax is $680.

Problem

Margaret Deitz lives in Mississippi. What is her state income tax on taxable income of $14,563?

Solution

Strategy
- Use the tax information for Mississippi. Find 3% of the first $5000.

  $0.03 × $5000 = $150

- Subtract to find the taxable income over $5000.

  $14,563 − $5000 = $9563

- Find 4% of the amount over $5000.

  $0.04 × $9563 = $382.52

- Add to find the total tax.

  $150 + $382.52 = $532.52

Conclusion
Margaret's state income tax is $532.52.

Related Problems

Find the state income tax to the nearest cent. Use the information on page 272.

	State	Taxable income		State	Taxable income
1.	Maryland	$3,895	**9.**	Michigan	$41,200
2.	Maryland	$11,429	**10.**	Mississippi	$6,792
3.	Maryland	$28,091	**11.**	Mississippi	$21,084
4.	Illinois	$8,655	**12.**	Mississippi	$39,000
5.	Illinois	$18,750	**13.**	California	$13,075
6.	Illinois	$35,620	**14.**	California	$27,825
7.	Michigan	$4,453	**15.**	California	$59,750
8.	Michigan	$17,680	**16.**	California	$73,430

Skills Tune-Up

Rounding whole numbers and decimals, pages 4-5

Round each number to the nearest thousand, nearest hundred, and nearest ten.

1. 834

2. 2481

3. 555

4. 8142

5. 9603

6. 5479

7. 1074

8. 29,928

9. 60,375

10. 72,186

11. 84,657

Round each number to the nearest whole number, nearest tenth, and nearest hundredth.

12. 7.368

13. 18.181

14. 36.911

15. 79.458

16. 783.142

17. 257.769

18. 546.803

19. 40.994

20. 59.608

21. 602.015

22. 85.971

Subtracting whole numbers and decimals, pages 6-7

1. $87 - 35$

2. $54 - 19$

3. $53 - 5$

4. $98 - 9$

5. $53 - 48$

6. $89 - 88$

7. $94.8 - 46.2$

8. $63.4 - 45.9$

9. $67.49 - 1.29$

10. $47.83 - 5.94$

11. $96.52 - 27.1$

12. $45.62 - 9.7$

13. $16.078 - 8.44$

14. $50.085 - 47.17$

15. $34.538 - 23.449$

16. $95.024 - 3.183$

17. $7.56 - 4.245$

18. $73.29 - 4.437$

19. $36.3 - 35.5$

20. $59.6 - 58.9$

21. $5.612 - 3$

22. $76.059 - 29$

23. $34 - 31.5$

24. $4 - 0.3$

25. $26 - 0.42$

26. $93 - 37.08$

27. $82.049 - 34.731$

28. $72.86 - 36.937$

Writing percents, decimals, and fractions, pages 32-33

Write as a fraction in lowest terms.

1. 12% **11.** 70%

2. 80% **12.** 31%

3. 55% **13.** 27%

4. 10% **14.** 40%

5. 47% **15.** 65%

6. 25% **16.** 28%

7. 62% **17.** 225%

8. 30% **18.** 132%

9. 16% **19.** 103%

10. 97% **20.** 450%

Write as a percent.

21. $\frac{1}{2}$ **32.** $\frac{11}{20}$

22. $\frac{1}{5}$ **33.** $\frac{3}{8}$

23. $\frac{1}{10}$ **34.** $\frac{15}{20}$

24. $\frac{3}{4}$ **35.** $\frac{9}{16}$

25. $\frac{3}{5}$ **36.** $\frac{7}{8}$

26. $\frac{1}{4}$ **37.** $\frac{9}{40}$

27. $\frac{7}{10}$ **38.** $\frac{13}{16}$

28. $\frac{9}{20}$ **39.** $\frac{17}{4}$

29. $\frac{19}{50}$ **40.** $\frac{11}{2}$

30. $\frac{4}{25}$ **41.** $\frac{38}{5}$

31. $\frac{9}{25}$ **42.** $\frac{13}{8}$

Chapter 13 Review

Who must file a tax return, pages 258-259

1. Ann and Tom White Eagle are 62 and 66 years old. They file a joint tax return. This year their incomes were $3822.50 and $2692.75. Are they required to file a tax return? (Use the information on page 258.)

Adjusted gross income and tax credit, pages 260-262

2. Mitzi Smith is single. Her salary was $14,950. She received $248 in interest and $180 in dividends. What is her adjusted gross income? (Use the information on page 261 for exclusion for dividend income.)

3. Mitzi contributed $80 to a candidate running for public office and had $2157 withheld for federal income tax. What is her tax credit? (Use the information on page 261 for credit for contributions to candidates.)

Tax liability, page 263

4. A single person is filing a tax return claiming 2 exemptions. What is the tax liability on an adjusted gross income (line 11, Form 1040A) of $16,725? (Use the tax tables on pages 406-408.)

Tax refund or balance due, pages 264-265

5. Myung Lee has a tax liability of $1987 and a tax credit of $1822. What is his refund or balance due? Give the amount, and write *refund* or *balance due*.

Completing Form 1040A, pages 266-267

6. The Menards file a joint tax return and claim 5 exemptions. Their salary income was $26,816 and they received $518 in interest. They have a tax credit of $3950. What is their refund or balance due? Give the amount, and write *refund* or *balance due*. (Use the tax tables on pages 406-408.)

Tax consultant, pages 268-270

7. Elaine Webster is single, claims 2 exemptions, and has an adjusted gross income of $17,500 and a tax credit of $2697. She itemizes these deductions:

Medical and dental expenses: $685
State and local taxes: $1598
Interest expenses: $560
Contributions to charity: $165

What is Elaine's refund or balance due? Give the amount, and write *refund* or *balance due*. (Use the information on page 268 for zero bracket amounts. Use the tax tables on pages 406-408.)

8. What is the tax liability for a single person with taxable income of $45,200? (Use Schedule X or Y on page 409.)

State income tax, pages 272-273

9. The state income tax in Michigan is 4.6% of the taxable income. What is the state income tax on taxable income of $16,500?

10. Maryland's state income tax for taxable income over $3000 is $90 plus 5% of the amount over $3000. What is the state income tax on taxable income of $10,900?

Chapter 13 Test

1. A single person must file a federal income tax return if he or she is under 65 and has an income of at least $3300, or if he or she is 65 or over and has an income of at least $4300. Sara McDonald, age 70, is single and had incomes of $2387, $1543, and $175. Is she required to file a tax return?

2. A married couple filing a joint return can take a $200 exclusion for dividend income. The Yonans are filing a joint return. Their salary was $19,500. They received $83 in interest and $250 in dividends. What is their adjusted gross income?

3. A married couple filing a joint return can claim one half of all contributions to candidates running for office up to a $100 maximum credit. The Yonans contributed $130 to a candidate and had $2155 withheld for federal income tax. What is their tax credit?

4. A married couple is filing a joint return claiming 3 exemptions. What is the tax liability on an adjusted gross income (line 11, Form 1040A) of $25,725? (Use the tax tables on pages 406-408.)

5. Louise Brown has a tax liability of $2188 and a tax credit of $2397. What is her refund or balance due? Give the amount, and write *refund* or *balance due*.

6. Kay Murray is single and claims 1 exemption. Her salary was $17,100 and she received $125 in interest. She has a tax credit of $2714. What is her refund or balance due? Give the amount, and write *refund* or *balance due*. (Use the tax tables on pages 406-408.)

7. The zero bracket amount for a married couple filing a joint return is $3400. The Garzas file a joint return and claim 4 exemptions. They have an adjusted gross income of $26,700 and a tax credit of $3782. They itemized these deductions:

   Medical and dental expenses: $975
   State and local taxes: $2180
   Interest expenses: $1250

   What is their refund or balance due? Give the amount, and write *refund* or *balance due*. (Use the tax tables on pages 406-408.)

8. What is the tax liability for a single person with a taxable income of $60,000? (Use Schedule X or Y on page 409.)

9. The state income tax in Illinois is 2.5% of the taxable income. What is the tax on taxable income of $14,500?

10. Mississippi's state income tax is 3% of the first $5000 of taxable income and 4% of the taxable income over $5000. What is the state income tax on taxable income of $18,900?

Chapter 14 Health, Life, and Retirement Insurance

Health Insurance

Most people have some type of **health insurance** that pays for part or all of their medical expenses for doctors, hospitals, and medicine. The person covered by the insurance policy is called the **insured**.

Many health insurance policies have a deductible clause. The insurance company usually pays a certain portion of the total expenses after the deductible amount is subtracted. The insured pays the deductible amount and the remaining expenses.

Problem

Robert Pottinger works for a company that carries medical insurance on its employees. The insurance is a $50-deductible policy. The insurance company pays 80% of the amount over the deductible.

Robert had surgery on his foot and was in the hospital for two days. His medical expenses amounted to $1615. How much did the insurance company pay? How much did Robert pay?

Solution

Strategy
• Subtract to find the amount over the deductible.

$1615 − $50 = $1565

• Multiply by 80% to find the amount the insurance company paid.

0.80 × $1565 = $1252

• Subtract to find the amount Robert paid.

$1615 − $1252 = $363

Conclusion
The insurance company paid $1252. Robert paid $363.

Related Problems

For problems 1–10, find the amount paid by insurance and the amount paid by the insured.

	Insured	Deductible amount	Percent paid by insurance over deductible	Medical expenses	Paid by insurance	Paid by insured
	Robert Pottinger	$50	80%	$1615.00	$1252.00	$363.00
1.	Leonard Kaplan	$50	80%	$840.00		
2.	Elsie Garden	$0	80%	$3165.00		
3.	Prudence Cook	$200	90%	$5100.00		
4.	Jaime Fisher	$100	90%	$3555.00		
5.	Elliott Cartier	$150	85%	$2750.00		
6.	Lydia Mayfair	$100	85%	$7600.00		
7.	Jake Momaday	$0	75%	$4276.00		
8.	Maxine Rice	$125	87%	$5714.00		
9.	Arturo Ruiz	$60	92%	$1980.00		
10.	Joan Fine	$40	84%	$6216.50		

11. Chong Sun Lee has a $90-deductible health insurance policy. After $90, the insurance company pays 75% of all medical expenses including prescription medicines. Last year, Chong had $485 in doctor bills and spent $43 on prescription medicines. How much did the insurance company pay?

12. Melissa Greenwald has a $60-deductible health insurance policy. After $60, the insurance company pays 80% of all medical expenses. Melissa's expenses totaled $5405. How much did Melissa pay?

13. Frances Zilliox has a $70-deductible health insurance policy. She has medical expenses that total $2482.60. Her insurance will pay whichever is less of these two amounts:

    a. 85% of the amount over the deductible
    b. $2000

    How much will Frances pay?

14. Mike Delgado has a $50-deductible health insurance policy. The insurance company pays 80% of all covered medical expenses from $50 through $3000. Above $3000, the insurance company pays 100%. Mike was in the hospital for major surgery. His medical expenses amounted to $8470. How much did the insurance company pay?

Term Life Insurance

The main purpose of life insurance is to provide money for dependents of the insured person in case of his or her death. The persons named in the policy to receive the insurance money are called the **beneficiaries**. The amount of money that the beneficiaries would receive is the **face value** of the policy.

The least expensive type of life insurance is **term life insurance**. It is issued for a certain period of time, such as 5 or 10 years. If the insured does not die during that time, no money is paid by the insurance company and the policy is canceled.

This table shows annual premiums for a certain 5-year term insurance policy.

5-Year Term Insurance Annual Premiums per $1000					
	Premium			Premium	
Age	Male	Female	Age	Male	Female
18	$2.69	$2.05	32	$3.51	$2.94
19	2.71	2.13	33	3.66	3.05
20	2.72	2.21	34	3.71	3.16
21	2.74	2.27	35	3.98	3.29
22	2.76	2.31	36	4.19	3.44
23	2.78	2.36	37	4.43	3.60
24	2.79	2.41	38	4.69	3.77
25	2.80	2.47	39	4.98	3.95
26	2.87	2.53	40	5.27	4.14
27	2.95	2.58	41	5.56	4.35
28	3.05	2.63	42	5.85	4.56
29	3.16	2.68	43	6.15	4.78
30	3.27	2.74	44	6.46	5.01
31	3.38	2.83	45	6.77	5.26

Problem

Sally Geraci is 26 years old. She and her husband have two young children. Sally is buying a 5-year term life insurance policy with a face value of $70,000 to provide money to help her husband raise their children in case she dies. What is Sally's annual premium? How much will she pay for term insurance protection for 5 years?

Solution

Strategy

- Read the table to find the rate per $1000 for a 26-year-old female.

  $2.53

- Multiply by 70 to find the annual premium for $70,000.

  70 × $2.53 = $177.10

- Multiply by 5 to find the total amount of premiums for 5 years.

  5 × $177.10 = $885.50

Conclusion

Sally's annual premium is $177.10. She will pay $885.50 for 5 years of term insurance protection.

Related Problems

For problems 1-5, find the annual premium for each 5-year term policy.

	Age	Sex	Face value
1.	25	Male	$60,000
2.	39	Female	$80,000
3.	40	Male	$75,000
4.	38	Male	$250,000
5.	27	Female	$80,000

6. Betty Neal is 30 years old. She is buying 5-year term insurance. How much will her annual premium be for a $55,000 policy?

7. Jack Gomez is buying a 5-year term insurance policy with a face value of $25,000. He is 20 years old. How much will Jack pay for term insurance protection for 5 years?

8. Theresa Banak is buying a 5-year term insurance policy with a face value of $90,000. She is 34 years old. If Theresa dies after three years, how much will her beneficiary receive? How much will Theresa pay for term insurance protection for 3 years?

9. Dan Ohira is 27 years old. He is buying a 5-year term insurance policy with a face value of $45,000. If Dan dies after four years, how much will his beneficiary receive? How much will Dan pay for term insurance protection for 4 years?

10. Kèn Sawyer is 29 years old. How much 5-year term insurance (sold only in multiples of $1000) can he buy if he can spend no more than $125 a year?

11. Alice Reinhardt is 33 years old. How much 5-year term insurance (sold only in multiples of $1000) can she buy if she can spend no more than $100 a year?

Straight Life, Limited Payment Life, and Endowment Insurance

Besides providing financial protection in case of death, some life insurance policies are a form of savings. After premiums have been paid for a certain length of time, the policy has a **cash value**. This amount of money increases as the policy gets older. The policy can be **surrendered**, or traded in, for its cash value. The insured can also borrow against the cash value at a very low rate of interest. Because these policies have a cash value, they are more expensive than term insurance.

One of the most common types of life insurance that has a cash value is **straight life insurance**. The insured pays premiums for life or until a certain age, usually 65 or 70. The insurance remains in force until the insured dies.

Another type of life insurance that has a cash value is **limited payment life insurance**. This type of policy is similar to straight life, but the premiums are paid for a specific length of time, usually 20 or 30 years. For this reason, the premiums are higher than for straight life. A limited payment policy that is paid for in 20 years is called a **20-payment life insurance** policy. The insurance remains in force until the insured dies.

The most expensive type of insurance is **endowment insurance**. Again, the premiums are paid for a specific length of time, usually 20 or 30 years. At the end of that time, the face value of the policy is paid to the insured and the insurance is no longer in force.

This table shows premium rates for certain life insurance policies. Rates given are for men. This table may also be used to figure premiums for a woman. Subtract 3 years from the woman's age and use the premiums for the resulting age.

Annual Insurance Premiums per $1000 (Rates shown are for a male. For a female, subtract 3 years from her age.)			
Age	Straight life	20-payment life	20-year endowment
15	$11.05	$17.42	$41.80
16	11.35	17.84	41.86
17	11.66	18.27	41.92
18	11.99	18.72	41.98
19	12.31	19.15	42.04
20	12.67	19.63	42.08
21	13.02	20.08	42.12
22	13.39	20.54	42.16
23	13.79	21.04	42.20
24	14.21	21.54	42.24
25	14.64	22.07	42.27
26	15.06	22.55	42.30
27	15.51	23.07	42.33
28	15.97	23.60	42.36
29	16.46	24.14	42.39
30	16.98	24.69	42.44
31	17.52	25.27	42.51
32	18.07	25.87	42.60
33	18.67	26.49	42.70
34	19.29	27.14	42.82

Problem

Lisa Snowbird is 25 years old. She bought $20,000 worth of straight life insurance. What is her annual premium?

Solution

Strategy

- Subtract 3 years from Lisa's age.

  25 − 3 = 22

- Read the table on page 282 to find the annual premium for each $1000 of straight life insurance at age 22.

  $13.39

- Multiply by 20 to find the annual premium for $20,000.

  20 × $13.39 = $267.80

Conclusion

Lisa's annual premium is $267.80.

Related Problems

Find the annual premium for each policy.

	Policy	Age	Sex	Face value
1.	Straight life	23	Male	$30,000
2.	Straight life	23	Female	$30,000
3.	20-year endowment	32	Male	$45,000
4.	20-payment life	32	Male	$45,000
5.	Straight life	18	Female	$20,000
6.	20-year endowment	18	Female	$20,000
7.	Straight life	34	Male	$57,000
8.	20-year endowment	26	Female	$25,000
9.	20-payment life	29	Male	$32,000
10.	20-payment life	19	Male	$32,000
11.	Straight life	20	Female	$26,000
12.	20-year endowment	15	Male	$30,000
13.	20-payment life	24	Female	$50,000
14.	20-payment life	30	Female	$50,000
15.	20-year endowment	21	Male	$40,000

The cash value of a policy is the cash amount available to the insured if he or she were to surrender the policy or to borrow against the policy. This table shows the cash values for the straight life insurance policy included in the table on page 282.

Straight Life—Cash Value per $1000					
Age at time of issue	Cash value at end of year				Cash value at age 65
	5	10	15	20	
15	$21	$ 77	$133	$210	$729
16	22	79	136	216	726
17	23	82	140	222	723
18	24	84	144	228	719
19	25	86	148	234	714
20	26	89	152	241	710
21	27	91	156	247	703
22	28	94	161	254	696
23	29	97	165	262	690
24	30	99	171	270	682
25	31	102	176	278	673
26	32	105	181	286	663
27	33	109	186	295	651
28	34	112	192	303	639
29	35	115	198	313	625
30	36	119	204	323	611
31	37	123	210	333	596
32	38	126	217	343	578
33	39	131	224	355	560
34	40	135	231	367	540

Problem

Jason Williams is 20 years old. He wants to buy $25,000 worth of straight life insurance. What is the total amount he will pay in premiums in 15 years? What will be the cash value of his policy at the end of 15 years?

Solution

Strategy
• Read the table on page 282 to find the annual premium for each $1000 of straight life insurance at age 20.

$12.67

• Multiply by 25 to find the annual premium for $25,000.

25 × $12.67 = $316.75

• Multiply by 15 to find the total amount of premiums for 15 years.

15 × $316.75 = $4751.25

• Read the table at the left to find the cash value at the end of 15 years for each $1000 of a policy issued at age 20.

$152

• Multiply by 25 to find the cash value for $25,000 worth of insurance.

25 × $152 = $3800

Conclusion
Jason will pay $4751.25 in premiums in 15 years. The cash value of his policy at the end of 15 years will be $3800.

Related Problems

Use the tables on pages 282 and 284.

16. Alan Stansfield is 28 years old. He plans to buy $18,000 worth of straight life insurance. What is the total amount he will pay in premiums in 20 years?

17. What will be the cash value of Alan's insurance at the end of 20 years?

18. Jim Kuang is 19 years old. He plans to buy $15,000 worth of straight life insurance. What is the total amount he will pay in premiums in 10 years?

19. What will be the cash value of Jim's insurance at the end of 10 years?

20. David Kidd is 30 years old. He plans to buy $75,000 worth of straight life insurance. What will be his annual premium?

21. If David lives to be 65, how much will he have paid in premiums?

22. When David is 65, what will be the cash value of his insurance?

23. Carl Russell is 23 years old. He plans to buy $40,000 worth of straight life insurance. What will be the cash value of this insurance at the end of 5 years?

24. Quentin Jonas is 33 years old. He plans to buy $85,000 worth of straight life insurance. What will be the cash value of this insurance when Quentin is 65 years old?

25. Dennis Tunney is 22 years old. He plans to buy $50,000 worth of straight life insurance. What will be the cash value of this insurance when Dennis is 37 years old?

Insurance Agent

Career Cluster: Business Contact Roger Iverson is an insurance agent. Some of his customers prefer to pay their insurance premiums semiannually, quarterly, or monthly, instead of annually. These types of payments usually cost more per year than an annual payment. Roger uses a table like the one below to compute the amount of the premium.

Type of payment	Factor
Semiannually	0.51
Quarterly	0.26
Monthly	0.0875

Problem

Joan Nakamura, one of Roger's customers, wants to pay her insurance premiums monthly. Her insurance policy has an annual premium of $237.28. What is the amount of her monthly premium? How much more per year will she pay than if she pays annually?

Solution

Strategy
• Read the table to find the factor for monthly premiums.

0.0875

• Multiply times the annual premium to find the monthly premium. Round to the nearest cent.

0.0875 × $237.28 ≈ $20.76

• Multiply by 12 to find the total of her monthly premiums for the year.

12 × $20.76 = $249.12

• Subtract the annual premium from the total of the monthly premiums to find the additional cost per year.

$249.12 − $237.28 = $11.84

Conclusion
Joan's monthly premium will be $20.76. She will pay $11.84 more per year if she makes monthly payments.

Related Problems

1. The annual premium for Lisa Montel's straight life insurance policy is $342.50. What will be her monthly premium?

2. How much more per year will Lisa pay if she pays monthly?

3. Tony Falco's annual premium for his 5-year term life insurance is $149.30. If he pays quarterly, how much will his quarterly premium be?

4. How much more per year will Tony pay if he pays quarterly?

5. The annual premium for Jane Jansen's endowment policy is $462.80. What will be her semiannual premium?

6. How much more per year will Jane pay if she pays semiannually?

7. Jennifer Plain's annual premium for her 20-payment life insurance policy is $364.90. Her monthly premiums would be $31.93. What is the difference per year between paying annually and paying monthly?

8. Beth Duarte's endowment policy has an annual premium of $316.75. Her quarterly premium would be $82.36. What is the difference per year between paying annually and paying quarterly?

9. Justin Brown is 25 years old. He bought a $40,000, 20-year endowment policy. What is Justin's annual premium? (Use the table on page 282.)

10. If Justin pays monthly, what will be his monthly premium?

11. At the end of 20 years, how much will Justin have saved if he pays his premiums annually rather than monthly?

CALCULATOR APPLICATIONS

Insurance Premiums

These tables show the annual premiums for various insurance policies. In the table headings, *A* means annual premium, *M* means monthly premium, *Q* means quarterly premium, and *S* means semiannual premium. Use your calculator and the factors given on page 286 to complete the tables.

For problems 1–7, the last column is the yearly difference between paying premiums monthly and annually.

	A	*M*	12*M*	12*M* − *A*
	$138.12	$12.09	$145.08	$6.96
1.	$172.49			
2.	$254.68			
3.	$127.46			
4.	$229.23			
5.	$148.77			
6.	$89.41			
7.	$124.55			

For problems 8–14, the last column is the yearly difference between paying premiums quarterly and annually.

	A	*Q*	4*Q*	4*Q* − *A*
	$127.19	$33.07	$132.28	$5.09
8.	$218.73			
9.	$157.42			
10.	$309.50			
11.	$148.71			
12.	$272.18			
13.	$197.45			
14.	$314.89			

For problems 15–20, the last column is the yearly difference between paying premiums semiannually and annually.

	A	*S*	2*S*	2*S* − *A*
	$237.80	$121.28	$242.56	$4.76
15.	$193.42			
16.	$246.55			
17.	$311.71			
18.	$275.84			
19.	$329.09			
20.	$254.81			

Break Time

On Monday, Mrs. Lee put two pitchers of juice into the refrigerator.

On Tuesday, Willy Lee poured from the black pitcher into the tan pitcher the amount of juice the tan pitcher contained on Monday.

On Wednesday, Tilly Lee poured from the tan pitcher into the black pitcher the amount of juice the black pitcher contained on Tuesday.

On Thursday, Milly Lee poured from the black pitcher into the tan pitcher the amount of juice the tan pitcher contained on Wednesday.

On Friday, Lilly Lee poured from the tan pitcher into the black pitcher the amount of juice the black pitcher contained on Thursday.

On Saturday, Mr. Lee measured the amount of juice in the pitchers. He found that each one contained 960 milliliters of juice.

How much juice had each pitcher contained on Monday?

Choosing Insurance and Savings Plans

Many people combine their program of insurance protection with a long-term savings plan.

Problem

Fred Post is 25. An efficient way for him to provide insurance protection and save money is to buy straight life insurance, paying premiums monthly. How much straight life insurance (sold only in multiples of $1000) can he buy for a maximum of $60 a month? What will be the cash value of the insurance at the end of 20 years?

Solution

Strategy

• Read the table on page 282 to find the annual premium for each $1000 of straight life insurance at age 25.

$14.64

• Read the table on page 286 to find the factor for monthly premiums. Multiply this factor times the annual premium for each $1000 to find the monthly premium for each $1000. Round to the nearest cent.

$0.0875 \times \$14.64 \approx \$1.28$

• Divide $60 by $1.28. Then find the number of $1000 units that can be purchased for a maximum of $60 a month. Remember, this insurance is sold only in multiples of $1000.

$\$60 \div \$1.28 = 46.875 \longrightarrow 46$

• Multiply times $1000 to find the amount of insurance Fred can buy.

$46 \times \$1000 = \$46,000$

• Read the table on page 284 to find the cash value at the end of 20 years for each $1000 of a straight life insurance policy issued at age 25. Multiply by 46 to find the cash value for $46,000 worth of insurance.

$46 \times \$278 = \$12,788$

Conclusion

For a maximum of $60 a month, Fred can buy $46,000 worth of straight life insurance. The cash value of Fred's policy at the end of 20 years will be $12,788.

Related Problems

For each problem, find the amount of straight life insurance that can be purchased for no more than the given amount. Then give the cash value of each policy at the end of 20 years. Use the tables on pages 282, 284, and 286. Assume that each person is a male.

	Age	Amount to spend each month
1.	20	$75
2.	17	$40
3.	18	$85
4.	33	$85
5.	23	$45
6.	28	$65
7.	30	$60
8.	19	$70
9.	26	$90
10.	34	$80

This table shows the results of depositing $1 each month in a savings account for a certain amount of time. Interest has been compounded monthly.

Long-Term Savings Balance (For $1 deposited each month with interest compounded monthly)		
Years	6%	7%
5	$ 69.77	$ 71.59
10	163.88	173.08
15	290.82	316.96
20	462.04	520.93
25	692.99	810.07
30	1004.52	1219.97

Problem

Linda Miley is buying a $45,000 term life insurance policy that she plans to keep for 20 years. The annual premium is $155. She is setting aside $60 each month for insurance and savings. The amount that is not spent for her insurance premium each month will be put in a savings account that earns 6% interest. How much can Linda save each month? If Linda keeps all of the interest in the savings account, how much will she have in the account at the end of 20 years?

Solution

Strategy
- Multiply the annual insurance premium by 0.0875 to find the monthly insurance premium. Round to the nearest cent.

0.0875 × $155 ≈ $13.56

- Subtract to find the amount to be put in savings each month.

$60 − $13.56 = $46.44

- Read the table at the left to find the result at the end of 20 years of depositing $1 each month in a savings account at 6% interest.

$462.04

- Multiply by 46.44 to find the result at the end of 20 years of depositing $46.44 each month in a savings account at 6% interest. Round to the nearest cent.

46.44 × $462.04 ≈ $21,457.14

Conclusion
Linda can save $46.44 each month. At the end of 20 years, she will have $21,457.14 in her savings account.

Related Problems

11. Jeannie Pope is 33 years old. Her annual premium for $70,000 worth of term life insurance is $195. How much does she pay per month for this insurance? The factor for monthly premiums is 0.0875.

12. Jeannie spends a total of $60 per month for insurance and savings. What amount does she put in her savings account each month?

13. Jeannie's savings account pays 7% interest compounded monthly. If she continues to deposit the same amount each month, how much will be in the savings account at the end of 20 years?

14. Paul Jaeger spends a total of $75 a month for insurance and savings. His monthly insurance premium is $35.41. The amount that is not spent on his insurance premium is deposited each month in a savings account that earns 7% interest compounded monthly. How much will he have in the account at the end of 15 years?

Social Security Retirement Benefits

Most people in the United States are covered by social security. A portion of each person's paycheck is withheld for social security. When a person aged 62 or older **retires**, or stops working full-time, the government provides the person retirement benefits from the social security fund.

Problem

David Dawson wants to determine his average annual income subject to social security. The work sheet at the right gives the maximum annual income on which a person pays social security for 1955 through 1981. In the third column, David recorded his annual earnings that were covered by social security. He has been contributing to social security for 23 years. What is his average annual income subject to social security?

Solution

Strategy

• Use the information in the work sheet to list David's earnings that are subject to social security. If the earnings for any year are more than the maximum, list only the maximum. The last column of the work sheet shows these earnings.

• Add the earnings that are subject to social security. Then divide by the number of years to find the average annual income subject to social security. Round to the nearest dollar.
$215,770 \div 23 \approx 9381

Conclusion

David's average annual income subject to social security is $9381.

Work Sheet			
Year	Maximum annual income on which social security is paid	Actual annual earnings	Earnings subject to social security
1955	$4,200		
1956	4,200		
1957	4,200		
1958	4,200		
1959	4,800	$3,380	$3,380
1960	4,800	3,580	3,580
1961	4,800	3,790	3,790
1962	4,800	4,020	4,020
1963	4,800	4,260	4,260
1964	4,800	4,700	4,700
1965	4,800	4,800	4,800
1966	6,600	5,450	5,450
1967	6,600	5,860	5,860
1968	7,800	6,300	6,300
1969	7,800	7,400	7,400
1970	7,800	8,500	7,800
1971	7,800	9,650	7,800
1972	9,000	10,300	9,000
1973	10,800	11,100	10,800
1974	13,200	12,800	12,800
1975	14,100	14,200	14,100
1976	15,300	15,300	15,300
1977	16,500	15,900	15,900
1978	17,700	16,050	16,050
1979	22,900	17,000	17,000
1980	25,900	17,670	17,670
1981	29,700	18,010	18,010
		Total	$215,770

Problem

David is planning to retire at age 65. He has one dependent. His average annual income subject to social security is $9381. What is the annual retirement benefit that David's family should receive?

Solution

Strategy

• In the table at the right, find the entry for average annual income subject to social security that is closest to $9381.

$9400

• Read the table for $9400 to find David's monthly benefit at age 65 and his dependent's monthly benefit.

For David: $520.40
For his dependent: $260.20

• Add to find the total monthly benefit. If the total of the monthly benefits exceeds the maximum shown in the table, then the maximum family benefit is received.

$520.40 + $260.20 = $780.60

• Multiply by 12 to find the family's annual retirement benefit.

12 × $780.60 = $9367.20

Conclusion

The annual retirement benefit for David's family is $9367.20.

Monthly Social Security Retirement Benefits						
Average annual income subject to social security	Benefit for worker, retirement at age				Benefit per dependent	Maximum family benefit
	65	64	63	62		
$923 or less	$121.80	$113.70	$105.60	$ 97.50	$ 60.90	$182.70
1,200	156.70	146.30	135.90	125.40	78.40	235.10
2,600	230.10	214.80	199.50	184.10	115.10	345.20
3,000	251.80	235.10	218.30	201.50	125.90	384.90
3,400	270.00	252.00	234.00	216.00	135.00	434.90
4,000	296.20	276.50	256.80	237.00	148.10	506.20
4,400	317.30	296.20	275.00	253.90	158.70	562.50
4,800	336.00	313.60	291.20	268.80	168.00	612.70
5,200	353.20	329.70	306.20	282.60	176.60	662.70
5,600	370.60	345.90	321.20	296.50	185.30	687.10
6,000	388.20	362.40	336.50	310.60	194.10	712.10
6,400	405.60	378.60	351.60	324.50	202.80	737.10
6,800	424.10	395.90	367.60	339.30	212.10	762.30
7,200	446.00	416.30	386.60	356.80	223.00	788.90
7,600	465.60	434.60	403.60	372.50	232.80	814.70
8,000	482.60	450.50	418.30	386.10	241.30	844.50
8,400	492.90	460.10	427.20	394.40	246.50	862.60
8,800	505.10	471.50	437.80	404.10	252.60	883.80
9,200	516.00	481.60	447.20	412.80	258.00	903.00
9,400	520.40	485.80	451.10	416.40	260.20	910.40
9,600	524.60	489.70	454.70	419.70	262.30	918.00
9,800	530.40	495.10	459.70	424.40	265.20	928.00
10,000	534.70	499.10	463.50	427.80	267.40	935.70

Related Problems

1. This table gives Clara Denby's annual earnings covered by social security. Use the information in the work sheet on page 292 to find Clara's average annual income subject to social security.

Year	Actual earnings	Year	Actual earnings	Year	Actual earnings
1958	$3,290	1966	$5,800	1974	$ 8,750
1959	3,760	1967	6,430	1975	9,060
1960	3,800	1968	6,890	1976	9,300
1961	4,270	1969	7,430	1977	9,470
1962	4,500	1970	7,900	1978	9,650
1963	4,960	1971	8,100	1979	9,970
1964	4,990	1972	7,460	1980	10,350
1965	5,300	1973	8,000	1981	10,850

2. The total of Jim Wald's annual earnings subject to social security is $171,160. He has been contributing to social security for 26 years. What is his average annual income subject to social security?

3. Anna Caliendo's annual earnings subject to social security total $228,740. She has been contributing to social security for 23 years. What is her average annual income subject to social security?

For problems 4-9, read the table on page 293 to find the annual retirement benefit.

	Average annual income	Retirement at age	Number of dependents
4.	$5815	64	0
5.	$7300	65	0
6.	$6142	65	1
7.	$7420	63	1
8.	$4616	62	2
9.	$9115	65	2

10. Albert Bach is planning to retire at age 62. He has no dependents. He has contributed to social security for 25 years. The total of his annual earnings subject to social security is $198,264. What is his annual retirement benefit?

Problem

Anita Romero is planning for her retirement. If she retires in 1981 at age 62, her monthly retirement benefit will be $339.30. Anita estimated that if she waits until 1984 when she is 65, she will receive $482.60 each month. What will be Anita's annual retirement benefit if she retires at age 62? at age 65? In what year will the total benefits for retirement at 65 be more than the total benefits for retirement at 62?

Solution

Strategy

• Multiply by 12 to find the annual retirement benefit at age 62.

12 × $339.30 = $4071.60

• Multiply by 12 to find the annual retirement benefit at age 65.

12 × $482.60 = $5791.20

• Construct a table to show the total benefits to be received by Anita if she retires at age 62 and if she retires at age 65.

Year	Retirement at 62	Retirement at 65
1981	$ 4,071.60	
1982	8,143.20	
1983	12,214.80	
1984	16,286.40	$ 5,791.20
1985	20,358.00	11,582.40
1986	24,429.60	17,373.60
1987	28,501.20	23,164.80
1988	32,572.80	28,956.00
1989	36,644.40	34,747.20
1990	40,716.00	40,538.40
1991	44,787.60	46,329.60

Conclusion

If Anita retires at age 62, her annual retirement benefit will be $4071.60. If she waits until she is 65 to retire, she will receive $5791.20 annually. In 1991, the total benefits received by Anita if she retires at age 65 will be more than the total received if she retires at age 62.

Related Problems

11. Judith Hank can retire in 1981 when she is 63 years old and receive $403.60 per month from social security. What will be her annual benefit?

12. If Judith retires at age 63, how much will she receive in retirement benefits in 5 years?

13. If Judith retires in 1983 when she is 65, she will receive $492.90 per month. What will be her annual benefit if she retires at age 65?

14. Construct a table to show the total benefits to be received by Judy if she retires at age 65 and if she retires at age 63. In what year will the total benefits for retirement at 65 be more than the total benefits for retirement at 63?

15. Rudy Aldinger receives $405.60 per month from social security. If social security benefits were increased by 14.2%, how much would Rudy receive each month? (Round to the nearest ten cents.)

Skills Tune-Up

Adding whole numbers and decimals, pages 6-7

1. 17 + 24 + 14
2. 6 + 29 + 18
3. 75 + 36 + 59
4. 39 + 28 + 97
5. 62 + 19 + 27
6. 91 + 25 + 46
7. 13 + 38 + 55 + 14
8. 7 + 89 + 68 + 32
9. 61 + 27 + 91 + 52
10. 98 + 25 + 13 + 43
11. 414 + 296 + 172
12. 867 + 329 + 541
13. 540 + 177 + 354
14. 805 + 643 + 784
15. 937 + 659 + 135
16. 5.7 + 4.27
17. 12.74 + 9.2
18. 11.35 + 43.43
19. 67.59 + 48.07
20. 0.2 + 0.4 + 0.3
21. 3.1 + 7.3 + 5.65
22. 1.97 + 0.14 + 0.68
23. 9.82 + 3.25 + 4.74
24. 3.4 + 6.68 + 2.52
25. 0.59 + 0.18 + 0.67
26. 2.82 + 9.95 + 4.59
27. 0.37 + 8.18 + 2.719
28. 7.1 + 2.58 + 5.1 + 8.9

Multiplying whole numbers, pages 8-9

1. 80 × 30
2. 40 × 500
3. 200 × 300
4. 9000 × 500
5. 3000 × 4000
6. 100 × 680
7. 35 × 40
8. 600 × 350
9. 50 × 6400
10. 2000 × 170
11. 150 × 2800
12. 170 × 1800
13. 450 × 1800
14. 5 × 17
15. 78 × 24
16. 70 × 36
17. 367 × 8
18. 2721 × 3
19. 388 × 76
20. 19 × 2193
21. 490 × 672
22. 2366 × 132
23. 506 × 397
24. 50 × 2409
25. 217 × 2965
26. 901 × 6867
27. 12,274 × 12
28. 7260 × 706

Percent problems, pages 34-37

1. 5% of 188 is ____.
2. $19\frac{1}{2}$% of 180 is ____.
3. $1\frac{1}{4}$% of 1600 is ____.
4. Find 80% of 30.
5. Find 89% of 2.
6. What number is 8.5% of 62?
7. What number is 12% of 750?
8. ____% of 76 is 19.
9. ____% of 84 is 79.8.
10. ____% of 60 is 7.5.
11. ____% of 40 is 34.
12. What percent of 900 is 288?
13. 2.38 is what percent of 68?
14. 559 is what percent of 860?
15. $3\frac{3}{4}$% of ____ is 30.
16. 25% of ____ is 2.05.
17. 72% of ____ is 28.8.
18. $42\frac{1}{2}$% of ____ is 3.06.
19. 32% of ____ is 64.
20. 8.3% of what number is 29.05?
21. 18.75 is 15% of what number?
22. 340.3 is 83% of what number?

Chapter 14 Review

Health insurance, pages 278-279

1. Pam Tanaka has a $50-deductible health insurance policy. The insurance company pays 75% of all covered medical expenses over the deductible amount. Her medical expenses amounted to $2735. How much did Pam pay?

Term life insurance, pages 280-281

2. Beth Bauer is 25 years old. She bought a 5-year term life insurance policy with a face value of $75,000. What is her annual premium?

5-Year Term Insurance Annual Premiums per $1000		
	Premium	
Age	Male	Female
24	$2.79	$2.41
25	2.80	2.47
26	2.87	2.53

Straight life, limited payment life, and endowment insurance, pages 282-285

3. Ted Larson bought $60,000 worth of straight life insurance at age 27. What is his annual premium?

Annual Insurance Premiums per $1000			
Age	Straight life	20-payment life	20-year endowment
26	$15.06	$22.55	$42.30
27	15.51	23.07	42.33
28	15.97	23.60	42.36

4. What will be the cash value of Ted's insurance at the end of 20 years?

Straight Life—Cash Value per $1000				
Age at time of issue	Cash value at end of year			
	5	10	15	20
26	$32	$105	$181	$286
27	33	109	186	295
28	34	112	192	303

Insurance agent, pages 286-287

5. The annual premium for Angela Manuel's insurance is $384.72. The factor for monthly premiums is 0.0875. How much more per year will Angela pay if she pays monthly rather than annually?

Choosing insurance and savings plans, pages 290-291

6. Andy Willoya, age 28, will pay monthly premiums for straight life insurance. The factor for monthly premiums is 0.0875. How much insurance (sold only in multiples of $1000) can he buy for a maximum of $65 a month? Use the table in problem 3.

7. Janet Martin deposits $40 each month in a savings account that pays 6% interest compounded monthly. How much will be in the account at the end of 20 years?

Savings Balance (For $1 deposited each month with interest compounded monthly)		
Years	6%	7%
20	$462.04	$520.93

Social security retirement benefits, pages 292-295

8. The total of Lou Gacek's annual earnings subject to social security is $171,175. He has been contributing to social security for 25 years. What is his average annual income subject to social security?

9. Meg Sowa plans to retire at age 64. She has no dependents. Her average annual income subject to social security is $7465. What will be Meg's annual retirement benefit?

Average annual income	Monthly benefit, retirement at age 64
$7200	$416.30
7600	434.60

10. Phil Damico is retired and receives $388.20 per month from social security. How much will he receive in 5 years?

Chapter 14 Test

1. Wilma Racine has a $60-deductible health insurance policy. The insurance company pays 80% of all medical expenses over the deductible amount. Her medical expenses amounted to $957. How much did Wilma pay?

2. Alma Torres is 30 years old. She bought a 5-year term insurance policy with a face value of $60,000. What is her annual premium?

5-Year Term Insurance Annual Premiums per $1000		
	Premium	
Age	Male	Female
29	$3.16	$2.68
30	3.27	2.74
31	3.38	2.83

3. Russell Elliot bought $50,000 worth of straight life insurance at age 32. How much is his annual premium?

Annual Insurance Premiums per $1000			
Age	Straight life	20-payment life	20-year endowment
31	$17.52	$25.27	$42.51
32	18.07	25.87	42.60
33	18.67	26.49	42.70

4. What will be the cash value of Russell's insurance at the end of 20 years?

Straight Life—Cash Value per $1000				
Age at time of issue	Cash value at end of year			
	5	10	15	20
31	$37	$123	$210	$333
32	38	126	217	343
33	39	131	224	355

5. The annual premium for Liz Diehl's insurance is $583.50. The factor for quarterly premiums is 0.26. How much more will Liz pay each year if she pays quarterly rather than annually?

6. Juan Carrido, age 33, is buying straight life insurance and will pay monthly premiums. The factor for monthly premiums is 0.0875. How much straight life insurance (sold only in multiples of $1000) can he buy for a maximum of $50 a month? Use the table in problem 3.

7. Marie Kwon deposits $30 each month in a savings account that pays 7% interest compounded monthly. How much will be in the account at the end of 20 years?

Savings Balance (For $1 deposited each month with interest compounded monthly)		
Years	6%	7%
20	$462.04	$520.93

8. The total of Ray Wuttunee's annual earnings subject to social security is $168,100. He has been contributing to social security for 25 years. What is his average annual income subject to social security?

9. Ginny Tufo is planning to retire at age 63. She has no dependents. Her average annual income subject to social security is $7364. What will be Ginny's annual retirement benefit?

Average annual income	Monthly benefit, retirement at age 63
$7200	$386.60
7600	403.60

10. Glen Conway is retired and receives $378.60 per month from social security. How much will he receive in 5 years?

Chapter 15 Investments

United States Savings Bonds

Many people purchase **Series EE Savings Bonds** as an investment.

Series EE Bonds can be purchased with **face values** of $50, $75, $100, $200, $500, $1000, $5000, and $10,000. The cost of these bonds is $\frac{1}{2}$ of the face value.

A bond can be **redeemed**, or cashed in, any time after six months from the date of purchase. The **redemption value** of the bond is the cost of the bond plus interest for the time the bond was held. If held to **maturity**, which is 8 years, the interest is 9% compounded semiannually on the cost of the bond. The redemption value of any Series EE bond is based on the redemption value of a $50 bond.

$50 Savings Bond Series EE (Cost: $25)	
After	Redemption value is
6 months	$25.56
1 year	$26.52
1.5 years	$27.31
2 years	$28.13
2.5 years	$28.98
3 years	$29.85
3.5 years	$30.74
4 years	$31.66
4.5 years	$32.61
5 years	$37.90
5.5 years	$39.51
6 years	$41.19
6.5 years	$42.94
7 years	$44.77
7.5 years	$46.67
8 years	$50.55
8.5 years	$52.83
9 years	$55.21
9.5 years	$57.69
10 years	$60.29
15 years	$93.63
20 years	$145.40

Maturity: 8 years

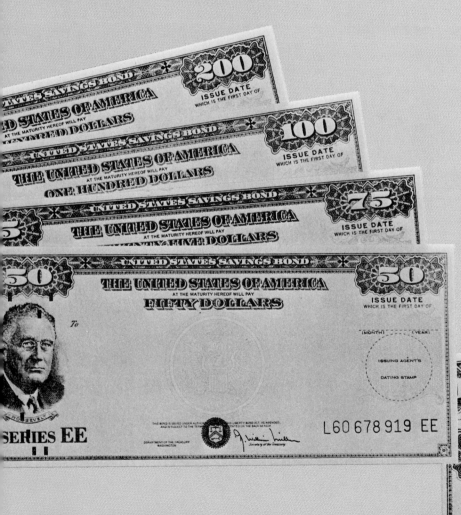

Problem

Bill Murphy wants to purchase a $200 Series EE Savings Bond. How much will the bond cost? If he redeems the bond in 8 years, how much will Bill receive?

Solution

Strategy

- Multiply $200 by $\frac{1}{2}$ to find the cost of the bond.

$\frac{1}{2} \times \$200 = \$100$

- Read the table on page 300 to find the redemption value after 8 years for a $50 bond.

$50.55

- Use a proportion to find the redemption value after 8 years for a $200 bond.

$\frac{50.55}{50} = \frac{r}{200}$ ⟵ Redemption value
⟵ Face value

$50r = 10,110$ Find the cross-products.

$r = 202.2$ Divide each side by 50.

Conclusion

The bond will cost $100. If Bill redeems the bond after 8 years, he will receive $202.20.

Related Problems

Complete the table.

	Number of bonds	Face value of each bond	Cost of 1 bond	Total cost
1.	1	$50		——
2.	1	$75		——
3.	3	$100		
4.	3	$500		
5.	6	$200		
6.	4	$75		
7.	12	$5,000		
8.	2	$10,000		
9.	20	$1,000		

Find the redemption value of each bond to the nearest cent.

	Years held	Face value
10.	3	$50
11.	7	$50
12.	5	$75
13.	8	$500
14.	2.5	$100
15.	9.5	$75
16.	15	$200
17.	3.5	$1,000
18.	6.5	$10,000
19.	20	$5,000

20. Karl bought these Series EE Savings Bonds: three $50 bonds, one $75 bond, and three $100 bonds. To the nearest cent, what will be the total redemption value of these bonds after 10 years?

Certificates of Deposit

Most banks and savings institutions offer their customers **certificates of deposit.** A certificate of deposit (CD) earns a higher interest rate than a regular savings account.

Some types of certificates require a minimum deposit, usually $1000. Money invested in a CD must be left on deposit a certain length of time to earn the higher interest rate. If the money is withdrawn early, part of the interest is lost. This penalty for early withdrawal is required by federal law.

Generally, the interest on a CD is compounded daily. A table for interest compounded daily is shown at the right.

Interest Factors per $1 Invested

Annual rate	Interest period			
	3 mo.	6 mo.	9 mo.	1 yr.
5.25%	0.01303	0.02623	0.03960	0.05390
5.5%	0.01365	0.02749	0.04152	0.05654
5.75%	0.01428	0.02876	0.04345	0.05918
6%	0.01490	0.03003	0.04538	0.06183
6.25%	0.01553	0.03130	0.04731	0.06449
6.5%	0.01616	0.03257	0.04925	0.06715
6.75%	0.01678	0.03384	0.05119	0.06982
7%	0.01741	0.03512	0.05314	0.07250
7.25%	0.01804	0.03640	0.05509	0.07519
7.5%	0.01866	0.03767	0.05704	0.07788
7.75%	0.01929	0.03895	0.05900	0.08057
8%	0.01992	0.04024	0.06096	0.08328

Problem

Millie Dunn decided to invest $2000 in a 4-year CD that earns 7.25% interest compounded daily. She agreed to leave her money on deposit for the full 4 years. The bank will send her a check for the interest each year. How much interest will Millie receive at the end of each year?

Solution

Strategy
• Read the table on page 302 to find the interest factor for 7.25% compounded daily for 1 year.

0.07519

• Multiply $2000 by the factor to find the annual interest.

0.07519 × $2000 = $150.38

Conclusion
Millie will receive $150.38 at the end of each year.

Related Problems

Complete the table.

	Amount invested	Annual rate	Interest period	Interest factor	Interest
1.	$1,000	7.5%	1 year		
2.	$5,000	7.75%	1 year		
3.	$10,000	8%	9 months		
4.	$3,000	6.25%	6 months		
5.	$4,000	6.5%	6 months		
6.	$2,000	6%	3 months		
7.	$2,500	5.75%	3 months		

8. Gail bought a $2000, 1-year CD that earns 7.5% interest compounded daily. She withdrew her money after 6 months. She received 6 months' interest at the regular savings-account rate of 5.25% compounded daily. How much interest did she receive?

9. How much interest did Gail lose by withdrawing her money early?

One method used to compare certificates of deposit is to find the **annual yield** of each CD. The CD with the highest annual yield will earn the most interest.

$$\text{Annual yield} = \frac{\text{Amount earned in 1 year}}{\text{Amount invested}}$$

Annual yield is usually expressed as a percent.

Problem

Millie's $2000 CD earned $150.38 interest each year. What was the annual yield to the nearest hundredth of a percent on this investment?

Solution

Strategy
• Use the formula to find the annual yield. Round to the nearest hundredth of a percent.

$$\text{Annual yield} = \frac{\$150.38}{\$2000} \approx 7.52\%$$

Conclusion
The annual yield was about 7.52%.

Related Problems

Complete the table. Round the annual yield to the nearest hundredth of a percent.

	Amount invested	Annual rate	Interest period	Interest paid every period	Amount earned in 1 year	Annual yield
10.	$1000	7.5%	1 year	$77.88	$77.88	
11.	$3000	7.5%	6 months	$113.01	(2 × $113.01)	
12.	$2000	5.75%	1 year			
13.	$5000	6.25%	1 year			
14.	$5000	6.5%	6 months			
15.	$2000	5.75%	3 months			
16.	$1000	7.5%	3 months			

17. Which has the higher annual yield: a $1000 CD at 6% that earns $61.83 each year, or a $2000 CD at 6% that earns $60.06 every 6 months?

18. Which has the higher annual yield: a $1000 CD at 7.5% that earns $77.88 each year, or a $5000 CD at 7% that earns $362.50 each year?

CALCULATOR APPLICATIONS

Compound Interest

The Acoyas bought a $2500 CD that earns 7.75% interest compounded daily. They plan to leave the $2500 and the interest it earns in the account for 10 years.

After the first year, the interest earned is 0.08057 × $2500, or $201.43. The compound amount, or the amount invested plus the interest earned, is $2500 + $201.43, or $2701.43. Notice that the amount invested each year is the same as the compound amount for the previous year.

Complete the table to find the value of the CD after 10 years. Round each answer to the nearest cent.

	Year	Amount invested	Interest factor	Interest	Compound amount
	1	$2500	0.08057	$201.43	$2701.43
1.	2	$2701.43	0.08057		
2.	3		0.08057		
3.	4		0.08057		
4.	5		0.08057		
5.	6		0.08057		
6.	7		0.08057		
7.	8		0.08057		
8.	9		0.08057		
9.	10		0.08057		

10. Subtract the original $2500 invested from the compound amount after 10 years to find the amount of interest this CD will earn in 10 years.

11. This CD earned $201.43 in interest the first year. If the interest had been withdrawn each year, the total interest earned in 10 years would have been $201.43 × 10. Find this amount.

12. If the amount invested and the interest are compounded daily for the full 10 years, how much more interest will be earned than if the interest is withdrawn each year?

13. Study the compound amounts for the 10 years. How many years does it take for the $2500 to double in value?

Common Stock

Many people invest their money in **common stock**. The holder of **shares** of common stock is a partial owner of the company that issues the stock. If the company makes a profit during the year, it may pay **dividends**, or part of the profits, to its stockholders.

To purchase stocks, a buyer usually contacts a **broker**. The broker buys and sells stocks for the buyer, and can give advice about which stocks may be good investments. The buyer pays the broker a commission, or a fee for services, each time stocks are bought and sold.

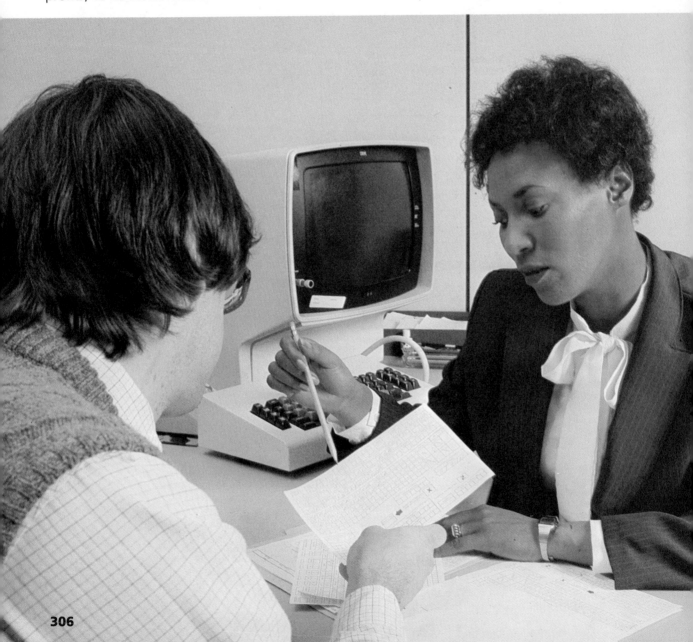

The current prices of many stocks are listed in the financial sections of most newspapers. Part of a listing for a given day is shown below. An explanation of the columns is also given.

1	2	3	4	5	6	7	8
	Div	P.E.	Sales (hds.)	High	Low	Close	Net Chg.
AAR	.44	8	28	11¾	11½	11½ −	⅛
ACF	2.76	10	89	48	47⅝	47⅞ −	⅛
AMF	1.24	13	136	24⅞	24⅝	24⅞ −	⅛
AM Intl		...	673	14¾	13½	13½ −	¾
APL		...	19	6⅛	6⅛	6⅛ −	⅛
ARA	1.94	7	138	33⅞	33	33⅜ +	⅛
ASA	5.00a	...	273	49¼	48⅝	49 −	¼
AVX	.32	24	223	35½	34¼	35 +	¼
AbtLb s		17	852	30½	29⅞	30½ +	⅞
AcmeC	1.40	8	6	27⅞	27⅞	27⅞	......
AdmDg	.04	8	27	6	5¾	5⅞ −	⅛
AdaEx	1.88e	...	75	14⅝	14⅜	14½	......
AdmMl	.20e	6	17	6¼	6⅛	6⅛	......
AMD s		17	328	26¾	26	26¾ +	⅞
AetnL f	2.32	6	2767 u	42¾	41⅜	42¾ +	1⅝

1 An abbreviation for the name of the stock.

2 *Div* Dividends paid in the last year. For example, .44 means \$0.44 per share was paid in dividends in the last year.

3 *P.E.* Price-earnings ratio. The ratio of the market price per share to the earnings per share.

4 *Sales* (*hds.*) Hundreds of shares sold. 28 means 2800 shares were sold.

5 *High* The highest price paid for a share. $11\frac{3}{4}$ means $11\frac{3}{4}$ dollars, or \$11.75.

6 *Low* The lowest price paid.

7 *Close* The last price paid.

8 *Net Chg.* Net change. The amount by which the closing price is different from the previous day's closing price. For example, $-\frac{1}{8}$ means that the closing price was $\frac{1}{8}$ of a dollar, or \$0.125, per share lower than the previous day's closing price.

Problem

Craig Jarvis bought 25 shares of stock at $35\frac{3}{8}$, or \$35.375, per share. He paid a commission of \$21.50. To the nearest cent, what was the total amount that Craig invested?

Solution

Strategy

- Multiply to find the cost of the shares. Round to the nearest cent.

  $25 \times \$35.375 \approx \$884.38$

- Add the commission Craig paid to find the total amount invested.

  $\$884.38 + \$21.50 = \$905.88$

Conclusion

The total amount that Craig invested was \$905.88.

Related Problems

For each problem, find the total amount invested to the nearest cent.

	Number of shares	Cost per share	Commission paid
1.	45	\$4.125	\$8.25
2.	90	\$15.25	\$28.00
3.	55	\$10.375	\$15.00
4.	20	\$35.25	\$18.50
5.	75	\$28.875	\$36.50
6.	100	\$63.625	\$79.25
7.	200	\$58.875	\$140.00
8.	150	\$26.25	\$57.50
9.	60	\$103.375	\$76.00
10.	120	\$100.50	\$148.61

Problem

Craig sold his 25 shares of stock several months after he bought them. The sale price was $36.75 per share. He paid a commission of $22. What was the profit or loss on the $905.88 that Craig invested?

Solution

Strategy
- Multiply the price per share by 25 to find the total sale price of the stock.

$$25 \times \$36.75 = \$918.75$$

- Subtract the amount of commission to find the amount received from the sale of the stock.

$$\$918.75 - \$22 = \$896.75$$

- Since the amount received was less than the amount invested, there was a loss. Subtract to find the loss.

$$\$905.88 - \$896.75 = \$9.13$$

Conclusion
Craig had a loss of $9.13 on his investment.

Related Problems

Complete the table.

| | Amount invested | Sale of stock | | | | |
		Number of shares	Sale price per share	Commission paid	Amount received	Profit or loss
	$905.88	25	$36.75	$22.00	$896.75	$9.13 loss
11.	$116.25	16	$5.625	$6.75		
12.	$2320.00	40	$63.50	$43.00		
13.	$740.75	50	$15.75	$20.00		
14.	$1150.30	100	$13.375	$29.50		
15.	$5950.15	100	$57.625	$74.00		
16.	$1484.00	65	$27.25	$31.25		
17.	$320.00	10	$32.125	$11.00		
18.	$6880.49	200	$41.00	$107.75		

Problem

Sandy MacKay invested $550 in 30 shares of stock. During the following year, the company paid dividends of $1.20 per share. To the nearest hundredth of a percent, what was the annual yield on Sandy's investment?

Solution

Strategy
• Multiply the dividend per share by 30 to find the total amount received.

$30 \times \$1.20 = \$36$

• Use the formula on page 304 to find the annual yield. Round to the nearest hundredth of a percent.

Annual yield = $\dfrac{\$36}{\$550} \approx 6.55\%$

Conclusion
The annual yield on Sandy's investment was about 6.55%.

Related Problems

Complete the table. Round the annual yield to the nearest hundredth of a percent.

	Amount invested	Number of shares	Dividends per share	Amount of dividends	Annual yield
19.	$2100	40	$3.00		
20.	$6400	100	$4.20		
21.	$4000	150	$1.06		
22.	$3100	100	$2.15		
23.	$7000	210	$1.72		
24.	$2225	125	$5.76		
25.	$5750	250	$3.10		

Break Time

Copy each figure. Then trace each figure without lifting your pencil from the paper. Do not trace any line more than once.

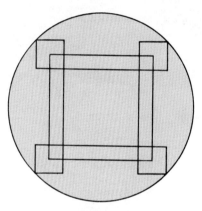

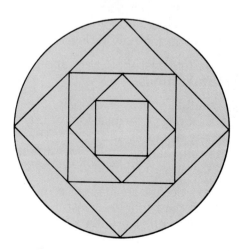

309

Investment Counselor

Career Cluster: Social Service As an investment counselor, Carla Reyes helps people decide how to invest their money.

Carla told Melinda Collier about **mutual funds.**

A mutual fund is a company that combines the money of its investors to buy a large variety of stocks and bonds. The money that the fund earns from its investments is paid to the shareholders as dividends.

The value of one share of a mutual fund is the amount that an investor would receive by selling one share back to the fund.

The amount that a new investor would have to pay to buy a share of a mutual fund sometimes includes a sales charge, or **load**. Thus, the price (buy price) is the value of a share (sell price) plus the load.

Mutual funds that do not have a sales charge are called **no-load** (NL) mutual funds. For these funds, the buy price is the same as the sell price.

The current prices of many funds are listed in the financial sections of most daily newspapers.

Problem

Melinda was considering two mutual funds, the AB Mut. F. and the DX Mut. F. How much would Melinda pay for 50 shares of each fund?

Solution

Strategy

• Read the table to find the buy price per share for each fund.

$10.86   AB Mut. F. (no-load)
$10.90   DX Mut. F. (includes load)

• Multiply each buy price by 50 to find the total price.

50 × $10.86 = $543   50 shares of AB Mut. F.
50 × $10.90 = $545   50 shares of DX Mut. F.

Conclusion

Melinda would pay $543 for 50 shares of the AB Mut. F. and $545 for 50 shares of the DX Mut. F.

MUTUAL FUNDS		
Name	Sell	Buy
AB Mut. F.	10.86	NL
AE Fund	13.05	14.26
BG Inv.	11.01	12.00
DX Mut. F.	9.97	10.90
GV Fund	7.63	8.34
Fin. Pln.	4.50	NL
HTH Grp.	12.12	13.25
Jay Fund	19.91	NL
MBT Grp.	5.79	NL
New Inv.	19.53	21.23
Park Fd.	24.97	NL
Va. Fund	4.01	NL

Related Problems

Complete the table.

	Number of shares	Mutual fund	Buy price	Total cost
1.	5	Jay Fund		
2.	20	New Inv.		
3.	15	AE Fund		
4.	50	Va. Fund		
5.	75	Fin. Pln.		
6.	40	BG Inv.		
7.	12	GV Fund		
8.	21	MBT Grp.		
9.	16	Park Fd.		

10. How much would Melinda receive if she sold 50 shares of the GV Fund back to the fund?

11. How much would Melinda receive if she sold 40 shares of the Jay Fund back to the fund?

12. What is the sales charge on each share of the DX Mut. F.?

13. What is the sales charge on each share of the HTH Grp. fund?

14. How many shares of the Fin. Pln. fund can be bought for $500? Round to the nearest ten-thousandth.

15. How many shares of the BG Inv. fund can be bought for $500? Round to the nearest ten-thousandth.

Skills Tune-Up

Rounding whole numbers and decimals, pages 4-5

Round each number to the nearest thousand, nearest hundred, and nearest ten.

1. 719
2. 653
3. 3491
4. 6137
5. 9359
6. 4773
7. 56,202
8. 2815
9. 999
10. 50,744

Round each number to the nearest whole number, nearest tenth, and nearest hundredth.

11. 5.628
12. 12.195
13. 47.459
14. 81.604
15. 376.287
16. 140.436
17. 764.972
18. 99.181
19. 68.018
20. 417.905
21. 346.997

Dividing decimals, pages 12-13

Find the quotient to the nearest hundredth.

1. $27.3 \div 9$
2. $60.6 \div 7$
3. $33.22 \div 37$
4. $19.41 \div 43$
5. $7.036 \div 78$
6. $3.277 \div 63$
7. $0.0027 \div 0.11$
8. $0.0089 \div 0.58$
9. $0.8 \div 3.6$
10. $5.3 \div 8.3$
11. $16.89 \div 6.1$
12. $11.47 \div 9.5$
13. $0.291 \div 0.08$
14. $0.289 \div 0.03$
15. $56 \div 0.7$
16. $96 \div 0.4$
17. $5.2 \div 1.11$
18. $4.71 \div 9.43$
19. $1.07 \div 28$
20. $2.81 \div 9.06$
21. $0.4877 \div 27$
22. $0.725 \div 0.648$
23. $0.932 \div 0.423$
24. $0.6525 \div 0.042$
25. $9.524 \div 0.039$
26. $9.41 \div 1.04$

Ratio and proportion, pages 30-31

Find the cross-products. Tell whether the ratios are equal.

1. $\frac{3}{5}$ $\frac{2}{3}$
2. $\frac{4}{6}$ $\frac{30}{45}$
3. $\frac{3}{7}$ $\frac{2}{12}$
4. $\frac{9}{2.7}$ $\frac{2}{0.6}$
5. $\frac{20.4}{100}$ $\frac{1.8}{9}$
6. $\frac{6}{9.95}$ $\frac{2}{2.99}$

Solve and check.

7. $\frac{5}{8} = \frac{15}{a}$
8. $\frac{5}{4} = \frac{c}{28}$
9. $\frac{49}{n} = \frac{14}{18}$
10. $\frac{d}{8} = \frac{3.6}{6}$
11. $\frac{0.75}{1} = \frac{18}{x}$
12. $\frac{4.5}{a} = \frac{0.09}{0.2}$
13. $\frac{0.48}{0.06} = \frac{y}{2}$
14. $\frac{n}{6.3} = \frac{1.2}{2.7}$

Chapter 15 Review

United States Savings Bonds, pages 300-301

1. The cost of any Series EE Savings Bond is $\frac{1}{2}$ of the face value. Find the cost of a $75 Series EE Savings Bond.

2. The redemption value of a $50 bond is $41.19 after 6 years. What is the redemption value of a $100 bond after 6 years?

Certificates of deposit, pages 302-304

3. Marie Wong bought a $4000 CD that earns 5.75% interest compounded daily. She receives an interest check every 3 months. How much interest does she receive every 3 months? A table for interest compounded daily is given below.

Interest Factors per $1 Invested

Annual rate	Interest period			
	3 mo.	6 mo.	9 mo.	1 yr.
5.25%	0.01303	0.02623	0.03960	0.05390
5.5%	0.01365	0.02749	0.04152	0.05654
5.75%	0.01428	0.02876	0.04345	0.05918
6%	0.01490	0.03003	0.04538	0.06183

4. Stan Larsen has a $3000 CD that earns $46.59 interest every 3 months. What is the annual yield on Stan's investment? Round to the nearest hundredth of a percent.

Common stock, pages 306-309

5. Ellen Drake bought 70 shares of stock for $43.375 per share. She paid a commission of $54. What was the total amount Ellen invested?

6. Ronald May sold 50 shares of stock for $63.625 per share. He paid a commission of $49. How much did Ronald receive from the sale?

7. Ronald's original investment was $3000. What was the profit or loss on his investment?

8. Kirk invested $800 in 30 shares of stock. During the following year, he was paid dividends of $1.25 per share. What was the annual yield on his investment? Round to the nearest hundredth of a percent.

Investment counselor, pages 310-311

Use the table below for problems 9 and 10.

MUTUAL FUNDS		
Name	Sell	Buy
RV Fund	14.85	NL
Est. Grp.	12.20	14.00

9. Find the total price of 20 shares of the RV Fund.

10. Find the sales charge on each share of the Est. Grp. fund.

Chapter 15 Test

1. The cost of any Series EE Savings Bond is $\frac{1}{2}$ of the face value. Find the cost of a $500 Series EE Savings Bond.

2. The redemption value of a $50 bond is $37.90 after 5 years. What is the redemption value of a $500 bond after 5 years?

3. David Tooley bought a $3000 CD that earns 6% interest compounded daily. He receives an interest check every 6 months. How much interest does he receive every 6 months? A table for interest compounded daily is given below.

Interest Factors per $1 Invested

Annual rate	Interest period			
	3 mo.	6 mo.	9 mo.	1 yr.
5.25%	0.01303	0.02623	0.03960	0.05390
5.5%	0.01365	0.02749	0.04152	0.05654
5.75%	0.01428	0.02876	0.04345	0.05918
6%	0.01490	0.03003	0.04538	0.06183

4. Barbara Vernon has a $5000 CD that earns $150.15 interest every 6 months. What is the annual yield on Barbara's investment? Round to the nearest hundredth of a percent.

5. Eva Ventura bought 30 shares of stock for $42.875 per share. She paid a commission of $32. What was the total amount Eva invested?

6. Donald Ross sold 40 shares of stock for $52.625 per share. He paid a commission of $43. How much did Donald receive from the sale?

7. Donald's original investment was $2625. What was the profit or loss on his investment?

8. Renee invested $575 in 25 shares of stock. During the following year, she was paid dividends of $2.50 per share. What was the annual yield on her investment? Round to the nearest hundredth of a percent.

Use the table below for problems 9 and 10.

MUTUAL FUNDS		
Name	Sell	Buy
Ntl. Inv.	27.10	NL
QA Fund	7.50	8.14

9. Find the total price of 30 shares of the Ntl. Inv. fund.

10. Find the sales charge on each share of the QA Fund.

Unit 5 Test

Choose the best answer.

1. Last year, Elena earned $1545.25, $698, $1128.50, and $58.25. Find her gross income.

A $2740.50   C $3430

B $3421   D $15,478.75

2. Last year, Terry received $11,250 in salary, $140 in interest, and $250 in dividends. Find her adjusted gross income. Terry can claim a $100 exclusion for dividend income.

A $11,540   C $11,640

B $11,470   D $11,740

3. Al and Sue Mendoza file a joint tax return and claim 2 exemptions. Their adjusted gross income (line 11, Form 1040A) is $19,475. Use the tax table below to find their tax liability.

1980 Tax Table B/Married Filing Joint Return						
If line 11, Form 1040A, or line 34, Form 1040, is—		**And the total number of exemptions claimed on line 6 is—**				
Over	But not over	2	3	4	5	6	7
		Your tax is—					
19,400	19,450	2,607	2,367	2,144	1,934	1,724	1,514
19,450	19,500	2,619	2,379	2,155	1,945	1,735	1,525
19,500	19,550	2,631	2,391	2,165	1,955	1,745	1,535
19,550	19,600	2,643	2,403	2,176	1,966	1,756	1,546
19,600	19,650	2,655	2,415	2,186	1,976	1,766	1,556

A $2379   C $2619

B $2155   D $2607

4. Kate has a tax liability of $2975 and a tax credit of $2892. Find her refund or balance due.

A $5867 refund   C $83 refund

B $83 balance due   D $5867 balance due

5. The Red Clouds file a joint tax return and claim 5 exemptions. Their adjusted gross income is $19,565 and their tax credit is $2173. Find their refund or balance due. (Use the tax table in problem 3.)

A $207 balance due   C $218 refund

B $207 refund   D $218 balance due

6. Use the information below and the tax table in problem 3 to find the Edmonds' tax liability on a joint return.

Number of exemptions: 3
Adjusted gross income: $19,700
Zero bracket amount: $3400
Itemized deductions
   State and local taxes: $1575
   Interest expenses: $2100

A $2391   C $2379

B $2415   D $2367

7. Michigan's state income tax is 4.6% of taxable income. Find the tax on $12,500.

A $575   C $57.50

B $5750   D $83,950

8. A health insurance company pays 80% of all medical expenses over the $50-deductible amount. What will the company pay on medical expenses of $1495?

A $1196   C $289

B $1236   D $1156

9. The annual premium for a 5-year term life insurance policy for an 18-year-old male is $2.69 per $1000. Find the annual premium on a $50,000 policy.

A $672.50   C $134.50

B $1345   D $2690

10. Quan bought $75,000 worth of straight life insurance at age 21. Find the total cash value at age 65.

Straight Life—Cash Value per $1000			
Age at time of issue	Cash value at end of year		Cash value at age 65
	10	20	
20	$89	$241	$710
21	91	247	703
22	94	254	696

A $52,725 **C** $53,250

B $527,250 **D** $52,200

11. Beth's annual insurance premium is $508.50. How much more will she pay per year if she pays quarterly rather than annually? The factor for quarterly payments is 0.26.

A $132.21 **C** $376.29

B $528.84 **D** $20.34

12. Larry is buying straight life insurance at age 24. He wants to pay monthly premiums. How much of this insurance can he buy for a maximum of $60 a month? The factor for monthly premiums is 0.0875.

Annual Premiums per $1000 for Males			
Age	Straight life	20-payment life	20-year endowment
23	$13.79	$21.04	$42.20
24	14.21	21.54	42.24
25	14.64	22.07	42.27

A $40,000 **C** $49,000

B $48,000 **D** $45,000

13. The Cords can receive monthly social security retirement benefits of $419.70 plus $262.30 for one dependent. Find their annual retirement benefit.

A $682 **C** $3147.60

B $5036.40 **D** $8184

14. The cost of any Series EE Savings Bond is $\frac{1}{2}$ of the face value. Find the cost of a $100 bond.

A $100. **C** $75

B $50 **D** $200

15. Chad bought a $3000 CD that earns 7% interest compounded daily. He receives an interest check at the end of each year. How much interest does he receive at the end of each year?

Interest Factors per $1 Invested			
Annual rate	Interest period		
	6 mo.	9 mo.	1 yr.
6.75%	0.03384	0.05119	0.06982
7%	0.03512	0.05314	0.07250
7.25%	0.03640	0.05509	0.07519

A $217.50 **C** $3217.50

B $225.60 **D** $225.57

16. Mrs. Leonard sold 80 shares of stock at $24.75 per share. She paid a commission of $36. How much did she receive?

A $1944 **C** $2016

B $1980 **D** $2880

17. DJR Mutual Fund is a no-load fund. The current selling price is $14.07 per share. Find the cost of 60 shares.

A $882.60 **C** $8826.40

B $844.20 **D** $8442.50

Break Time

Often it is easy to find percentages mentally. Study these examples for some helpful hints. The answers are rounded to the nearest cent.

Problem	Hint	THINK	Answer
10% of $18	10% $= \frac{1}{10}$, so divide by 10.	$18 ÷ 10 = $1.80	$1.80
10% of 18¢	Divide by 10.	18¢ ÷ 10 = 1.8¢ ≈ 2¢	2¢
5% of 79¢	5% $= \frac{1}{2}$ of 10%, so divide by 10 and then divide by 2.	79¢ ÷ 10 = 7.9¢ ≈ 8¢ 8¢ ÷ 2 = 4¢	4¢
20% of $25	20% = 2 × 10%, so divide by 10 and then multiply by 2.	$25 ÷ 10 = $2.50 2 × $2.50 = $5	$5
40% of $1.50	40% = 4 × 10%, so divide by 10 and then multiply by 4.	$1.50 ÷ 10 = $0.15 = 15¢ 4 × 15¢ = 60¢	60¢
50% of 75¢	50% $= \frac{1}{2}$, so divide by 2.	75¢ ÷ 2 = 37.5¢ ≈ 38¢	38¢
25% of $12	25% $= \frac{1}{4}$, so divide by 4.	$12 ÷ 4 = $3	$3
$33\frac{1}{3}$% of $3.60	$33\frac{1}{3}$% $= \frac{1}{3}$, so divide by 3.	$3.60 ÷ 3 = $1.20	$1.20

Find the answers mentally. Round each answer to the nearest cent. Write only the answer.

1. 10% of $45
2. 10% of 45¢
3. 5% of $98
4. 5% of 98¢
5. 20% of $30
6. 20% of 30¢
7. 40% of $27
8. 40% of 27¢

9. 50% of $15
10. 50% of 15¢
11. 25% of $48
12. 25% of 48¢
13. $33\frac{1}{3}$% of $63
14. $33\frac{1}{3}$% of 63¢
15. 10% of $3.79
16. 10% of $14.25

17. 20% of $2.95
18. $33\frac{1}{3}$% of $6.39
19. 50% of $5.50
20. 5% of $8.79
21. 25% of $12.50
22. 40% of $2.50
23. 30% of $12
24. 80% of $20

COMPUTER APPLICATIONS

Payroll Deductions

John Weber works in the payroll department of a small company. The computational methods for finding the amount of federal income tax withheld were entered into the computer using the program shown.

Lines 50, 70, 90, and 110   These values need to be entered.

Data required	Name
Number of pay periods per year	P
Gross pay for this period	G
Number of exemptions	E
Filing status (Use O for single and 1 for married.)	S

Line 20   Rounding, to be used throughout the program, is defined.

Lines 30–38   These are DATA statements. Each line of data indicates a tax bracket. The first three numbers of each line are for single taxpayers, while the last three numbers of each line are for married taxpayers.

Line 120   The gross pay for the year (I) is estimated.

Line 130   Each exemption is a $1000 deduction which is subtracted from the yearly gross pay to compute the adjusted gross income (A).

Line 140   The RESTORE statement is placed before the READ statements so that the DATA lines can be reused.

Line 150   An IF . . . THEN statement is used to separate the calculations for a single filing status and a married filing status.

Lines 160, 170, 240, and 250   X eliminates data items in these statements. The entire DATA statement is read but numbers for X are not used.

Lines 160–230 and 240–310   These lines are used to find the line of data to use for the computations. The DATA lines are read until the adjusted gross income is less than B1, the first number used from the DATA statement that was read last. Then the computer is sent to line 320.

Line 320   D is the amount by which the adjusted gross income exceeds the bottom of the tax bracket from B to B1.

Line 330   Y, the federal tax for the year, is made up of two parts: a flat tax (F) for the bracket and a tax on the excess (D).

Line 340   The amount of federal withholding tax for the year is divided by the number of pay periods per year to find W, the amount to be withheld for one pay period.

```
10  REM   FEDERAL INCOME TAX                      150  IF S=1 THEN 240
20  DEF FNR(Z)=INT(Z*100+.5)/100                  160  READ B,F,T,X,X,X
30  DATA 0,0,0,0,0,0                              170  READ B1,F1,T1,X,X,X
31  DATA 1420,0,.15,2400,0,.15                    180  IF B1=0 THEN 320
32  DATA 3300,282,.18,6600,630,.18                190  IF A<B1 THEN 320
33  DATA 6800,912,.21,10900,1404,.21              200  LET B=B1
34  DATA 10200,1626,.26,15000,2265,.24            210  LET F=F1
35  DATA 14200,2666,.30,19200,3273,.28            220  LET T=T1
36  DATA 17200,3566,.34,23600,4505,.32            230  GO TO 170
37  DATA 22500,5368,.39,28900,6201,.37            240  READ X,X,X,B,F,T
38  DATA 0,0,0,0,0,0                              250  READ X,X,X,B1,F1,T1
40  PRINT "NUMBER OF PAY PERIODS";                260  IF B1=0 THEN 320
50  INPUT P                                       270  IF A<B1 THEN 320
60  PRINT "GROSS PAY";                            280  LET B=B1
70  INPUT G                                       290  LET F=F1
80  PRINT "NUMBER OF EXEMPTIONS";                 300  LET T=T1
90  INPUT E                                       310  GO TO 250
100 PRINT "FILING STATUS";                        320  LET D=FNR(A-B)
110 INPUT S                                       330  LET Y=FNR(T*D+F)
120 LET I=FNR(P*G)                                340  LET W=FNR(Y/P)
130 LET A=FNR(I-E*1000)                           350  PRINT "FEDERAL WITHHOLDING TAX";W
140 RESTORE                                       360  END
```

Give the output for the program above when

1. P is 52, G is 155, E is 2, and S is 0.

2. P is 26, G is 264.44, E is 4, and S is 1.

3. P is 26, G is 572.87, E is 3, and S is 1.

4. P is 52, G is 302.18, E is 1, and S is 0.

5. P is 26, G is 488.76, E is 2, and S is 1.

6. a married person has 3 exemptions, there are 52 pay periods, and the pay for this pay period is $432.07.

7. a single person has 1 exemption, there are 52 pay periods, and the pay for this pay period is $432.07.

8. a single person has 3 exemptions, there are 26 pay periods, and the pay for this pay period is $678.45.

9. a married person has 5 exemptions, there are 26 pay periods, and the pay for this pay period is $872.11.

10. Modify the program so that the number of pay periods per year, the gross pay for this period, the number of exemptions, and the filing status are included in the printout.

11. Give the output when there are 26 pay periods, the gross pay for this period is $478.93, there is 1 exemption, and the filing status is married.

12. Modify the program to calculate a state withholding tax. For this tax, use 2.5% of the adjusted gross pay. (Adjusted gross pay is the amount after subtracting the deductions for exemptions.)

13. Give the output when there are 52 pay periods, the gross pay for this period is $392.61, there is 1 exemption, and the filing status is single.

Unit 6 Purchasing and Budgeting

Chapter 16 Buying Food

Nutritionist

Career Cluster: Health Henry Robinson is a nutritionist at a hospital. His job is to plan nutritious, well-balanced meals.

When Henry plans meals for people, he takes into consideration these four main food groups.

— Meat, poultry, eggs, and fish
— Milk and dairy products
— Fruits and vegetables
— Breads and cereals

He also uses a calorie chart. A portion of one is shown below. A **calorie** is a heat unit that is used to express the fuel value of foods.

CALORIE CHART	Portion	Calories
Meat, poultry		
Bacon	1 slice	45
Chicken, broiled	1 piece	185
Meat loaf	1 slice	200
Dairy products and eggs		
Butter	1 pat	50
Cheddar cheese	55 g	225
Cottage cheese	55 g	50
Egg, poached	1	80
Milk	240 mL	160
Fruits		
Apple	1	70
Grapefruit	$\frac{1}{2}$	55
Orange juice	120 mL	55
Peaches, canned	1 serving	100
Vegetables		
Lettuce	2 leaves	10
Peas	1 serving	60
Potato, baked	1	90
Tomato	1	30
Breads and cereals		
Oatmeal	240 mL	150
Whole-wheat bread	1 slice	55
Sandwiches		
Chicken salad	1	280
Tuna salad	1	280
Miscellaneous		
French dressing	15 mL	60
Vegetable soup	240 mL	80

Problem

Henry is planning a low-calorie diet for Rose Benson. Find the number of calories in the breakfast that Henry has planned for Rose.

Monday breakfast
$\frac{1}{2}$ grapefruit
240 mL oatmeal
120 mL milk
2 slices bacon

Solution

Strategy

• Use the calorie chart to compute the number of calories in each item.

Grapefruit: 55 cal.
Oatmeal: 150 cal.
Milk: 80 cal. (160 ÷ 2)
Bacon: 90 cal. (45 × 2)

• Add to find the total number of calories.
55 + 150 + 80 + 90 = 375

Conclusion

The breakfast contains 375 calories.

Related Problems

Find the number of calories in each meal.

1. Monday lunch

240 mL vegetable soup
$\frac{1}{2}$ tomato
240 mL milk
1 tuna salad sandwich

2. Monday dinner

2 pieces broiled chicken
55 g cottage cheese
1 serving peas
240 mL milk
1 serving canned peaches

3. Tuesday breakfast

120 mL orange juice
2 poached eggs
1 slice whole-wheat toast
1 pat butter
240 mL milk

4. Tuesday lunch

$\frac{1}{2}$ chicken salad sandwich
55 g cheddar cheese
240 mL milk
1 apple

5. Tuesday dinner

1 slice meat loaf
1 baked potato
4 leaves of lettuce
15 mL French dressing
240 mL milk

6. Find the total number of calories planned for Monday. Include breakfast.

7. Find the total number of calories planned for Tuesday.

Calorie Usage

Jed Horton's doctor gave him information about the number of calories used in certain activities. Jed kept track of how long he participated in each activity one day. Then he completed the table below.

Activity	Calories used per kilogram of body weight in one hour	Number of hours spent one day
Sleeping	0.9	$7\frac{3}{4}$

Sitting quietly
    reading, writing, talking on the telephone,
    watching TV, attending classes
	1.8	$9\frac{1}{2}$

Light exercise
    walking slowly, playing the piano, typing,
    driving a car
	2.4	$4\frac{1}{2}$

Moderate exercise
    bicycling 8 km per hour, walking briskly,
    bowling, playing catch
	3.9	$\frac{1}{2}$

Active exercise
    dancing, doing calisthenics, raking leaves,
    playing table tennis
	5.7	$\frac{1}{4}$

Very active exercise jogging 8 km per hour, swimming, playing tennis	6.4	$1\frac{1}{2}$
	Total hours	24

Problem

Jed weighs 69 kg. How many calories did he use while sleeping?

Solution

Strategy

• Read the table to find the factor for sleeping.

0.9

• Multiply times Jed's weight to find the number of calories used in one hour of sleeping.

$0.9 \times 69 = 62.1$

• Read the table to find the number of hours Jed slept. Rename as a decimal.

$7\frac{3}{4} = 7.75$

• Multiply times the number of calories used in one hour of sleeping. Round to the nearest whole number.

$7.75 \times 62.1 \approx 481$

Conclusion

Jed used about 481 calories while sleeping.

Related Problems

For problems 1–5, find the number of calories used during each activity listed in the chart. Round each answer to the nearest whole number.

1. Sitting quietly

2. Light exercise

3. Moderate exercise

4. Active exercise

5. Very active exercise

6. Find the total number of calories Jed used on that day. Include the calories used for sleeping.

Find the number of calories used by Betty Granville during each activity listed. The number of hours Betty spent on each activity on Monday is given. She weighs 58 kg.

7. Sleeping, 8 hours

8. Sitting quietly, $10\frac{1}{2}$ hours

9. Light exercise, $2\frac{3}{4}$ hours

10. Moderate exercise, $1\frac{1}{4}$ hours

11. Active exercise, 1 hour

12. Very active exercise, $\frac{1}{2}$ hour

13. Find the total number of calories used by Betty on Monday.

14. Betty is trying to use more calories than are in the food she eats. On Monday her meals contained 1375 calories. How many more calories did Betty use than were in the food she ate?

325

Grocery Shopping

Jaime and Alicia Lorenzo plan their weekly menus before they shop. From these menus the Lorenzos make a shopping list. This helps them buy only the items they need. They use ads in the newspaper to find the cost of the items they want to buy.

Problem

Bananas cost $0.87 per kilogram. Find the cost of 1.3 kg of bananas.

Solution

Strategy
- Multiply the weight of the bananas times the cost per kilogram. Round up to the next whole cent.

  $1.3 \times \$0.87 \approx \$1.14$

Conclusion
1.3 kg of bananas cost $1.14.

Problem

Beef gravy mix is marked 3/$1.00. This means 3 packages cost $1.00. How much would 2 packages of gravy mix cost?

Solution

Strategy
- Divide by 3 to find the cost of one package. Round up to the next whole cent.

  $\$1.00 \div 3 \approx \$0.34$

- Multiply by 2 to find the cost of 2 packages.

  $2 \times \$0.34 = \$0.68$

Conclusion
2 packages of gravy mix cost $0.68.

Related Problems

Find the cost of each item listed.

1. 1.2 kg of apples at $1.54 per kilogram
2. 3 cans of pears at $0.69 each
3. 0.5 kg of steak at $6.05 per kilogram
4. 2 cans of peas at 4 for $1.00
5. 2 bottles of salad dressing at 3 for $2.00
6. 3 packages of pudding mix at 5 for $1.29
7. 2 cans of fruit drink at $0.62 each
8. 3.6 kg of onions at $0.65 per kilogram
9. 3 cans of pork and beans at 2 for $0.95
10. 8 cans of soup at 3 for $0.98

When Jaime and Alicia shop, they often compare prices to determine the best buys. To do this, they find the **unit price** of each item. This is the price per unit of measure.

Problem

Find the unit price of a 300-gram jar of peanut butter priced at $1.28.

Solution

Strategy
- Write the price in cents.

  $\$1.28 = 128¢$

- Divide by the number of grams. Round to the nearest hundredth of a cent.

  $128¢ \div 300 \approx 0.43¢$

Conclusion
The unit price is about 0.43¢ per gram.

Related Problems

Find the unit price for each item to the nearest hundredth of a cent.

11. 340-gram bottle of chili sauce for $0.63

12. 312-gram box of raisins for $1.40

13. 675-gram jar of applesauce for $0.81

14. 3.5-liter bottle of bleach for $0.77

15. 950-milliliter bottle of apple juice for $0.89

16. 908-gram can of peaches for $0.99

17. 535-milliliter can of tomato juice for $0.45

18. 0.5-kilogram bag of noodles for $0.65

19. 300-gram jar of mustard for $0.48

20. 1.5-liter bottle of vinegar for $0.74

Problem

Which is the better buy for vegetable oil?

1.2-liter bottle for $1.99   1.6-liter bottle for $2.89

Solution

Strategy

- Find the unit price for each $1.99 ÷ 1.2 ≈ $1.66   1.2-liter bottle
  item to the nearest whole cent. $2.89 ÷ 1.6 ≈ $1.81   1.6-liter bottle

- Compare the unit prices. $1.66 < $1.81

Conclusion

The 1.2-liter bottle is the better buy.

Related Problems

This table shows some of the items on the Lorenzos' grocery list.
For each brand, find the unit price to the nearest whole cent.
Then find the cost of the item if the Lorenzos choose the better
buy. Round each cost up to the next whole cent.

	Item	Name brand	Unit price	Store brand	Unit price	Cost
	Vegetable oil, 1 bottle	1.2-L bottle: $1.99	$1.66/L	1.6-L bottle: $2.89	$1.81/L	$1.99
21.	Milk, 4 L	2-L carton: $0.99		4-L carton: $1.89		
22.	Flour, 5 kg	2.5-kg sack: $1.39		5-kg sack: $2.69		
23.	Detergent, 10 kg	5-kg box: $7.29		2-kg box: $2.55		
24.	Swiss cheese, 1 kg	0.5-kg chunk: $3.19		1-kg chunk: $6.45		
25.	Potatoes, 5 kg	2.5-kg sack: $1.47		$0.53/kg		
26.	Butter, 1 kg	1-kg package: $4.39		0.5-kg package: $2.35		
27.	Bread, 1 loaf	0.5-kg loaf: $0.89		0.6-kg loaf: $0.95		
28.	Orange juice, 2 L	1-L bottle: $0.89		2-L bottle: $1.69		

29. Find the total cost.

30. If a $1-off coupon can be applied to either size, which is the better
    buy: 5 kg of charcoal for $2.89, or 10 kg of charcoal for $5.09?

CALCULATOR APPLICATIONS

Sometimes a proportion can be used to find the price of
an item.

Find the price of 1.4 kg of pears priced at 2 kg for $1.99.

Write a proportion.

$$\frac{1.99}{2} = \frac{n}{1.4}$$ ← Price (dollars)
← Weight (kilograms)

Solve the proportion, rounding up to the next whole cent.

$$1.99 \times 1.4 = 2 \times n$$

$$\frac{2.786}{2} = \frac{2n}{2}$$

$$1.40 \approx n$$

1.4 kg of pears cost $1.40.

Find the cost of each item listed. Round each answer up
to the next whole cent.

1. 3.1 kg of oranges at 2 kg for $2.39

2. 0.7 kg of steak at $6.05 per kilogram

3. 7 cans of tomato sauce at 5 for $0.99

4. 2 packages of gelatin at 3 for $1.00

5. 2.6 kg of onions at 4 kg for $2.77

6. 1.2 kg of ham at 0.5 kg for $3.69

7. 1 jar of jelly at 3 for $1.66

8. 25 cans of juice at 2 for $0.79

9. 0.4 kg of nuts at $7.12 per kilogram

10. 5 cantaloupes at 3 for $1.39

11. 12 lemons at 5 for $0.79

12. 5 bars of soap at 2 for $0.49

13. 3 loaves of bread at 2 for $1.39

14. 0.8 kg of cheese at 0.5 kg for $2.99

15. 4 cans of soup at 3 for $0.98

16. 10 cans of dog food at 4 for $0.59

Comparing Meat Prices

Ned Kuri belongs to a food-buying cooperative. He and his friends
save money by sharing in the purchase of large quantities of food. The
cooperative is interested in buying a side of beef. A side of beef is half of all
the meat obtained from the animal. During butchering, there is a 20% to
30% loss due to trimming away fat, discarding bone, and normal shrinkage.

Problem

Before butchering, a side of beef weighed
135 kg. After butchering, the usable meat
weighed 97.2 kg. What was the percent of
loss?

Solution

Strategy
• Subtract to find the amount of loss.

  $135 - 97.2 = 37.8$

• Divide by the total weight of the side of
  beef to find the percent of loss.

  $\frac{37.8}{135} = 28\%$

Conclusion
The percent of loss was 28%.

Problem

The price of the 135-kilogram side of beef
before butchering was $3.29 per kilogram.
Find the cost per kilogram of usable meat
(97.2 kg).

Solution

Strategy
• Multiply to find the total cost of the side of
  beef before butchering.

  $135 \times \$3.29 = \$444.15$

• Divide to find the cost per kilogram of
  usable meat. Round to the nearest whole
  cent.

  $\$444.15 \div 97.2 \approx \$4.57$

Conclusion
The usable meat cost $4.57 per kilogram.

Related Problems

Complete the table. Round each cost to the nearest whole cent.

	Weight of beef before butchering	Amount of usable meat	Percent of loss	Cost per kilogram before butchering	Cost per kilogram of usable meat
	135 kg	97.2 kg	28%	$3.29	$4.57
1.	130 kg	91.0 kg		$3.29	
2.	145 kg	107.3 kg		$3.19	
3.	125 kg	95.0 kg		$3.33	
4.	155 kg	116.6 kg		$3.19	
5.	165 kg	123.75 kg		$3.19	

Problem

A 140-kilogram side of beef yields 15.5 kg of ground beef. The current price for ground beef in a grocery store is $3.99 per kilogram. Using this price, find the value of the ground beef obtained from the side of beef.

Solution

Strategy
• Multiply to find the store value of the ground beef. Round up to the next whole cent.   15.5 × $3.99 ≈ $61.85

Conclusion
The ground beef would cost about $61.85 in a grocery store.

Related Problems

The 140-kilogram side of beef yields the amounts listed in the table. Find the value for each cut of meat. Round up to the next whole cent.

	Cut of meat	Amount obtained	Current cost per kilogram	Value at the current price
	Ground beef	15.5 kg	$3.99	$61.85
6.	Round steak	15.4 kg	$4.89	
7.	Stew meat	14.4 kg	$5.99	
8.	Chuck blade roast	12.5 kg	$4.09	
9.	Sirloin steak	11.6 kg	$5.39	
10.	Rib roast	8.5 kg	$5.89	
11.	Chuck arm roast (boneless)	8.1 kg	$5.09	
12.	Porterhouse, T-bone, club steaks	7.1 kg	$8.99	
13.	Rump roast (boneless)	4.7 kg	$4.59	
14.	Brisket (boneless)	2.9 kg	$5.29	
15.	Flank steak	0.7 kg	$8.09	
16.	Kidney	0.4 kg	$1.99	

17. What is the total store value of the meat?

18. The price of the 140-kilogram side of beef is $3.29 per kilogram before butchering. What is the difference between the total cost of the side of beef and the total value of the meat at current store prices?

Comparing Meal Costs

There are alternatives to preparing and eating meals at home. Many people choose to eat in restaurants or to purchase prepared foods and carry-out meals.

When eating at a restaurant, most people give the waiter or waitress a tip for serving the food. This amount is usually about 15% of the bill.

Problem

Irene and Stan Ochita want to compare the cost of eating in a restaurant with the cost of having the same dinner at home. They recently had fish dinners at a restaurant. The bill was $12.35 plus $0.62 tax. They left a 15% tip. Preparing the same meal at home costs $8.25. How much more does the restaurant meal cost?

Solution

Strategy
• Round the food bill to the nearest dollar.

$12.35 ≈ $12.00

• Mentally calculate the amount of a 15% tip.

$1.20	10% of bill (10% of $12.00 = $1.20)
+ 0.60	5% of bill (5% = $\frac{1}{2}$ of 10%; $\frac{1}{2}$ of $1.20 = $0.60)
$1.80	Tip (15% = 10% + 5%)

• Find the total restaurant cost.

$12.35	Food bill
0.62	Tax
1.80	Tip
$14.77	Total cost

• Subtract the cost of preparing the same meal at home.

$14.77 − $8.25 = $6.52

Conclusion
The restaurant meal costs $6.52 more.

Related Problems

Find the total cost for two people for each meal listed.

1. *Chicken carry-out*
Bucket of 8 pieces	$4.88
Cole slaw	$0.84
Beverage at home	$0.20 per person

2. *Chicken prepared at home*
Whole chicken	$2.10
Cole slaw ingredients	$0.52
Beverage	$0.20 per person

3. *Chicken at a restaurant*
Chicken and cole slaw dinner for two	$8.80
Beverage	$0.55 per person
Sales tax	$0.50
Include 15% tip.	

4. Find the difference in the total costs of the most expensive and the least expensive chicken dinners.

5. *Beef stew dinner served at home*
Frozen beef stew	$3.59
Salad ingredients	$0.55
Beverage	$0.20 per person

6. *Beef stew prepared at home*
Beef	$1.70
Potatoes	$0.35
Carrots	$0.07
Salad ingredients	$0.55
Beverage	$0.20 per person

7. *Beef stew dinner at a restaurant*
Stew and salad for two	$8.40
Beverage	$0.60 per person
Sales tax	$0.42
Include 15% tip.	

8. Find the difference in the total costs of the most expensive and the least expensive beef stew dinners.

Break Time

Fill in the squares in the diagram with all the numbers from 1 to 8. No two consecutive numbers can be next to each other vertically, horizontally, or diagonally.

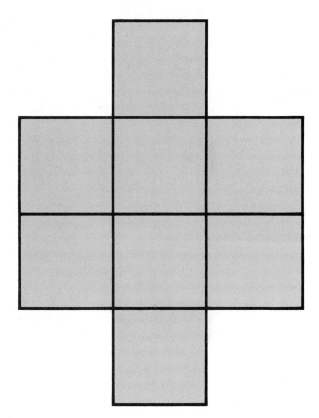

Skills Tune-Up

Multiplying decimals, pages 10-11

1. 0.6×0.5
2. 0.1×0.7
3. 0.03×0.3
4. 0.04×0.4
5. 0.07×0.05
6. 0.06×0.07
7. 0.004×0.01
8. 0.09×0.011
9. 300×0.4
10. 800×0.8
11. 900×0.02
12. 0.04×150
13. 0.004×300
14. 500×0.011
15. 0.005×0.008
16. 0.007×0.004
17. 6000×0.0011
18. 0.0013×8000
19. 4.3×9.7
20. 1.56×7.1
21. 6.7×3.02
22. 14.1×0.035
23. 3.276×5.15
24. 6.776×12.9
25. 273.6×558
26. 0.55×0.0023
27. 0.446×0.0068

Dividing fractions and mixed numbers, pages 16-17

1. $\frac{1}{2} \div \frac{5}{8}$
2. $\frac{2}{3} \div \frac{3}{4}$
3. $\frac{5}{8} \div \frac{15}{16}$
4. $\frac{2}{5} \div \frac{1}{10}$
5. $\frac{5}{8} \div \frac{2}{7}$
6. $\frac{2}{5} \div \frac{4}{7}$
7. $6 \div \frac{3}{4}$
8. $\frac{1}{4} \div 4$
9. $\frac{4}{5} \div 3$
10. $6 \div \frac{3}{8}$
11. $1\frac{3}{4} \div \frac{7}{10}$
12. $\frac{2}{3} \div 1\frac{1}{5}$
13. $11\frac{3}{4} \div 4$
14. $12 \div 2\frac{2}{7}$
15. $9 \div 7\frac{1}{2}$
16. $1\frac{4}{5} \div 2\frac{1}{10}$
17. $2\frac{4}{5} \div 1\frac{3}{4}$
18. $1\frac{13}{14} \div 1\frac{1}{7}$
19. $9\frac{2}{7} \div 1\frac{6}{7}$
20. $4\frac{5}{6} \div 1\frac{2}{3}$
21. $7\frac{7}{8} \div 8\frac{1}{6}$

Percent problems, pages 34-37

1. $12\frac{1}{2}\%$ of 10 is ____.
2. 30% of 20 is ____.
3. 5% of 300 is ____.
4. 5.5% of 85 is ____.
5. Find 12% of 5.
6. Find $2\frac{1}{2}\%$ of 700.
7. What number is 24% of 35?
8. What number is 6.6% of 50?
9. ____% of 32 is 24.
10. ____% of 50 is 47.5.
11. ____% of 70 is 17.5.
12. ____% of 5.78 is 2.89.
13. What percent of 64 is 48?
14. What percent of 60 is 15?
15. 81 is what percent of 120?
16. 35% of ____ is 2.52.
17. 7.25% of ____ is 4.06.
18. 3% of ____ is 0.84.
19. $12\frac{1}{2}\%$ of ____ is 2.5.
20. 6% of what number is 2.22?
21. 60% of what number is 90?
22. 5.4 is $4\frac{1}{2}\%$ of what number?

Chapter 16 Review

1. Use the chart to find the number of calories in this meal.

Lunch

55 g cottage cheese
2 slices whole-wheat bread
2 pats butter
1 apple
240 mL milk

CALORIE CHART	Portion	Calories
Meat		
Meat loaf	1 slice	200
Pot roast	1 slice	220
Dairy products		
Butter	1 pat	50
Cottage cheese	55 g	50
Milk	240 mL	160
Fruits and vegetables		
Apple	1	70
Cantaloupe	$\frac{1}{2}$	40
Cole slaw	1 serving	35
Green beans	1 serving	15
Breads		
Whole-wheat bread	1 slice	55
Roll	1	100

Calorie usage, pages 324-325

2. Angela weighs 60 kg. She went bicycling for $2\frac{1}{2}$ hours. Bicycling requires 3.9 calories per kilogram of body weight each hour. How many calories did she use? Round the answer to the nearest whole number.

Grocery shopping, pages 326-328

3. Apples cost $1.39 per kilogram. Find the cost of 1.6 kg of apples.

4. Find the cost of 2 cans of beans at 3 for $0.98.

5. Find the unit price of a 520-gram box of macaroni for $0.69. Round the answer to the nearest hundredth of a cent.

6. Which is the better buy for onions?

3.5-kilogram bag for $2.19
5-kilogram bag for $3.65

Comparing meat prices, pages 330-331

7. Before butchering, a side of beef weighed 145 kg. After butchering, the usable meat weighed 107.3 kg. What was the percent of loss?

8. The price of a 145-kilogram side of beef before butchering was $3.19 per kilogram. The usable meat weighed 107.3 kg. Find the cost per kilogram of usable meat. Round the answer to the nearest whole cent.

9. The current price for sirloin steak in a grocery store is $5.39 per kilogram. Using this price, find the value of 11.9 kg of sirloin steak. Round the answer up to the next whole cent.

Comparing meal costs, pages 332-333

10. Lana and Jay had fish dinners at a restaurant. The bill was $9.00 plus $0.45 tax. They left a 15% tip. Making the same meal at home costs $5.25. How much more does the restaurant meal cost?

Chapter 16 Test

1. Use the chart to find the number of calories in this meal.

Dinner

2 slices pot roast
1 serving cole slaw
$\frac{1}{2}$ cantaloupe
1 roll
240 mL milk

CALORIE CHART	Portion	Calories
Meat		
Meat loaf	1 slice	200
Pot roast	1 slice	220
Dairy products		
Butter	1 pat	50
Cottage cheese	55 g	50
Milk	240 mL	160
Fruits and vegetables		
Apple	1	70
Cantaloupe	$\frac{1}{2}$	40
Cole slaw	1 serving	35
Green beans	1 serving	15
Breads		
Whole-wheat bread	1 slice	55
Roll	1	100

2. Stu weighs 78 kg. He played table tennis for $1\frac{1}{2}$ hours. Playing table tennis requires 5.7 calories per kilogram of body weight each hour. How many calories did he use? Round the answer to the nearest whole number.

3. Find the cost of 0.7 kg of pork chops at $3.99 per kilogram.

4. Find the cost of 3 cans of tomatoes at 4 for $1.19.

5. Find the unit price of a 350-milliliter can of soup for $0.33. Round the answer to the nearest hundredth of a cent.

6. Which is the better buy for fabric softener?

2-liter bottle for $1.79
3.5-liter bottle for $3.23

7. Before butchering, a side of beef weighed 140 kg. After butchering, the usable meat weighed 99.4 kg. What was the percent of loss?

8. The price of a 140-kilogram side of beef before butchering was $3.29 per kilogram. The usable meat weighed 99.4 kg. Find the cost per kilogram of usable meat. Round the answer to the nearest whole cent.

9. The current price for rump roast in a grocery store is $4.59 per kilogram. Using this price, find the value of 4.9 kg of rump roast. Round the answer up to the next whole cent.

10. Michelle and Doug had spaghetti dinners at a restaurant. The bill was $11.00 plus $0.44 tax. They left a 15% tip. Making the same meal at home costs $5.80. How much more does the restaurant meal cost?

Chapter 17 Buying, Making, and Renting Goods

Catalog Buying

Dave and Diane Tomlinson order many items from catalogs. Together they can look through the catalogs at home and choose the items they want to buy.

When people buy merchandise shown in a catalog, they usually pay shipping and handling charges. These charges are shown in the table.

Shipping and Handling Charges				
Shipping weight	Local zone	Zones 1 & 2	Zone 3	Zone 4
1 oz. to 8 oz.	$1.27	$1.34	$1.36	$1.40
9 oz. to 15 oz.	$1.49	$1.60	$1.64	$1.68
1 lb. to 2 lb.	$1.97	$2.11	$2.14	$2.26
2 lb. 1 oz. to 3 lb.	$2.07	$2.39	$2.43	$2.53
3 lb. 1 oz. to 5 lb.	$2.20	$2.57	$2.63	$2.68
5 lb. 1 oz. to 10 lb.	$2.43	$2.84	$2.91	$3.04
10 lb. 1 oz. to 15 lb.	$2.73	$2.99	$3.21	$3.60
15 lb. 1 oz. to 25 lb.	$3.89	$4.14	$4.48	$5.02
25 lb. 1 oz. to 45 lb.	$4.77	$5.03	$5.59	$6.56

Problem

Diane wants to buy the woman's warm-up suit shown on page 339. She wants the jacket and pants in tan, both in size 10. The sales tax rate in her state is 4%. She lives in zone 3. Fill in the order form for Diane's warm-up suit. What is the total amount she must enclose with the order?

Solution

Strategy
- Fill in the merchandise information in the order form below.

- Add to find the total cost of the items.

- Multiply to find the tax. Round to the nearest cent.

- Add to find the total weight of the items. Remember, 1 pound = 16 ounces.

- Read the table for shipping and handling charges.

- Add to find the total cost of the order.

Conclusion
Diane must enclose $30.69 with the order.

Item	Catalog number	How many	Size	Color	Price for one	Total price	Shipping weight lb.	oz.
Jacket	G 38-0672	1	10	tan	$14.99	$14.99	1	8
Pants	G 38-0677	1	10	tan	11.99	11.99	1	10

		Total weight	
Merchandise total	26.98		
4% of $26.98 → Tax	1.08	lb.	oz.
Charges for 3 lb. 2 oz. in zone 3 → Shipping and handling	2.63	3	2
Total cost → AMOUNT ENCLOSED	$30.69		

A WARM-UP JACKET—Acrylic knit with fleece lining. Full zip front. Colors: Blue, red, tan. Sizes: Misses 6, 8, 10, 12, 14, 16. Wt. 1 lb. 8 oz.
G38-0672 ....$14.99

B WARM-UP PANTS—Acrylic knit with fleece lining. Elasticized waist. Colors: Blue, red, tan. Sizes: Misses 6, 8, 10, 12, 14, 16. Wt. 1 lb. 10 oz.
G38-0677 ....$11.99

C RUNNING SHOES—Nylon and leather uppers. Colors: Tan, blue, brown. D-width sizes: $7\frac{1}{2}$, 8, $8\frac{1}{2}$, 9, $9\frac{1}{2}$, 10, $10\frac{1}{2}$, 11, $11\frac{1}{2}$, 12. Wt. 1 lb. 14 oz.
W33-7881 ....$26.50

D RUNNING SOCKS—65% cotton, 35% nylon. White with striped trim. Colors: Gold, brown, blue, burgundy. Sizes: M, L. Wt. 4 oz.
T59-5218 ....$1.79

E RUNNING SUIT—100% polyester tricot. Elasticized waist. Colors: Green, blue, brown, gray. Sizes: S, M, L, XL. Wt. 1 lb. 10 oz.
N45-8603 ....$17.99

Related Problems

Dave wants to buy the running suit, running shoes, and socks shown here. He wants all of them in blue. His suit size is Large. He wears a $10\frac{1}{2}$D shoe. And his sock size is Large.

1. What is the total cost of the items?

2. What is the amount of tax if the sales tax rate is 4%? Round to the nearest cent.

3. What is the total weight of the items?

4. What are the shipping and handling costs for zone 3?

5. What is the total amount Dave must enclose with his order?

11

339

A **SHOULDER PADS**—Durable construction. 100% nylon covering. Sizes: S(26-28), M(28-30), L(30-32)
Wt. 2 lb. 2 oz.
P 232-9851 ....$15.99

B **FOOTBALL**—Genuine cowhide-leather football. Official size. Tee included. Wt. 1 lb. 7 oz.
M 430-4562 ....$12.99

C **FIELDER'S GLOVE**—Large pocket with tough lacing across the top. For right-handed throwers.
Wt. 13 oz.
V 516-4392 ....$17.99

D **BASEBALL**—Little League approved. Wt. 7 oz.
W 916-7342 ....$4.99

E **BASEBALL CAP**—Colors: navy, red, gold, green. Sizes: S, M, L. Wt. 5 oz.
Y 327-8420 ....$5.69

F **SPORT SHOES**—Black leather uppers, white stripes, padded ankle collar. 13 molded cleats. Medium width. Sizes: 4-10.
Wt. 1 lb. 15 oz.
T 829-3901 ....$18.79

G **HELMET**—Fully padded for maximum protection, white only. Sizes: S($6\frac{1}{4}$-$6\frac{1}{2}$), M($6\frac{5}{8}$-7), L($7\frac{1}{8}$-$7\frac{3}{8}$).
Wt. 2 lb. 1 oz.
R 342-6917 ....$19.99

34

Clarence wants to buy a football, a helmet (size M), and shoulder pads (size M).

6. What is the total cost of these items?

7. Find the amount of tax if the sales tax rate is 5%. Round to the nearest cent.

8. Find the total weight of the merchandise.

9. Use the table on page 338 to find the shipping and handling charges. Clarence lives in the local zone.

10. What is the total amount Clarence must enclose with his order?

Nancy wants to buy a baseball, a fielder's glove, a cap (red, size M), and a pair of sport shoes (size 8).

11. What is the total cost of these items?

12. Find the amount of tax if the sales tax rate is 6%. Round to the nearest cent.

13. Find the total weight of the merchandise.

14. Use the table on page 338 to find the shipping and handling charges. Nancy lives in zone 4.

15. What is the total amount Nancy must enclose with her order?

CALCULATOR APPLICATIONS

Completing Order Forms

Sally D'Avito is ordering office supplies for her stationery store. She needs 200 portfolios at $0.96 each. The cost of the portfolios is 200 × $0.96, or $192.00.

The portfolios are packed 10 to a box. The number of boxes needed is 200 ÷ 10, or 20, boxes.

Each box weighs 1 lb. 6 oz. The total weight of the 20 boxes is 20 × 1 lb. 6 oz., or 20 lb. 120 oz. Since 1 pound = 16 ounces, the total weight is 27 lb. 8 oz.

Complete this order form.

	Name of item	Quantity	Catalog number	Unit price	Total price	Number per box	Number of boxes	Weight each box LB. OZ.	Total weight LB. OZ.
	Portfolios	200	3-47A	$0.96	$192.00	10	20	1 6	27 8
1.	Legal ruled pads	180	5-62X	$0.35		12		1 4	
2.	Payroll record pads	50	9-51C	$0.45		10		2 7	
3.	Requisition pads	72	7-13R	$0.40		12		1 12	
4.	Letter openers	24	1-34T	$1.59		12		2 12	
5.	Legal-size envelopes	7 boxes	8-21B	$9.32		——		3 13	
6.	Staplers	25	2-63F	$5.65		5		4 6	
7.	Pencils	288	6-40D	$1.35/doz.		12		7	
8.	Pens	96	6-37Y	$3.17/doz.		12		15	
9.	Total for goods							Total	
10.	Tax (5%)								
11.	Shipping charges ($0.11/lb.)								
12.	TOTAL								

Sewing Costs

The cast of the Aberdeen High School Variety Show need costumes for some of the dance numbers. They want skirts for the girls and matching vests for the boys. The school is willing to pay for the material if some of the cast members will make the skirts and the vests.

There are 32 girls and 21 boys in the cast. Seven of the girls wear size 8. Ten wear size 10. Eleven wear size 12. And four wear size 14. Six of the boys need a small (S) vest. Ten need a medium (M). And five need a large (L).

Skirt
$1.75   SIZE **8**

Skirt

Size	8	10	12	14
Fabric width	Yards required			
35/36 in.	3¼	3¼	3⅜	3½
44/45 in.	1⅞	2	2	2⅛
54 in.	1⅞	1⅞	1⅞	1⅞

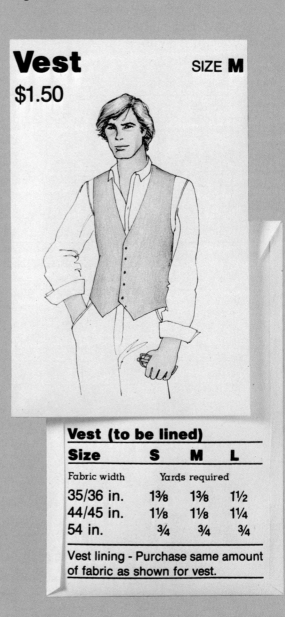

Vest
$1.50   SIZE **M**

Vest (to be lined)

Size	S	M	L
Fabric width	Yards required		
35/36 in.	1⅜	1⅜	1½
44/45 in.	1⅛	1⅛	1¼
54 in.	¾	¾	¾

Vest lining - Purchase same amount of fabric as shown for vest.

Problem

The fabric selected for the skirts is 45 inches wide. How many yards are needed for the seven skirts in size 8?

Solution

Strategy

• Read the chart. Find the row for 45-inch fabric and the column for size 8.

$$1\frac{7}{8}$$

• Multiply by 7 to find the amount needed for 7 skirts.

$$7 \times 1\frac{7}{8} = 7 \times \frac{15}{8} = \frac{105}{8} = 13\frac{1}{8}$$

Conclusion

The amount of fabric needed for the 7 skirts is $13\frac{1}{8}$ yards.

Related Problems

1. How many yards of 45-inch fabric are needed for 10 skirts, size 10?

2. How many yards of 45-inch fabric are needed for 11 skirts, size 12?

3. How many yards of 45-inch fabric are needed for 4 skirts, size 14?

4. How many yards of 45-inch fabric are needed for 6 vests, size S?

5. How many yards of 45-inch fabric are needed for 10 vests, size M?

6. How many yards of 45-inch fabric are needed for 5 vests, size L?

7. What is the total number of yards needed for the 32 skirts and 21 vests? Include the fabric for the size 8 skirts.

8. At $4.80 per yard, what is the cost of fabric for the skirts and vests?

9. The 45-inch lining is $1.60 per yard. What is the cost of the lining for the vests?

10. Each skirt pattern costs $1.75. The cast decides to buy two patterns for each size. Find the cost of the skirt patterns.

11. Each vest pattern costs $1.50. The cast decides to buy one pattern for each size. Find the cost of the vest patterns.

12. Each skirt has a zipper and a fastener. At $0.55 each, what is the total cost of the zippers?

13. There are 3 fasteners in a package. How many packages of fasteners are needed?

14. At $0.79 per package, what is the total cost of the fasteners?

15. Five buttons are required for each vest. How many buttons are needed for all the vests?

16. There are 6 buttons in a package. How many packages of buttons are needed?

17. At $1.35 per package, what is the total cost of the buttons?

18. Thread costs $0.60 per spool. The cast estimates that they will need 12 spools. What is the cost of the thread?

19. What is the total cost of all the materials (fabric, lining, patterns, zippers, fasteners, buttons, and thread)?

20. If the fabric store gives a 15% discount to the school, what is the cost of the materials? (Round the discount to the nearest cent.)

Seasonal Sales

When Barbara and Jim King plan some of their purchases, they use a chart like the one shown here. It gives the best times of the year for buying certain items.

Problem

Jim needs a new coat. The regular price of the coat that Jim wants is $75.99. He expects to save at least 15% by shopping during the best months. What are the best months for buying men's coats? What can Jim expect to pay for the coat?

Solution

Strategy

- Read the chart to find the best months for buying men's coats.   January and August

- Multiply the cost of the coat by 15% to find the discount. Round to the nearest cent. $0.15 \times \$75.99 \approx \$11.40$

- Subtract to find the sale price. $\$75.99 - \$11.40 = \$64.59$

Conclusion

The best months for buying men's coats are January and August. Jim can expect to pay about $64.59 for the coat.

January	February	March	April
Men's coats Dresses Shoes Books Linens Toys	Men's shirts Furniture Curtains Rugs Small appliances	Winter clothes Ski equipment Hosiery Housewares Gardening supplies	Dresses Infants' wear Men's suits Shoes Paint
May	**June**	**July**	**August**
Handbags Linens Wallpaper Jewelry Luggage	Sleepwear Dresses Building materials TV sets	Fabric Bathing suits Men's shirts Shoes	Women's coats Men's coats School clothes School supplies New cars Linens
September	**October**	**November**	**December**
Dishes Bicycles Carpeting	Hosiery School clothes Women's coats Lamps	Blankets Used cars Major appliances Water heaters	Women's coats Shoes Party goods Men's and children's wear

Related Problems

For each problem, list the best month or months to buy each item. Then find the amount of the expected discount, rounded to the nearest cent, and the expected sale price of the item.

	Item	Best months to buy	Regular price	Expected discount	Amount of discount	Sale price
	Man's coat	January, August	$75.99	15%	$11.40	$64.59
1.	Shoes		$37.00	15%		
2.	Paint		$13.69	20%		
3.	Clothes dryer		$359.95	25%		
4.	TV set		$689.95	15%		
5.	Bedroom set		$895.99	20%		
6.	Sheets		$9.99	30%		
7.	Handbag		$17.50	15%		
8.	Curtains		$37.47	25%		
9.	Bathing suit		$26.30	35%		
10.	Dress		$48.00	40%		

Break Time

There are 16 small squares in this large square. ABEF forms a square. ABCEFGIJK forms another square. How many new squares can you form?

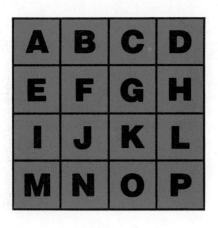

The small squares can also form rectangles. AB forms a rectangle. ABCEFG and BCDFGH form two more rectangles. How many new rectangles can you form?

345

Buying Craft Supplies

Many people enjoy making items for their homes or themselves, or as gifts. This stained-glass window was made from various colors of glass, solder, copper foil, and edging. The solder is sold in 1-pound reels for $7.75 a pound. The foil comes in rolls for $3.00 a roll. The edging is sold in 8-foot strips for $3.75 each. Glass is sold only in 1- or $\frac{1}{2}$ - square foot sections. The prices are listed below.

Color	Price (sq. ft.)	Color	Price (sq. ft.)
Black	$5.00	Orange	$7.00
Blue	$3.00	Red	$9.00
Brown	$4.00	Salmon	$4.00
Camel	$4.00	White	$4.00
Gray	$4.50	Yellow	$5.00
Green	$5.00		

Problem

Find the total cost of materials for the scuba-diver window. The amounts of glass needed are listed below. The window takes 2 pounds of solder, 1 roll of foil, $7\frac{1}{2}$ feet of edging, and 17 glass bubbles at $0.15 each.

Black—1 square foot

Blue—$1\frac{1}{2}$ square feet

Brown—$1\frac{1}{3}$ square feet

Camel—$\frac{1}{3}$ square foot

Gray—3 square feet

Green—$3\frac{1}{2}$ square feet

White—$\frac{1}{3}$ square foot

Yellow—2 square feet

Solution

Strategy

- Multiply to find the cost for each color of glass. Remember, glass is sold only in 1- or $\frac{1}{2}$ - square foot sections. Add to find the total cost for the glass.

$1 \times \$5.00 =$	$\$5.00$	Black
$1\frac{1}{2} \times \$3.00 =$	$\$4.50$	Blue
$1\frac{1}{2} \times \$4.00 =$	$\$6.00$	Brown
$\frac{1}{2} \times \$4.00 =$	$\$2.00$	Camel
$3 \times \$4.50 =$	$\$13.50$	Gray
$3\frac{1}{2} \times \$5.00 =$	$\$17.50$	Green
$\frac{1}{2} \times \$4.00 =$	$\$2.00$	White
$2 \times \$5.00 =$	$\underline{\$10.00}$	Yellow
	$\$60.50$	Total

- Multiply to find the costs for the solder and bubbles.

$2 \times \$7.75 = \$15.50$ Solder

$17 \times \$0.15 = \$2.55$ Bubbles

- Add to find the total cost including foil and edging.

$\$60.50 + \$15.50 + \$2.55 + \$3.00 + \$3.75 = \$85.30$

Conclusion

The total cost of materials for the window is $85.30.

Related Problems

Find the total cost for each stained-glass project. Use the prices on page 346.

1. Glass (sq. ft.)   **Solder**—1 pound

    Brown—$\frac{1}{4}$ **Foil**—$\frac{1}{2}$ roll

    Green—$1\frac{1}{2}$ **Edging**—4 feet

    Orange—$\frac{1}{4}$

    Salmon—$1\frac{1}{2}$

    White—$\frac{2}{3}$

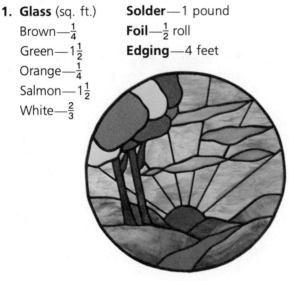

2. Glass (sq. ft.)   **Solder**—$1\frac{1}{2}$ pounds

    Blue—$\frac{1}{2}$ **Foil**—$\frac{2}{3}$ roll

    Brown—1   **Edging**—7 feet

    Gray—4

    Red—2

    Orange—$\frac{1}{2}$

    White—$\frac{1}{4}$

Find the cost for each needlepoint project. Yarn is $0.04 per strand.

3. Yarn (strands)   **Painted canvas**

    Blue—38   **mesh**—$17.50

    Gold—2

    Green—10

    Red—1

    Yellow—2

4. Yarn (strands)

    Black—8

    Blue—2

    Gold—5

    Gray—36

    Red—48

    White—1

Stuffing—
2 pounds at
$1.59 a pound

Buttons—4 at
$0.10 each

Felt—1 square
at $0.29

Ribbon—$\frac{1}{4}$ yard at
$0.60 a yard

**Painted canvas
mesh**—$12.50

Buying Building Materials

Virginia and Walter Harbold are buying various materials to build this frame storage shed.

Nails are referred to by their size. A 2-penny nail (2d), for example, is 1 in. long. A 20d nail is 4 in. long. Nails are often sold by the pound.

Lumber is also specified by size. The actual thickness and width of a board are smaller than the given measurements because the wood has been sawed and smoothed. The length, however, is about the same as given. For example, a 2 in. by 4 in. by 10 ft. board actually measures about $1\frac{1}{2}$ in. by $3\frac{1}{2}$ in. by 10 ft.

Lumber can be purchased in several ways. One way is by the linear foot. The cost of the lumber depends on just the length of the board. Another way is by the board foot. A board foot is the amount of lumber in a board 1 in. thick, 1 ft. wide, and 1 ft. long.

Problem

Two boards, each 2 in. by 6 in. by 14 ft., are needed for the ridge beam of the shed. At $0.33 per board foot, find the cost of the two boards.

Solution

Strategy

- Multiply the measurements to find the number of board feet in one board. Remember, 6 inches = $\frac{1}{2}$ foot.

Thickness in inches		Width in feet		Length in feet		Board feet
2	×	$\frac{1}{2}$	×	14	=	14

- Multiply to find the total cost.

Number of boards		Board feet per board		Cost per board foot		Total cost
2	×	14	×	$0.33	=	$9.24

Conclusion

The cost of the two boards is $9.24.

Problem

Battens are strips of wood that fasten the main structure. The shed requires 40 battens, each 1 in. by 3 in. by 8 ft. At $0.09 per linear foot, what is the cost of the 40 battens?

Solution

Strategy

- Multiply to find the total cost.

Number of battens		Length in feet		Cost per linear foot		Total cost
40	×	8	×	$0.09	=	$28.80

Conclusion

The cost of the 40 battens is $28.80.

Related Problems

Find the cost of each item for the storage shed. Round costs up to the next cent.

	Description	Size	Amount	Unit price	Cost
	Ridge beam	2 in. by 6 in. by 14 ft.	2	$0.33/board foot	$9.24
1.	Battens	1 in. by 3 in. by 8 ft.	40	$0.09/ linear foot	$28.80
		1 in. by 3 in. by 10 ft.	2	$0.09/linear foot	
2.	Framing and forms for concrete	2 in. by 2 in. by 6 ft.	6	$0.33/board foot	
		2 in. by 8 in. by 12 ft.	4	$0.33/board foot	
		2 in. by 4 in. by 4 ft.	1	$0.33/board foot	
		2 in. by 4 in. by 8 ft.	8	$0.33/board foot	
		2 in. by 4 in. by 10 ft.	11	$0.33/board foot	
		2 in. by 4 in. by 12 ft.	5	$0.33/board foot	
		2 in. by 4 in. by 14 ft.	24	$0.33/board foot	
3.	Galvanized nails	3d	$\frac{1}{2}$ lb.	$1.09/lb.	
		6d	5 lb.	$1.09/lb.	
4.	Common nails	10d	$3\frac{1}{2}$ lb.	$0.89/lb.	
		16d	7 lb.	$0.89/lb.	
		20d	3 lb.	$0.89/lb.	
5.	T-hinges	Heavy steel	2 pairs	$3.95/pair	
6.	Anchor bolts	$\frac{1}{2}$ in. by $5\frac{1}{2}$ in.	8	$0.65 each	
7.	Plywood	$\frac{1}{2}$ in. by 4 ft. by 8 ft.	28 sheets	$16.95/sheet	
8.	Concrete for pad		1.6 cu. yd.	$50/cu. yd.	
9.	Gravel for pad		3100 lb.	$8/ton	
10.	Roofing shingles	240 lb./100 sq. ft.	180 sq. ft.	$27.95/100 sq. ft.	
11.	Door trim and doorway	1 in. by 4 in. by 10 ft.	2	$0.17/linear foot	
		1 in. by 4 in. by 8 ft.	4	$0.17/linear foot	
		1 in. by 4 in. by 7 ft.	7	$0.17/linear foot	
12.	Door stop	1 in. by 2 in. by 4 ft.	1	$0.07/linear foot	
		1 in. by 2 in. by 7 ft.	2	$0.07/linear foot	

13. Find the total cost of all the materials for the storage shed.

Rental Clerk

Career Cluster: Business Contact Leslie Deutsch works at Park Rental. This company rents various types of equipment to its customers. Leslie's job is to explain to the customers how to use the items they rent.

Leslie also fills out rental receipts. Customers pay a deposit when they pick up the equipment. If the rental charge is different when the equipment is returned, they either get a refund or pay the extra amount.

When Leslie computes the rental charge, she refers to the schedule of charges given in the table. First, she uses the hourly rate. Then she compares this charge to the minimum charge and the daily rate. The customer must pay at least the minimum charge. The daily rate is the maximum charge the customer will have to pay for each 24-hour period.

Item	Minimum charge	Hourly rate	Daily rate
Circular saw	$4.50	$1.50	$9.00
Drill	$3.00	$1.00	$6.00
Disc sander	$4.50	$1.50	$8.50
Hand-belt sander	$6.00	$2.00	$12.00
Metal detector	$10.50	$3.50	$15.00
Car polisher	$5.25	$1.75	$10.50
Chain saw	$20.00	$5.00	$28.00
Rug shampooer	$6.00	$2.00	$12.00
Rug steamer	$9.00	$3.00	$17.00
Wet vacuum	$9.00	$3.00	$13.00
Floor sander	$12.00	$4.00	$20.00
Extension ladder	$4.50	$1.50	$9.00
Tiller	$12.00	$6.00	$32.00
Lawn aerator	$8.00	$2.50	$12.00

Problem

Elliott Dakota rented a disc sander one day. He used it for $6\frac{1}{4}$ hours. What did Leslie charge Elliott for the rental?

Solution

Strategy

• Round the number of hours up to the next full hour.

$6\frac{1}{4} \rightarrow 7$

• Multiply the hourly rate by 7 to find the rental cost for 7 hours.

$7 \times \$1.50 = \$10.50$

• Compare the rental cost for 7 hours to the minimum charge.

$\$10.50 > \$4.50$

• Compare the rental cost for 7 hours to the daily rate.

$\$10.50 > \$8.50$

Conclusion

Leslie charged Elliott $8.50.

Related Problems

Find the cost of renting each item for the number of hours given. Remember, the cost must be at least as much as the minimum charge, but not more than the daily rate.

	Item	Time
1.	Chain saw	4 hours
2.	Wet vacuum	$5\frac{1}{2}$ hours
3.	Extension ladder	$3\frac{1}{2}$ hours
4.	Drill	2 hours
5.	Rug steamer	9 hours
6.	Lawn aerator	$8\frac{1}{4}$ hours
7.	Floor sander	$7\frac{1}{4}$ hours
8.	Metal detector	1 hour
9.	Circular saw	4 hours
10.	Hand-belt sander	3 hours

11. Fred uses a tiller for 2 full days a year. A tiller costs about $525. After how many years will the total rental costs exceed the price of the tiller?

12. The price of a rug shampooer is $75. Kazuko shampoos her rugs twice a year. It takes a full day each time. After how many years will the total rental costs exceed the price of a rug shampooer?

13. The owner of Park Rental bought a new car polisher for $45 and a new wet vacuum for $85. Based on the hourly rate, which one "pays for itself" sooner?

14. One of the circular saws at Park Rental needs replacement after about 330 hours of rental. The owner had paid $55 for it. Based on the hourly rate, find the number of times the saw had "paid for itself."

Skills Tune-Up

Dividing whole numbers, pages 12-13

1. $6564 \div 3$
2. $2846 \div 8$
3. $7993 \div 9$
4. $8214 \div 3$
5. $1358 \div 7$
6. $8108 \div 7$
7. $2203 \div 52$
8. $4295 \div 89$
9. $9786 \div 14$
10. $4803 \div 83$
11. $5373 \div 47$
12. $9180 \div 64$
13. $5333 \div 77$
14. $7938 \div 27$
15. $2770 \div 97$
16. $5840 \div 73$
17. $3047 \div 41$
18. $23,397 \div 43$
19. $86,210 \div 27$
20. $93,016 \div 44$
21. $285,797 \div 24$
22. $484,569 \div 88$
23. $957,671 \div 78$
24. $828,129 \div 206$
25. $156,648 \div 696$
26. $638,668 \div 530$
27. $880,528 \div 964$

Adding fractions and mixed numbers, pages 18-19

1. $\frac{8}{15} + \frac{2}{5}$
2. $\frac{4}{5} + \frac{7}{10}$
3. $\frac{5}{8} + \frac{1}{12}$
4. $\frac{3}{14} + \frac{5}{7}$
5. $\frac{1}{2} + \frac{1}{3}$
6. $\frac{1}{3} + \frac{5}{8}$
7. $\frac{7}{20} + \frac{9}{10}$
8. $\frac{1}{9} + \frac{7}{45}$
9. $\frac{5}{6} + \frac{2}{9}$
10. $\frac{1}{3} + 5\frac{1}{12}$
11. $7\frac{3}{10} + \frac{1}{2}$
12. $2\frac{7}{10} + 2\frac{13}{30}$
13. $5\frac{5}{6} + 2\frac{1}{3}$
14. $5\frac{2}{7} + 12\frac{5}{7}$
15. $15\frac{5}{9} + 5\frac{5}{18}$
16. $10\frac{2}{5} + 6\frac{1}{3}$
17. $4\frac{11}{24} + 2\frac{1}{4}$
18. $3\frac{1}{15} + 7\frac{4}{5}$
19. $9\frac{11}{20} + \frac{1}{5} + 8\frac{3}{5}$
20. $5\frac{1}{2} + 4\frac{4}{9} + 8\frac{1}{18}$

Subtracting fractions and mixed numbers, pages 18-19

1. $\frac{5}{6} - \frac{1}{2}$
2. $\frac{3}{5} - \frac{7}{15}$
3. $\frac{5}{6} - \frac{1}{8}$
4. $\frac{25}{36} - \frac{2}{9}$
5. $\frac{1}{6} - \frac{1}{8}$
6. $\frac{3}{5} - \frac{8}{15}$
7. $\frac{5}{7} - \frac{13}{21}$
8. $\frac{11}{24} - \frac{1}{8}$
9. $18 - 3\frac{6}{7}$
10. $8 - 2\frac{1}{4}$
11. $4 - \frac{1}{2}$
12. $12\frac{49}{64} - 8\frac{57}{64}$
13. $10 - \frac{3}{5}$
14. $4 - \frac{2}{3}$
15. $7\frac{1}{3} - 7\frac{1}{8}$
16. $17\frac{1}{2} - 9\frac{3}{10}$
17. $37\frac{3}{8} - 29\frac{23}{24}$
18. $22\frac{23}{30} - 18\frac{5}{6}$
19. $26\frac{5}{8} - 9\frac{19}{24}$
20. $11\frac{2}{15} - 9\frac{5}{6}$

Chapter 17 Review

Catalog buying, pages 338-340

Kaye Kwail wants to buy 2 AM-FM radios from the catalog.

> **AM-FM RADIO**—100% solid state chassis with 3-inch speaker. Built-in AM, telescoping FM antennas. Operates on AC cord or 4 optional "C" batteries. Black plastic case with handle. Wt. 2 lb. 10 oz.
> S 5-398 ....$38.95

1. What is the total cost of the merchandise?

2. What is the amount of sales tax if the tax rate is 5%? Round to the nearest cent.

3. Kaye lives in zone 2. Use this table to find the shipping and handling charges.

Shipping and Handling Charges			
Shipping weight	Local zone	Zones 1 & 2	Zone 3
1 oz. to 8 oz.	$1.27	$1.34	$1.36
9 oz. to 15 oz.	$1.49	$1.60	$1.64
1 lb. to 2 lb.	$1.97	$2.11	$2.14
2 lb. 1 oz. to 3 lb.	$2.07	$2.39	$2.43
3 lb. 1 oz. to 5 lb.	$2.20	$2.57	$2.63
5 lb. 1 oz. to 10 lb.	$2.43	$2.84	$2.91

4. What is the total amount Kaye must enclose with her order?

Sewing costs, pages 342-343

5. If $1\frac{1}{4}$ yd. of fabric is needed to make one vest, how much fabric is needed to make 9 vests?

Seasonal sales, pages 344-345

6. TV sets are often on sale in June. The regular price of a certain model is $375. With a 15% discount, what is the sale price of the TV set?

Craft supplies, pages 346-347

7. A stained-glass window takes the amounts of glass listed. Find the total cost. Remember, glass is sold only in 1- or $\frac{1}{2}$ - square foot sections.

   Blue—$2\frac{1}{2}$ sq. ft. at $3 a square foot
   Green—1 sq. ft. at $5 a square foot
   Red—$2\frac{3}{4}$ sq. ft. at $9 a square foot
   Yellow—3 sq. ft. at $5 a square foot

8. The stained-glass window in problem 7 takes $1\frac{1}{2}$ pounds of solder at $7.75 a pound, $\frac{2}{3}$ of a roll of foil at $3 a roll, and 8 feet of edging at $3.75 for 8 feet. Find the total cost of materials, including glass.

Buying building materials, pages 348-349

9. Find the cost of three boards, each 1 in. by 4 in. by 6 ft. at $0.18 per linear foot. Remember, when lumber is priced by the linear foot, the cost of each board depends only on its length.

Rental clerk, pages 350-351

10. Find the cost of renting a car polisher for 4 hours at $1.75 per hour.

Chapter 17 Test

George Wright wants to buy 2 sweaters from the catalog.

SWEATER—100% wool. Pull-over style with ribbed neckline, wrist, and bottom edge. Long sleeve, raglan shoulder. Machine wash warm, tumble dry low. Colors: navy, brown, light blue, yellow, red. Sizes: S, M, L, XL. Wt. 15 oz.
Q 5-391 . . . .$24.98

1. What is the total cost of the merchandise?

2. What is the amount of sales tax if the tax rate is 4%? Round to the nearest cent.

3. George lives in zone 1. Use this table to find the shipping and handling charges.

Shipping and Handling Charges			
Shipping weight	Local zone	Zones 1 & 2	Zone 3
1 oz. to 8 oz.	$1.27	$1.34	$1.36
9 oz. to 15 oz.	$1.49	$1.60	$1.64
1 lb. to 2 lb.	$1.97	$2.11	$2.14
2 lb. 1 oz. to 3 lb.	$2.07	$2.39	$2.43
3 lb. 1 oz. to 5 lb.	$2.20	$2.57	$2.63
5 lb. 1 oz. to 10 lb.	$2.43	$2.84	$2.91

4. What is the total amount George must enclose with his order?

5. If $3\frac{1}{4}$ yd. of fabric is needed to make one skirt, how much fabric is needed to make 7 skirts?

6. Men's suits are often on sale in April. The regular price of one suit is $145. With a 20% discount, what is the sale price of the suit?

7. A stained-glass planter takes the amounts of glass listed. Find the total cost. Remember, glass is sold only in 1- or $\frac{1}{2}$ - square foot sections.

Gold—$1\frac{1}{3}$ sq. ft. at $4 a square foot
Clear—$1\frac{1}{2}$ sq. ft. at $3 a square foot
Yellow—2 sq. ft. at $5 a square foot

8. The stained-glass planter in problem 7 takes 2 pounds of solder at $7.75 a pound and 1 roll of foil at $3 a roll. Find the total cost of materials, including glass.

9. Find the cost of five boards, each 2 in. by 8 in. by 12 ft., at $0.36 per linear foot. Remember, when lumber is priced by the linear foot, the cost of each board depends only on its length.

10. Find the cost of renting a lawn aerator for 3 hours at $2.50 per hour.

Chapter 18   Budgeting

Analyzing Spending Habits

A **budget** is an organized plan for spending money. The first step in making a budget is to find out how money is currently being spent.

The expenses that usually change from one month to the next are **variable monthly expenses**. Julie Brown, a high-school senior with a part-time job, started recording her variable expenses in February.

February	Week 1	
Gasoline	$5.00	
Bowling	4.50	
Sandwich	1.05	✓
Contribution	1.00	
Belt	5.00	
Stamps	1.80	

February	Week 2	
Gasoline	$5.00	
Lunch	3.95	✓
Knee socks	2.50	
Paperback book	1.75	
Notebook paper	.89	

February	Week 3	
Gas, Oil	$6.29	
Dave's Cafe	3.00	✓
Theater	3.25	
Drycleaners	2.75	
Magazine	1.25	
Birthday gift	5.80	

February	Week 4	
Magazine	$1.00	
Collection for flowers	1.00	
Tolls	.90	
Parking garage	1.50	
Groceries (Dad's birthday breakfast)	5.37	✓
Basketball game	2.50	
Sandwich	1.49	✓

Problem

Julie realized that her expenses fall into categories, such as food and entertainment. How much did Julie spend for food during February?

Solution

Strategy

• Read Julie's spending records. List all of her food expenses and add to find the total amount spent for food. Round the answer to the nearest dollar.

$1.05 + $3.95 + $3.00 + $5.37 + $1.49 ≈ $15.00

Conclusion

Julie spent about $15 for food during February.

Related Problems

Julie chose six categories of spending, including a category for miscellaneous purchases. Find the monthly total for each category and the total of all variable expenses for the month. Round each total to the nearest dollar.

	Variable Expenses for *February*					
	Category	Week 1	Week 2	Week 3	Week 4	Category total
	Food	$1.05	$3.95	$3.00	$5.37 + $1.49	$15
1.	Car					
2.	Entertainment		——			
3.	Clothes and clothing care				——	
4.	Gifts, contributions		——			
5.	Miscellaneous (All other spending)					
6.	TOTAL					

The Wright family's variable expenses for February are given below. Helen Wright drives to and from work. Her husband Robert takes the bus. Their children, Andy and Tina, are in junior high school.

Unlike Julie Brown, the Wrights consider eating in a restaurant as part of their entertainment. Other eating costs are included under "Food." Personal expenses like magazines and haircuts are not listed here because they are covered by a fixed monthly allowance that each family member receives.

February — Variable Expenses

FIRST WEEK

Groceries	45.50	Contributions	10.00
Robert's lunches	15.50	Dry cleaner	22.00
Helen's lunches	10.20	Groceries	20.17
Gas bill	65.32	Movie	12.00
Electric bill	41.71	2 pr. jeans	32.90
Gasoline	15.00	Miscellaneous	9.85

SECOND WEEK

Groceries	57.25	Basketball game	7.25
Robert's lunches	12.50	Restaurant	9.25
Helen's lunches	9.00	Tina's boots (on sale)	21.95
Gasoline	17.50	Miscellaneous	8.50
Helen's shoes	24.00		

THIRD WEEK

Groceries	58.88	Chelsea's Restaurant	37.82
Robert's lunches	12.57	Contributions	13.00
Helen's lunches	8.47	Miscellaneous	1.42
Telephone	25.40	Miscellaneous	6.00
Gasoline	18.00		

FOURTH WEEK

Groceries	60.04	Museum	6.00
Robert's lunches	13.75	Robert's jacket	75.00
Helen's lunches	14.00	Parking	1.25
Gasoline	17.25	Miscellaneous	13.00

Related Problems

Use the Wrights' record of variable expenses to complete the following table. Round each total to the nearest dollar.

	Variable Expenses for *February*				
	Category	Week 1	Week 2	Week 3	Week 4	Category total
7.	Food					
8.	Utilities (gas, phone, electric)		—		—	
9.	Car					
10.	Entertainment					
11.	Contributions		—		—	
12.	Clothing and maintenance			—		
13.	Miscellaneous					
14.	TOTAL					

Break Time

Except for one counterfeit stone, all of these diamonds have the same weight. The counterfeit is slightly heavier than each of the other stones.

Describe how to use no more than two weighings of the diamonds on a balance scale to decide which stone is counterfeit.

Budgeting Variable Expenses

Julie Brown has been recording her variable expenses for three months. If she averages the amounts she has spent in each category, she can predict expenses for the next month. Each average becomes the **amount budgeted**.

Problem

Julie's records show that in the last three months she has spent $15, $19, and $18 for food. How much should she allow in her budget for food for next month?

Solution

Strategy
• Add to find the total amount spent for food.

$15 + $19 + $18 = $52

• Divide by 3 to find the average amount. Round the answer to the nearest dollar.

$52 ÷ 3 ≈ $17

Conclusion
Julie should allow about $17 for food next month.

Related Problems

Complete each chart to find the amounts that should be budgeted for the next month. Round each answer to the nearest dollar.

Julie Brown

	Variable monthly expenses	February	March	April	Amount budgeted
	Food	$ 15	$ 19	$ 18	$ 17
1.	Car	$ 19	$ 23	$ 20	$
2.	Entertainment	$ 10	$ 11	$ 15	$
3.	Clothes and clothing care	$ 10	$ 7	$ 10	$
4.	Gifts, contributions ...	$ 8	$ 5	$ 9	$
5.	Miscellaneous	$ 7	$ 5	$ 5	$
6.	Total amount to be budgeted for next month				$

The Wright family

	Variable monthly expenses	February	March	April	Amount budgeted
7.	Food	$338	$347	$370	$
8.	Utilities	$132	$165	$113	$
9.	Car	$ 69	$ 81	$ 75	$
10.	Entertainment	$ 72	$ 60	$ 64	$
11.	Contributions	$ 23	$ 20	$ 30	$
12.	Clothing and maintenance	$176	$125	$130	$
13.	Miscellaneous	$ 39	$ 65	$ 46	$
14.	Total amount to be budgeted for next month				$

Making a Budget

After graduation, Julie Brown will be working full time. Her monthly take-home pay will be about $540. To plan her spending, she filled out a budget sheet.

Under variable monthly expenses, Julie increased the amounts she budgets for clothes and clothing care and for miscellaneous spending.

Fixed monthly expenses, such as a car payment and rent, do not vary from month to month. Some people also consider amounts that they save or invest each month as fixed expenses. Julie intends to open a savings account.

Budget sheet for *Julie Brown*

Monthly take-home pay $ 540

Variable monthly expenses

Food *($17 budgeted now)*	$ 17
Car *($21 now)*	$ 21
Entertainment *($12 now)*	$ 12
Clothes and clothing care *($9 now)*	$ 40
Gifts, contributions *($7 now)*	$ 7
Miscellaneous *($6 now)*	$ 15
TOTAL	$112

Fixed monthly expenses

Car payment	$125
Rent *(Room and board)*	$100
Savings account	$ 35
TOTAL	$260

Annual expenses

Car insurance	$ 500
Car repairs	$ 300
License plates	$ 18
Medical, dental bills	$100
Vacation	$ 300
Miscellaneous *(Computer course)*	$ 80
TOTAL	$

Monthly reserve (TOTAL ÷ 12) .... $ ____

MONTHLY SPENDING PLAN

Total variable expenses	$ ____
Total fixed expenses	$ ____
Monthly reserve for annual expenses	$ ____
SUBTOTAL	$ ____
Plus 5% of subtotal for unexpected expenses	$ ____
SPENDING TOTAL	$ ____

Everyone is faced with expenses that occur only occasionally, such as bills for insurance or car repair. These expenses are listed as **annual expenses**.

Problem

What is the total of Julie's annual expenses? How much money should she set aside each month (monthly reserve) for these expenses?

Solution

Strategy

- Use Julie's budget sheet to list her annual expenses. Then add to find the total.

$500	Car insurance
300	Car repairs
18	License plates
100	Medical, dental bills
300	Vacation
+ 80	Computer course
$1298	Total

- Divide by 12 to find the monthly reserve. Round to the nearest dollar.

$$\$1298 \div 12 \approx \$108$$

Conclusion

Julie's annual expenses will be about $1298. She should set aside $108 each month for these expenses.

Related Problems

To complete Julie's monthly spending plan, find the sum of monthly variable expenses, monthly fixed expenses, and the monthly reserve. Then add on 5% of this sum to find the spending total.

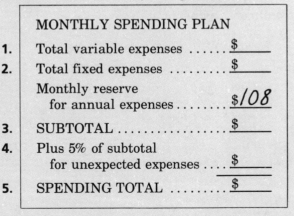

MONTHLY SPENDING PLAN

1. Total variable expenses ...... $_____
2. Total fixed expenses .... $_____
   Monthly reserve
       for annual expenses $108
3. SUBTOTAL .... $_____
4. Plus 5% of subtotal
       for unexpected expenses .... $_____
5. SPENDING TOTAL .... $_____

6. If the spending total is greater than the monthly take-home pay, the budget must be revised. Does Julie need to revise her budget?

This budget sheet for the Wright family includes budgeted amounts for variable monthly expenses as determined on page 361. Complete the budget sheet. In problem 9, round the answer to the nearest dollar.

Budget sheet for *The Wrights*

Monthly take-home pay $ *2166*

Variable monthly expenses

Food	$ *352*
Utilities	$ *137*
Car	$ *75*
Entertainment	$ *65*
Contributions	$ *24*
Clothing and maintenance	$ *144*
Miscellaneous	$ *50*
TOTAL	$ *847*

Fixed monthly expenses

Mortgage (including real estate tax payment)	$ *335*
Installment payments	
a. Car	$ *170*
b. Furniture	$ *68*
Savings	$ *100*
Miscellaneous	
Robert's bus fare	$ *22*
School lunches	$ *40*
Robert's allowance	$ *35*
Helen's allowance	$ *35*
Andy's allowance	$ *15*
Linda's allowance	$ *15*

7. TOTAL .... $ _____

Annual expenses

Homeowner's insurance	$ *250*
Home repairs	$ *500*
Water, garbage bills *(4 x $45)*	$ *180*
Car insurance	$ *435*
Car repairs	$ *200*
License plates	$ *22*
City registration	$ *12*
Life insurance	$ *375*
Medical, dental bills	$ *500*
Clubs, professional organizations	$ *25*
Vacation	$ *600*
Gifts	$ *120*
Newspaper, magazine subscriptions	$ *75*

8. TOTAL .... $ _____

9. Monthly reserve (TOTAL ÷ 12) .... $ _____

MONTHLY SPENDING PLAN

10. Total variable expenses .... $ _____
11. Total fixed expenses .... $ _____
12. Monthly reserve for annual expenses .... $ _____
13. SUBTOTAL .... $ _____
14. Plus 5% of subtotal for unexpected expenses .... $ _____
15. SPENDING TOTAL .... $ _____

16. Which is greater, the spending total or the take-home pay for one month?

17. Do the Wrights need to revise their budget?

CALCULATOR APPLICATIONS

A year ago, George Vanda moved from a small city to a large city. He wants to find the **percent of increase** in some of his spending categories.

George spent $500 in contributions during the last year and $467 the previous year. To find the percent of increase, first find the difference between the two amounts.

   $500 − $467 = $33

Divide the difference by the previous year's expense. Write the answer as a decimal rounded to the nearest hundredth.

   $33 ÷ $467 ≈ 0.07

Write the decimal as a percent.

   0.07 = 7%

George's expenses for contributions increased by 7%.

Find the percent of increase in each of these categories of George's spending.

	Category	Last year's expense	Previous year's expense	Difference	Difference ÷ previous year's expense	Percent of increase
	Contributions	$500	$467	$33	0.07	7%
1.	Food	$1322	$1172			
2.	Rent	$3660	$2400			
3.	Car insurance	$523	$278			
4.	Other car expenses	$887	$650			
5.	Clothing	$616	$565			

Adjusting a Budget

Two of Julie Brown's girlfriends want her to move in with them when their roommate leaves in six months. This change would create new expenses for Julie. She cannot increase her income right now, but she may be able to adjust her budget by reducing some current expenses.

Problem

The three girls would allow about $150 per month for groceries. Julie would also allow $15 for lunches and $20 per month for eating in a restaurant. What amount should Julie budget for food?

Solution

Strategy
• Divide by 3 to find Julie's share of the grocery expense.
 $150 ÷ 3 = $50

• Add to find the total amount she should budget for food.

$50	Groceries
15	Lunches
+ 20	Eating in a restaurant
$85	

Conclusion
Julie should budget $85 for food.

Related Problems

Besides sharing the cost of groceries, the three girls would also equally share the costs for telephone, electricity, and rent. Make the changes described in problems 1-10.

Variable monthly expenses

1. The girls budget $30 each month for the telephone bill. How much would Julie pay?

2. The girls budget $20 each month for electricity. How much would Julie pay?

3. If Julie cuts her budgeted amount of $40 for clothing in half, what would be the new amount?

4. Julie would budget $85 for food. Her other variable monthly expenses should stay the same, as listed below.

   Car $21
   Entertainment $12
   Gifts and contributions $7
   Miscellaneous $15

   Use these amounts, along with your answers to problems 1-3, to find the new total of Julie's variable monthly expenses.

Fixed monthly expenses

5. The $100 for room and board would be replaced by Julie's share of $330 for rent. How much would Julie pay for rent?

6. Add Julie's share of the rent to her car payment of $125 and her savings deposit of $35. What would be the new total for fixed monthly expenses?

Annual expenses

7. Julie would need renter's insurance to protect her stereo and some furniture. Premiums of $35 each are payable two times a year. What would be Julie's annual expense for this insurance?

8. If she reduces the $300 budgeted for a vacation by $100, what would be the new amount budgeted?

9. In six months, Julie would no longer have to budget $80 for her computer course, which would be completed. Her other annual expenses would stay about the same.

   Car insurance $500
   Car repairs $300
   License plates $18
   Medical, dental bills $100

   Use these amounts, along with your answers to problems 7 and 8, to find the new total of Julie's annual expenses.

10. How much would Julie have to reserve each month to pay for annual expenses?

Use the answers to problems 4, 6, and 10 to help you complete Julie's new monthly spending plan. Round your answers to the nearest dollar.

MONTHLY SPENDING PLAN	
11.	Total variable expenses . . . . $ _____
12.	Total fixed expenses . . . . $ _____
13.	Monthly reserve for annual expenses . . . . $ _____
14.	SUBTOTAL . . . . $ _____
15.	Plus 5% of subtotal for unexpected expenses . . . . $ _____
16.	SPENDING TOTAL . . . . $ _____

17. Julie's take-home pay from the full-time job will be $540. Can she afford to move into the apartment in six months?

18. In nine months, Julie will have a chance to get a promotion. Her take-home pay would be increased by 10%. What would be her new monthly take-home pay?

19. Could Julie afford to move if she gets the promotion?

20. If Julie does not get the promotion but cuts out the vacation allowance entirely, could she afford to move?

Economist

Career Cluster: Science Tony Bartlett is an economist and a university instructor. He is involved in a research project that will explain how people spend their money, depending on their level of income and the part of the country in which they live. The country is divided into six regions, and eight different levels of income are included.

Tony made the bar graph on page 369. It shows how families of four in a certain region of the country spend their gross income. Three levels of income are used in the graph.

Problem

At income level B, how much money does the typical family spend for food?

Solution

Strategy

• Read the graph to determine what percent of income a family at level B spends for food.

29%

• Read the list of income levels to find the family's gross income.

$12,000

• Multiply $12,000 by 29% to find the amount spent for food.

0.29 × $12,000 = $3480

Conclusion

The typical family at income level B spends $3480 for food during the year.

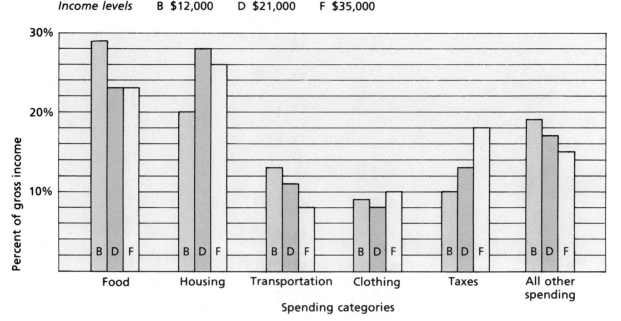

Region I
Annual spending for typical families of four

Income levels   B $12,000   D $21,000   F $35,000

Percent of gross income

Food   Housing   Transportation   Clothing   Taxes   All other spending

Spending categories

Related Problems

Find the amount spent for each category.

	Category	Income level		
		B	D	F
1.	Food	$3480		
2.	Housing			
3.	Transportation			
4.	Clothing			
5.	Taxes			
6.	All other spending			

Refer to your answers to problems 1-6.

What is the most expensive category for a family

7. at income level B?

8. at income level D?

9. at income level F?

10. How much more does a family at level B pay for food than for housing?

11. How much more does a family at level D pay in taxes than it spends for clothing?

12. How much more does a family at level F pay for housing than it spends for transportation?

Skills Tune-Up

Adding whole numbers and decimals, pages 6-7

1. $14 + 37 + 21$
2. $28 + 15 + 7$
3. $43 + 97 + 21$
4. $81 + 49 + 23$
5. $97 + 55 + 47$
6. $67 + 80 + 79$
7. $26 + 43 + 78 + 55$
8. $17 + 83 + 48 + 24$
9. $97 + 39 + 27 + 70$
10. $668 + 202 + 341$
11. $548 + 913 + 188$
12. $300 + 784 + 456$
13. $224 + 384 + 170$
14. $3.5 + 4.24$
15. $13.42 + 4.65$
16. $33.17 + 19.05$
17. $15.85 + 82.76$
18. $0.29 + 0.32 + 0.13$
19. $5.8 + 8.3 + 3.75$
20. $0.75 + 3.07 + 0.08$
21. $9.43 + 7.55 + 3.09$
22. $3.45 + 2.41 + 9.7$
23. $0.78 + 0.46 + 0.01$
24. $4.04 + 1.16 + 7.82$
25. $0.06 + 3.179 + 7.26$
26. $7.8 + 2.99 + 3.4 + 5.6$
27. $3.7 + 1.33 + 8.8 + 7.4$

Comparing and renaming fractions and mixed numbers, pages 14-15

Compare these fractions.
Replace ⬤ with $<$, $>$, or $=$.

1. $\frac{3}{5}$ ⬤ $\frac{2}{7}$
2. $\frac{3}{4}$ ⬤ $\frac{8}{9}$
3. $\frac{2}{3}$ ⬤ $\frac{7}{8}$
4. $\frac{5}{9}$ ⬤ $\frac{1}{3}$
5. $\frac{1}{2}$ ⬤ $\frac{4}{7}$
6. $\frac{11}{12}$ ⬤ $\frac{5}{8}$
7. $\frac{5}{9}$ ⬤ $\frac{6}{7}$
8. $\frac{3}{7}$ ⬤ $\frac{1}{2}$
9. $\frac{6}{7}$ ⬤ $\frac{12}{14}$
10. $\frac{5}{8}$ ⬤ $\frac{11}{16}$
11. $\frac{1}{2}$ ⬤ $\frac{4}{9}$
12. $\frac{7}{8}$ ⬤ $\frac{8}{9}$
13. $\frac{2}{3}$ ⬤ $\frac{5}{12}$
14. $\frac{5}{7}$ ⬤ $\frac{10}{14}$
15. $\frac{4}{7}$ ⬤ $\frac{3}{4}$
16. $\frac{9}{14}$ ⬤ $\frac{1}{2}$
17. $\frac{1}{3}$ ⬤ $\frac{3}{8}$
18. $\frac{8}{11}$ ⬤ $\frac{4}{5}$

Rename as a mixed number.

19. $\frac{9}{2}$
20. $\frac{15}{4}$
21. $\frac{21}{6}$
22. $\frac{19}{5}$
23. $\frac{18}{12}$
24. $\frac{21}{8}$
25. $\frac{13}{2}$
26. $\frac{26}{3}$
27. $\frac{25}{10}$
28. $\frac{37}{5}$
29. $\frac{31}{8}$
30. $\frac{45}{36}$
31. $\frac{48}{11}$
32. $\frac{29}{7}$
33. $\frac{44}{33}$
34. $\frac{57}{8}$
35. $\frac{65}{10}$
36. $\frac{25}{15}$

Dividing fractions and mixed numbers, pages 16-17

1. $\frac{1}{4} \div \frac{1}{3}$
2. $\frac{8}{9} \div \frac{4}{7}$
3. $\frac{2}{5} \div \frac{2}{3}$
4. $\frac{3}{7} \div \frac{3}{8}$
5. $\frac{1}{10} \div \frac{2}{3}$
6. $\frac{21}{25} \div \frac{7}{15}$
7. $7 \div \frac{7}{8}$
8. $\frac{8}{15} \div 16$
9. $4 \div \frac{3}{7}$
10. $\frac{15}{16} \div 3$
11. $5\frac{5}{6} \div \frac{5}{6}$
12. $\frac{3}{7} \div 2\frac{2}{3}$
13. $1\frac{1}{5} \div 10$
14. $20 \div 6\frac{1}{4}$
15. $1\frac{2}{5} \div 2\frac{1}{3}$
16. $9\frac{1}{6} \div 1\frac{4}{7}$
17. $1\frac{1}{7} \div 1\frac{1}{3}$
18. $4\frac{3}{8} \div 1\frac{1}{6}$
19. $2\frac{6}{7} \div 8\frac{3}{4}$
20. $2\frac{5}{14} \div 3\frac{1}{7}$

Chapter 18 Review

Analyzing spending habits, pages 356-359

Use the spending record below. Round each answer to the nearest dollar.

Sweater $20.00	Food $3.30
Food $7.80	Shirt $13.50
Movie $4.50	Bus tokens $4.50
Books $7.15	Dance $10.00
Miscellaneous $2.45	Food $8.50
Mittens $7.20	Art exhibit $3.50
Ball game $3.50	

1. Find the total expense for clothing.

2. Find the total expense for entertainment.

Budgeting variable expenses, pages 360-361

3. Use this 3-month spending record. Find the amount that should be budgeted for this variable expense. Round to the nearest dollar.

	May	June	July	Amount budgeted
Food	$40	$55	$60	$_____

4. The budgeted amounts for Rae's variable monthly expenses are: food, $15; car, $20; entertainment, $20; clothes, $15; gifts, $7; and miscellaneous, $10. What is the total of her variable monthly expenses?

Making a budget, pages 362-364

5. Rae's fixed expenses are $25 for savings and $18 to repay a loan from her parents. What is the total of her fixed monthly expenses?

6. The total of Rae's annual expenses is $920. To the nearest dollar, how much should she set aside each month to pay her annual expenses?

7. Complete this monthly spending plan for the Etheridge family.

MONTHLY SPENDING PLAN	
Total variable expenses	$650
Total fixed expenses	$492
Monthly reserve for annual expenses	$298
SUBTOTAL	$
Plus 5% of subtotal for unexpected expenses	$
SPENDING TOTAL	$

8. Take-home pay for the Etheridges is $1550 per month. Does their budget need to be revised?

Adjusting a budget, pages 366-367

9. The Springer family budgets $78 per month for car expenses. If Mr. Springer joins a car pool, he can cut this expense in half. What would be the new amount budgeted?

Economist, pages 368-369

10. In one part of the country, a typical family spends 27% of its gross income for housing. If the family's income is $19,000 per year, what is the amount spent for housing?

Chapter 18 Test

Use the spending record below. Round each answer to the nearest dollar.

Gas $8.20	*Gift* $8.75
Food $3.55	*Charity* $4.00
○ *Album* $6.15	*Gas – oil* $7.90
Miscellaneous $3.27	*Food* $7.00
Tennis $7.50	*Haircut* $4.75
Food $2.30	*Books* $6.30
Gas $4.25	

1. Find the total expense for food.

2. Find the total expense for gas and oil.

3. Use this 3-month spending record. Find the amount that should be budgeted for this variable expense.

	May	June	July	Amount budgeted
Utilities	$92	$100	$117	$

4. The budgeted amounts for Brian's variable expenses are: food, $25; car, $60; entertainment, $35; and miscellaneous, $20. What is the total of Brian's variable monthly expenses?

5. Brian's fixed expenses are $210 per month for his car payment and $45 per month for savings. What is the total of Brian's fixed monthly expenses?

6. The total of Brian's annual expenses is $850. To the nearest dollar, how much should he set aside each month to pay his annual expenses?

7. Complete this monthly spending plan for the Hahn family.

MONTHLY SPENDING PLAN	
Total variable expenses	$617
Total fixed expenses	$500
Monthly reserve for annual expenses	$423
SUBTOTAL	$
Plus 5% of subtotal for unexpected expenses	$
SPENDING TOTAL	$

8. Take-home pay for the Hahns is $1682 per month. Does their budget need to be revised?

9. The James family budgets $1825 annually for clothes. Mr. and Mrs. James hope to save $350 annually by making some of their clothes. What should be the new amount budgeted for clothes?

10. One survey showed that a typical family spends 22% of its income for food. If the family's income is $30,000 per year, what amount is spent for food?

Unit 6 Test

Choose the best answer.

1. Find the number of calories in 3 slices of bacon if 1 slice contains 45 calories.

   A 48 calories   C 135 calories

   B 125 calories   D 15 calories

2. Lori weighs 66 kilograms. She went bowling for 1.5 hours. At 3.9 calories per kilogram per hour, how many calories did she use? Round to the nearest whole number.

   A 386 calories   C 184 calories

   B 257 calories   D 92 calories

3. Find the cost of 1.5 kilograms of grapes at $1.79 per kilogram. Round to the nearest cent.

   A $1.19   C $3.29

   B $2.69   D $0.29

4. Before butchering, a side of beef weighed 150 kilograms. After butchering, the usable meat weighed 114 kilograms. What was the percent of loss?

   A 32%   C 24%

   B 76%   D 132%

5. Find the total cost of this meal for two people. The prices given are per person. Include a 15% tip.

Shrimp	$9.25
Beverage	$0.50
Salad	$1.25

   A $11   C $12.65

   B $22   D $25.30

6. Use the table below. Find the shipping and handling charges for an order weighing 3 lb. 7 oz. and going to zone 2.

Shipping and Handling Charges			
Shipping weight	Local zone	Zones 1 & 2	Zone 3
1 oz. to 8 oz.	$1.27	$1.34	$1.36
9 oz. to 15 oz.	$1.49	$1.60	$1.64
1 lb. to 2 lb.	$1.97	$2.11	$2.14
2 lb. 1 oz. to 3 lb.	$2.07	$2.39	$2.43
3 lb. 1 oz. to 5 lb.	$2.20	$2.57	$2.63
5 lb. 1 oz. to 10 lb.	$2.43	$2.84	$2.91

   A $2.07   C $7.71

   B $2.39   D $2.57

7. If $2\frac{1}{4}$ yards of fabric is needed to make one blouse, how much fabric is needed to make two blouses?

   A $4\frac{1}{16}$ yd.   C $4\frac{1}{4}$ yd.

   B $4\frac{1}{2}$ yd.   D $4\frac{1}{8}$ yd.

8. Laundry appliances are often on sale in March. The regular price of a clothes washer is $400. What is the sale price of the washer if the discount is 15%?

   A $385   C $340

   B $60   D $460

9. A stained-glass planter takes 5 sq. ft. of gold glass at $4 a square foot. It also takes 2 pounds of solder at $7.75 a pound and 1 roll of foil at $3 a roll. Find the total cost of the materials for the planter.

A $14.75   C $30.75

B $38.50   D $22.50

10. Find the total cost of 4 boards, each 2 in. by 4 in. by 8 ft. at $0.18 per linear foot. Remember, when lumber is priced by the linear foot, the cost of each board depends only on its length.

A $5.76   C $11.52

B $1.44   D $2.56

11. A rug shampooer rents for $2.50 per hour. Find the cost of renting the shampooer for 6 hours.

A $12   C $15

B $8.50   D $10

12. Find the total expense for entertainment for January. Round to the nearest dollar.

Entertainment expenses—January

Concert $6.00
Hockey game $8.75
Bowling $4.35

A $19   C $18

B $20   D $17

13. A 3-month spending record for gasoline, oil, and tolls is given below. Find the amount that should be budgeted per month for this variable expense.

June: $28
July: $31
August: $28

A $87   C $30

B $28   D $29

14. Don Kim's annual expenses total $585. To the nearest dollar, how much should he reserve each month to pay annual expenses?

A $600   C $49

B $59   D $40

15. The Stowe family usually budgets $1500 for a summer vacation. This year they hope to save $425 by driving instead of flying to their destination. How much should they budget this year for the vacation?

A $1925   C $1075

B $425   D $125

16. One survey indicates that an average family spends 28% of its income on housing. If the family income is $17,200 per year, what is the amount spent for housing?

A $12,384   C $401

B $4816   D $1433

Break Time

Winter carnival tickets cost 25¢ each. How much would a book of 18 tickets cost?

Here is a short way to find 18 × 25.

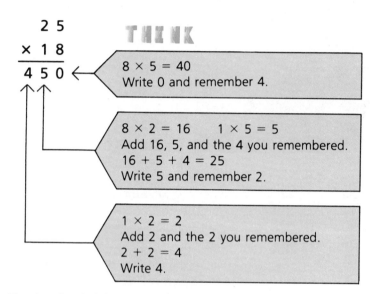

```
  2 5
× 1 8
─────
4 5 0
```

THINK

8 × 5 = 40
Write 0 and remember 4.

8 × 2 = 16   1 × 5 = 5
Add 16, 5, and the 4 you remembered.
16 + 5 + 4 = 25
Write 5 and remember 2.

1 × 2 = 2
Add 2 and the 2 you remembered.
2 + 2 = 4
Write 4.

The book of tickets would cost $4.50.

Find 59 × 67.

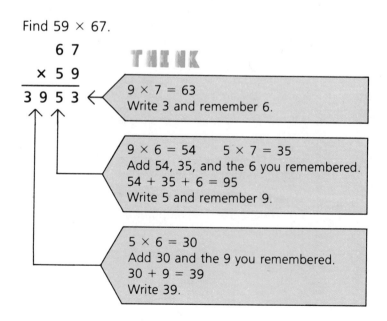

```
  6 7
× 5 9
─────
3 9 5 3
```

THINK

9 × 7 = 63
Write 3 and remember 6.

9 × 6 = 54   5 × 7 = 35
Add 54, 35, and the 6 you remembered.
54 + 35 + 6 = 95
Write 5 and remember 9.

5 × 6 = 30
Add 30 and the 9 you remembered.
30 + 9 = 39
Write 39.

Use the method described at the left to multiply mentally. Write only the answer.

1.	25 × 32	**8.**	43 × 15	**15.**	16 × 35
2.	24 × 31	**9.**	62 × 35	**16.**	45 × 36
3.	13 × 21	**10.**	46 × 28	**17.**	82 × 14
4.	23 × 42	**11.**	52 × 36	**18.**	46 × 33
5.	36 × 18	**12.**	19 × 28	**19.**	73 × 48
6.	21 × 43	**13.**	42 × 16	**20.**	56 × 37
7.	35 × 26	**14.**	63 × 24	**21.**	91 × 85

COMPUTER
APPLICATIONS

Cash Registers

Cash registers at many stores are computerized. They provide an accounting for money received and keep track of inventory. Some read labels on merchandise, ''ring up'' a sale without having their keys pressed by a clerk, and make change. The program shown causes a computer to figure change as a cash register does.

Lines 40 and 60   These values are entered.

Data required	Name
Amount of total bill	T
Amount given	A

Lines 30 and 50   A PRINT statement before each INPUT statement shows what data to enter.

Lines 20 and 25   DATA statements indicate the value and name of each bill and coin used to make change.

Line 80   The amount of the total bill is subtracted from the amount given to find the amount of change (S).

Line 90   The DATA statement is read. The bill with the highest value is read first.

Line 110   When the amount of change is less than the value of the bill or coin, the computer is sent to line 160.

Line 120   When the amount of change is equal to or greater than the value of the bill or coin, the value (V) of the bill or coin is subtracted.

Lines 100 and 130   N is used to keep track of the number of times a bill or coin is used.

Lines 70 and 140   C is used to keep a running total of the change received.

Line 150   The computer is sent back to line 110 and lines 110–140 are repeated to check if a bill or coin is used more than once.

Line 160   When a bill or coin is not used, the computer is sent to line 180.

Line 170   When a bill or coin is used, the name and the number of times it is used is printed.

Line 180   When the amount of change does not equal zero, the computer is sent back to read the next bill or coin.

Line 190   The total amount of change is printed.

```
10 REM  CASH REGISTER                100 LET N=0
20 DATA 20,"TWENTIES",10,"TENS",5,   110 IF S<V THEN 160
"FIVES",1,"ONES"                     120 LET S=S-V
25 DATA .25,"QUARTERS",.10,"DIMES",  130 LET N=N+1
.05,"NICKELS",.01,"PENNIES"          140 LET C=C+V
30 PRINT "TOTAL BILL";               150 GO TO 110
40 INPUT T                           160 IF N=0 THEN 180
50 PRINT "AMOUNT GIVEN";             170 PRINT D$,N
60 INPUT A                           180 IF S>=.01 THEN 90
70 LET C=0                           190 PRINT "CHANGE    $";C
80 LET S=A-T                         200 END
90 READ V,D$
```

Give the output for the program above when

1. T is 23.95 and A is 40.

2. T is 16.88 and A is 20.

3. T is 37.23 and A is 40.

4. T is 2.17 and A is 10.

5. T is 11.62 and A is 15.

6. the amount of the total bill is $3.46 and the amount given is $5.00.

7. the amount of the total bill is $43.78 and the amount given is $50.00.

8. the amount of the total bill is $22.45 and the amount given is $30.00.

9. the amount of the total bill is $2.56 and the amount given is $20.00.

10. the amount of the total bill is $10.50 and the amount given is $15.00.

11. purchases totaling $15.97 are paid for with $20.

12. purchases totaling $21.94 are paid for with $40.

13. purchases totaling $21.94 are paid for with $30.

14. purchases totaling $21.94 are paid for with $22.

15. Modify the program so that a statement is printed for the situation where the amount given is less than the total bill. Have the computer go back to line 50 so that another amount can be entered.

16. Give the output when the total cost is $22.78 and the first amount given is $20 and the next amount given is $25.

17. Modify the program so that instead of the amount of the total bill, the total cost of the merchandise is entered. Add a 5% sales tax to the total cost.

18. Give the output when the total cost is $37.26 and the amount given is $40.

19. Modify the program so that instead of the total cost, the number of items and the price per item are entered. Then have the total cost calculated in the program.

20. Give the output for 3 items for $0.78 each, 2 items for $1.99 each, 5 items for $0.87 each, 2 items for $1.44 each, and 1 item for $5.79. The amount given is $30.

Skills File

Rounding Whole Numbers and Decimals   *379*
Adding Whole Numbers and Decimals   *380*
Subtracting Whole Numbers and Decimals   *381*
Multiplying Whole Numbers   *382*
Multiplying Decimals   *383*
Dividing Whole Numbers   *384*
Dividing Decimals   *385*
Comparing and Renaming Fractions and Mixed Numbers   *386*
Multiplying Fractions and Mixed Numbers   *387*
Dividing Fractions and Mixed Numbers   *388*
Adding Fractions and Mixed Numbers   *389*
Subtracting Fractions and Mixed Numbers   *390*
Ratio and Proportion   *391*
Writing Percents, Decimals, and Fractions   *392*
Using Percent   *393*

Computer Literacy

The PRINT and END Statements   *394*
The LET and INPUT Statements   *395*
The GO TO and IF . . . THEN Statements   *396*
The READ, DATA, and REM Statements   *397*
The FOR and NEXT Statements   *398*
The INT and TAB Functions   *399*

Tables

Tables of Measure   *400*
Monthly Payment Table   *401*
Federal Withholding Tables   *402*
Tax Tables   *406*
Tax Rate Schedules   *409*

Careers Chart *410*

Glossary *414*

Selected Answers *418*

Index *452*

Skills File

Rounding whole numbers and decimals, pages 4–5

Round each number to the nearest thousand
and nearest ten.

1. 709	**13.** 5234	**25.** 6728	**37.** 96,932	**49.** 35,032
2. 518	**14.** 8891	**26.** 4102	**38.** 20,248	**50.** 10,791
3. 676	**15.** 7084	**27.** 2776	**39.** 84,853	**51.** 46,957
4. 983	**16.** 2498	**28.** 9383	**40.** 50,626	**52.** 52,385
5. 845	**17.** 9536	**29.** 8671	**41.** 61,472	**53.** 97,503
6. 597	**18.** 5167	**30.** 1867	**42.** 22,319	**54.** 71,807
7. 1386	**19.** 8698	**31.** 7561	**43.** 11,707	**55.** 25,013
8. 4427	**20.** 3094	**32.** 5555	**44.** 30,858	**56.** 47,203
9. 8391	**21.** 4972	**33.** 9674	**45.** 43,674	**57.** 58,689
10. 6852	**22.** 7889	**34.** 2021	**46.** 94,153	**58.** 62,474
11. 2416	**23.** 6503	**35.** 4999	**47.** 74,906	**59.** 79,619
12. 9637	**24.** 1484	**36.** 7903	**48.** 56,521	**60.** 89,795

Round each number to the nearest whole number
and nearest hundredth.

61. 4.167	**73.** 37.109	**85.** 79.5301	**97.** 268.866	**109.** 646.7184
62. 1.408	**74.** 94.014	**86.** 41.2674	**98.** 689.742	**110.** 439.8209
63. 7.856	**75.** 49.658	**87.** 26.3788	**99.** 912.049	**111.** 574.1852
64. 5.714	**76.** 88.761	**88.** 59.6684	**100.** 567.605	**112.** 671.4135
65. 6.293	**77.** 68.256	**89.** 86.0473	**101.** 403.188	**113.** 821.6397
66. 8.641	**78.** 40.322	**90.** 25.7857	**102.** 741.222	**114.** 757.2531
67. 2.9381	**79.** 31.493	**91.** 11.9353	**103.** 100.885	**115.** 248.3418
68. 3.0857	**80.** 22.945	**92.** 72.4822	**104.** 808.351	**116.** 189.7416
69. 9.7292	**81.** 71.547	**93.** 99.8294	**105.** 352.879	**117.** 545.5665
70. 2.3904	**82.** 55.008	**94.** 33.5738	**106.** 973.624	**118.** 337.2746
71. 3.4729	**83.** 90.232	**95.** 65.0687	**107.** 735.038	**119.** 499.8283
72. 6.5175	**84.** 16.874	**96.** 84.7111	**108.** 270.181	**120.** 986.9772

Skills File

Adding whole numbers and decimals, pages 6–7

1. 65
    + 18

2. 27
    + 43

3. 89
    + 57

4. 65
    + 96

5. 18
     7
    + 75

6. 21
    36
    + 3

7. 54
    78
    + 39

8. 17
    42
    + 73

9. 81
    40
    + 25

10. 50
     65
    + 94

11. 64
     37
    + 18

12. 45
      3
     22
    + 14

13. 41
     35
     14
    + 7

14. 56
     80
     21
    + 15

15. 92
     77
     23
    + 40

16. 11
     42
     30
    + 12

17. 56
     48
     70
    + 62

18. 19
     54
     68
    + 72

19. 96
     85
     22
    + 58

20. 371
    + 265

21. 203
    + 978

22. 189
    + 726

23. 426
    + 609

24. 404
     82
    + 360

25. 343
     261
    + 35

26. 472
     148
    + 606

27. 229
     705
    + 991

28. 316
     283
    + 257

29. 589
     884
    + 625

30. 873
     559
    + 167

31. 7.38
    + 2.9

32. 8.4
    + 3.56

33. 1.17
    + 4.39

34. 5.04
    + 6.79

35. 21.53
    + 65.08

36. 84.77
    + 40.62

37. 0.2
     0.7
    + 0.8

38. 2.4
     0.6
    + 3.2

39. 7.5
     3.23
    + 6.1

40. 8.49
     2.3
    + 1.52

41. 7.9
     9.04
    + 2.83

42. 5.46
     8.02
    + 0.63

43. 8.52
     0.04
    + 3.07

44. 4.67
     1.82
    + 9.05

45. 4.06
     5.72
    + 3.108

46. 4.452
     2.19
    + 9.68

47. 8.1
     2.8
     7.5
    + 5.4

48. 7.3
     0.7
     6.8
    + 4.39

49. 8.2
     3.04
     1.5
    + 9.7

50. 4.03
     0.14
     0.8
    + 1.9

51. 6.7
     2.05
     7.36
    + 0.4

52. 3.8
     5.27
     1.13
    + 5.05

53. 7.64
     4.38
     0.95
    + 8.5

54. 0.28
     9.51
     0.04
    + 2.97

55. 8.65
     0.23
     3.14
    + 6.37

56. 8.13
     0.285
     9.47
    + 0.39

57. 0.17
     9.59
     4.509
    + 1.26

58. 9.19
     5.26
     0.48
    + 2.606

59. 8.776
     4.81
     3.03
    + 6.45

Skills File

Subtracting whole numbers and decimals, pages 6–7

1. 78 − 35	**15.** 283 − 191	**29.** 88.4 − 53.7	**43.** 87.26 − 59.8	**57.** 61.4 − 48	**71.** 28 − 14.81
2. 94 − 83	**16.** 763 − 488	**30.** 74.8 − 2.5	**44.** 23.74 − 18.4	**58.** 80.7 − 49	**72.** 63 − 21.84
3. 34 − 9	**17.** 970 − 343	**31.** 17.5 − 6.9	**45.** 97.16 − 3.2	**59.** 93.2 − 57	**73.** 55 − 7.39
4. 21 − 8	**18.** 708 − 314	**32.** 90.1 − 65.3	**46.** 54.07 − 6.1	**60.** 26.6 − 8	**74.** 70 − 43.06
5. 52 − 3	**19.** 413 − 86	**33.** 76.47 − 21.35	**47.** 73.85 − 31.4	**61.** 73.7 − 48	**75.** 18.75 − 6.672
6. 60 − 4	**20.** 865 − 81	**34.** 41.96 − 38.59	**48.** 91.32 − 38.4	**62.** 42.61 − 35	**76.** 95.03 − 32.671
7. 94 − 69	**21.** 607 − 38	**35.** 53.07 − 21.64	**49.** 58.241 − 3.19	**63.** 28.53 − 19	**77.** 20.05 − 18.164
8. 76 − 47	**22.** 7946 − 2871	**36.** 17.42 − 8.17	**50.** 45.939 − 21.87	**64.** 71.29 − 55	**78.** 43.09 − 21.426
9. 63 − 17	**23.** 5126 − 3718	**37.** 47.79 − 0.38	**51.** 70.427 − 27.99	**65.** 90.14 − 67	**79.** 82.91 − 7.525
10. 44 − 25	**24.** 7103 − 1214	**38.** 28.537 − 14.216	**52.** 40.176 − 26.5	**66.** 87 − 4.1	**80.** 57.6 − 3.244
11. 80 − 37	**25.** 5001 − 3745	**39.** 32.045 − 18.637	**53.** 56.714 − 23.4	**67.** 27 − 6.3	**81.** 83.7 − 5.625
12. 50 − 19	**26.** 1782 − 649	**40.** 71.894 − 4.968	**54.** 15.673 − 8.8	**68.** 84 − 59.5	**82.** 92.1 − 17.066
13. 32 − 29	**27.** 8124 − 315	**41.** 27.158 − 6.253	**55.** 85.061 − 9.4	**69.** 52 − 18.3	**83.** 50.3 − 36.218
14. 87 − 79	**28.** 4334 − 702	**42.** 50.297 − 8.759	**56.** 59.347 − 18.9	**70.** 30 − 29.6	**84.** 41.2 − 29.489

Skills File

Multiplying whole numbers, pages 8–9

1. 700 × 3	**15.** 40 × 70	**29.** 300 × 90	**43.** 67 × 26	**57.** 325 × 89	**71.** 9053 × 80
2. 100 × 6	**16.** 60 × 10	**30.** 400 × 80	**44.** 41 × 53	**58.** 567 × 14	**72.** 5416 × 26
3. 200 × 8	**17.** 50 × 30	**31.** 7000 × 60	**45.** 34 × 22	**59.** 208 × 95	**73.** 6923 × 35
4. 900 × 5	**18.** 80 × 50	**32.** 3000 × 80	**46.** 40 × 67	**60.** 223 × 149	**74.** 7672 × 54
5. 400 × 7	**19.** 100 × 90	**33.** 9000 × 50	**47.** 82 × 80	**61.** 257 × 306	**75.** 6958 × 63
6. 200 × 5	**20.** 300 × 80	**34.** 800 × 900	**48.** 28 × 74	**62.** 803 × 142	**76.** 3042 × 51
7. 1000 × 8	**21.** 900 × 40	**35.** 500 × 700	**49.** 55 × 73	**63.** 643 × 718	**77.** 8821 × 68
8. 3000 × 4	**22.** 200 × 90	**36.** 100 × 600	**50.** 84 × 59	**64.** 978 × 535	**78.** 9455 × 26
9. 6000 × 9	**23.** 500 × 60	**37.** 4000 × 100	**51.** 388 × 45	**65.** 161 × 824	**79.** 7158 × 247
10. 9000 × 2	**24.** 700 × 10	**38.** 2000 × 800	**52.** 679 × 18	**66.** 432 × 218	**80.** 5904 × 832
11. 5000 × 4	**25.** 400 × 30	**39.** 7000 × 400	**53.** 612 × 33	**67.** 686 × 504	**81.** 9268 × 107
12. 7000 × 6	**26.** 800 × 50	**40.** 6000 × 2000	**54.** 507 × 86	**68.** 6530 × 49	**82.** 5296 × 308
13. 10 × 30	**27.** 600 × 20	**41.** 1000 × 3000	**55.** 801 × 45	**69.** 7238 × 72	**83.** 2087 × 645
14. 20 × 80	**28.** 200 × 70	**42.** 5000 × 4000	**56.** 428 × 67	**70.** 1472 × 40	**84.** 7009 × 836

Skills File

Multiplying decimals, pages 10–11

1. $\begin{array}{r} 0.6 \\ \times\ 0.4 \\ \hline \end{array}$	**15.** $\begin{array}{r} 0.004 \\ \times\ \ \ 0.5 \\ \hline \end{array}$	**29.** $\begin{array}{r} 9000 \\ \times\ \ \ 0.6 \\ \hline \end{array}$
2. $\begin{array}{r} 0.5 \\ \times\ 0.9 \\ \hline \end{array}$	**16.** $\begin{array}{r} 0.02 \\ \times\ \ \ \ \ 8 \\ \hline \end{array}$	**30.** $\begin{array}{r} 5000 \\ \times\ \ \ 0.3 \\ \hline \end{array}$
3. $\begin{array}{r} 0.7 \\ \times\ 0.8 \\ \hline \end{array}$	**17.** $\begin{array}{r} 0.08 \\ \times\ \ \ \ \ 1 \\ \hline \end{array}$	**31.** $\begin{array}{r} 0.004 \\ \times\ \ 0.06 \\ \hline \end{array}$
4. $\begin{array}{r} 0.01 \\ \times\ \ 0.6 \\ \hline \end{array}$	**18.** $\begin{array}{r} 0.05 \\ \times\ \ \ \ \ 7 \\ \hline \end{array}$	**32.** $\begin{array}{r} 0.003 \\ \times\ \ 0.08 \\ \hline \end{array}$
5. $\begin{array}{r} 0.02 \\ \times\ \ 0.7 \\ \hline \end{array}$	**19.** $\begin{array}{r} 0.03 \\ \times\ \ \ \ \ 2 \\ \hline \end{array}$	**33.** $\begin{array}{r} 0.007 \\ \times\ \ 0.02 \\ \hline \end{array}$
6. $\begin{array}{r} 0.08 \\ \times\ \ 0.3 \\ \hline \end{array}$	**20.** $\begin{array}{r} 0.001 \\ \times\ \ \ \ \ 3 \\ \hline \end{array}$	**34.** $\begin{array}{r} 0.002 \\ \times\ \ 0.04 \\ \hline \end{array}$
7. $\begin{array}{r} 0.04 \\ \times\ \ 0.5 \\ \hline \end{array}$	**21.** $\begin{array}{r} 0.004 \\ \times\ \ \ \ \ 9 \\ \hline \end{array}$	**35.** $\begin{array}{r} 300 \\ \times\ 0.06 \\ \hline \end{array}$
8. $\begin{array}{r} 0.03 \\ \times\ 0.01 \\ \hline \end{array}$	**22.** $\begin{array}{r} 0.007 \\ \times\ \ \ \ \ 6 \\ \hline \end{array}$	**36.** $\begin{array}{r} 100 \\ \times\ 0.09 \\ \hline \end{array}$
9. $\begin{array}{r} 0.07 \\ \times\ 0.04 \\ \hline \end{array}$	**23.** $\begin{array}{r} 0.008 \\ \times\ \ \ \ \ 2 \\ \hline \end{array}$	**37.** $\begin{array}{r} 700 \\ \times\ 0.04 \\ \hline \end{array}$
10. $\begin{array}{r} 0.02 \\ \times\ 0.09 \\ \hline \end{array}$	**24.** $\begin{array}{r} 0.005 \\ \times\ \ \ \ 50 \\ \hline \end{array}$	**38.** $\begin{array}{r} 200 \\ \times\ 0.06 \\ \hline \end{array}$
11. $\begin{array}{r} 0.06 \\ \times\ 0.08 \\ \hline \end{array}$	**25.** $\begin{array}{r} 0.003 \\ \times\ \ \ \ 70 \\ \hline \end{array}$	**39.** $\begin{array}{r} 4000 \\ \times\ \ \ 0.03 \\ \hline \end{array}$
12. $\begin{array}{r} 0.003 \\ \times\ \ \ 0.6 \\ \hline \end{array}$	**26.** $\begin{array}{r} 0.006 \\ \times\ \ \ \ 80 \\ \hline \end{array}$	**40.** $\begin{array}{r} 9000 \\ \times\ \ \ 0.05 \\ \hline \end{array}$
13. $\begin{array}{r} 0.001 \\ \times\ \ \ 0.7 \\ \hline \end{array}$	**27.** $\begin{array}{r} 2000 \\ \times\ \ \ 0.9 \\ \hline \end{array}$	**41.** $\begin{array}{r} 6000 \\ \times\ \ \ 0.01 \\ \hline \end{array}$
14. $\begin{array}{r} 0.008 \\ \times\ \ \ 0.2 \\ \hline \end{array}$	**28.** $\begin{array}{r} 4000 \\ \times\ \ \ 0.1 \\ \hline \end{array}$	**42.** $\begin{array}{r} 5000 \\ \times\ \ \ 0.08 \\ \hline \end{array}$

43. $\begin{array}{r} 770 \\ \times\ 0.68 \\ \hline \end{array}$	**57.** $\begin{array}{r} 0.723 \\ \times\ \ \ 1.4 \\ \hline \end{array}$	**71.** $\begin{array}{r} 30.5 \\ \times\ 8.5 \\ \hline \end{array}$
44. $\begin{array}{r} 580 \\ \times\ 0.34 \\ \hline \end{array}$	**58.** $\begin{array}{r} 0.639 \\ \times\ \ \ 9.2 \\ \hline \end{array}$	**72.** $\begin{array}{r} 0.124 \\ \times\ 0.362 \\ \hline \end{array}$
45. $\begin{array}{r} 409 \\ \times\ 0.23 \\ \hline \end{array}$	**59.** $\begin{array}{r} 0.741 \\ \times\ \ \ 3.6 \\ \hline \end{array}$	**73.** $\begin{array}{r} 0.819 \\ \times\ 0.703 \\ \hline \end{array}$
46. $\begin{array}{r} 604 \\ \times\ 0.19 \\ \hline \end{array}$	**60.** $\begin{array}{r} 0.873 \\ \times\ \ 0.72 \\ \hline \end{array}$	**74.** $\begin{array}{r} 0.376 \\ \times\ 0.105 \\ \hline \end{array}$
47. $\begin{array}{r} 0.24 \\ \times\ \ \ 89 \\ \hline \end{array}$	**61.** $\begin{array}{r} 0.206 \\ \times\ \ 0.63 \\ \hline \end{array}$	**75.** $\begin{array}{r} 8.051 \\ \times\ \ 36.8 \\ \hline \end{array}$
48. $\begin{array}{r} 0.36 \\ \times\ \ \ 37 \\ \hline \end{array}$	**62.** $\begin{array}{r} 0.592 \\ \times\ \ 0.78 \\ \hline \end{array}$	**76.** $\begin{array}{r} 4.695 \\ \times\ \ 73.2 \\ \hline \end{array}$
49. $\begin{array}{r} 0.68 \\ \times\ \ \ 16 \\ \hline \end{array}$	**63.** $\begin{array}{r} 0.749 \\ \times\ \ \ 3.16 \\ \hline \end{array}$	**77.** $\begin{array}{r} 2.597 \\ \times\ \ 98.6 \\ \hline \end{array}$
50. $\begin{array}{r} 0.7501 \\ \times\ \ \ \ \ 22 \\ \hline \end{array}$	**64.** $\begin{array}{r} 0.412 \\ \times\ \ 7.23 \\ \hline \end{array}$	**78.** $\begin{array}{r} 7.002 \\ \times\ \ 65.9 \\ \hline \end{array}$
51. $\begin{array}{r} 0.2034 \\ \times\ \ \ \ \ 58 \\ \hline \end{array}$	**65.** $\begin{array}{r} 40.2 \\ \times\ 5.07 \\ \hline \end{array}$	**79.** $\begin{array}{r} 0.076 \\ \times\ 29.08 \\ \hline \end{array}$
52. $\begin{array}{r} 0.5083 \\ \times\ \ \ \ \ 27 \\ \hline \end{array}$	**66.** $\begin{array}{r} 81.3 \\ \times\ 6.38 \\ \hline \end{array}$	**80.** $\begin{array}{r} 0.802 \\ \times\ 90.46 \\ \hline \end{array}$
53. $\begin{array}{r} 3652 \\ \times\ 0.15 \\ \hline \end{array}$	**67.** $\begin{array}{r} 57.8 \\ \times\ 5.81 \\ \hline \end{array}$	**81.** $\begin{array}{r} 0.538 \\ \times\ 74.13 \\ \hline \end{array}$
54. $\begin{array}{r} 7378 \\ \times\ 0.21 \\ \hline \end{array}$	**68.** $\begin{array}{r} 62.9 \\ \times\ 7.3 \\ \hline \end{array}$	**82.** $\begin{array}{r} 0.6087 \\ \times\ \ 23.41 \\ \hline \end{array}$
55. $\begin{array}{r} 5447 \\ \times\ 0.87 \\ \hline \end{array}$	**69.** $\begin{array}{r} 84.1 \\ \times\ 1.9 \\ \hline \end{array}$	**83.** $\begin{array}{r} 0.3043 \\ \times\ \ 91.82 \\ \hline \end{array}$
56. $\begin{array}{r} 0.452 \\ \times\ \ \ 8.1 \\ \hline \end{array}$	**70.** $\begin{array}{r} 47.8 \\ \times\ 2.7 \\ \hline \end{array}$	**84.** $\begin{array}{r} 0.5309 \\ \times\ \ 84.52 \\ \hline \end{array}$

Skills File

Dividing whole numbers, pages 12–13

1. 2)463
2. 7)821
3. 9)846
4. 8)702
5. 7)4136
6. 6)8256
7. 4)1273
8. 3)6728
9. 6)7108
10. 9)3618
11. 7)5920
12. 2)9523
13. 4)3007
14. 5)1234
15. 8)8867
16. 3)2050
17. 4)8756
18. 6)81429
19. 7)50633
20. 5)31954
21. 9)92648

22. 61)725
23. 14)359
24. 36)288
25. 42)176
26. 79)870
27. 82)563
28. 27)937
29. 51)428
30. 66)255
31. 93)986
32. 56)805
33. 31)172
34. 17)643
35. 64)781
36. 85)999
37. 77)200
38. 43)136
39. 50)487
40. 94)950
41. 22)215
42. 68)404

43. 42)5862
44. 76)4972
45. 91)2634
46. 23)1288
47. 39)8114
48. 75)3435
49. 57)3592
50. 63)1286
51. 27)8346
52. 32)3159
53. 70)9403
54. 81)7342
55. 65)7878
56. 51)9161
57. 31)8835
58. 47)1048
59. 66)3308
60. 25)2463
61. 88)9006
62. 94)5526
63. 46)4407

64. 22)39378
65. 52)39728
66. 60)48901
67. 72)65989
68. 17)83424
69. 91)85736
70. 87)90480
71. 37)30555
72. 49)86047
73. 28)94613
74. 56)823914
75. 20)149298
76. 64)173696
77. 16)181457
78. 97)482582
79. 33)347096
80. 71)375534
81. 46)920414
82. 68)234405
83. 86)261379
84. 32)974021

85. 441)89027
86. 703)24368
87. 282)76446
88. 927)42175
89. 870)10653
90. 376)68808
91. 135)87146
92. 564)55364
93. 656)23209
94. 488)70216
95. 834)625549
96. 263)248745
97. 454)476246
98. 622)818288
99. 185)140535
100. 506)345092
101. 313)920369
102. 911)702636
103. 586)900413
104. 204)863446
105. 781)532931

Skills File

Dividing decimals, pages 12-13

Find each quotient to the nearest hundredth.

1. 2)7.67	**21.** 95)98.9	**41.** 3.2)7.7	**61.** 0.19)0.82	**81.** 4.05)27
2. 7)35.63	**22.** 64)73.8	**42.** 7.4)1.3	**62.** 0.25)0.145	**82.** 8.33)42
3. 4)928.7	**23.** 39)80.4	**43.** 2.8)4.6	**63.** 0.64)0.309	**83.** 6.19)47
4. 3)640.9	**24.** 41)51.2	**44.** 6.1)9.2	**64.** 0.38)0.918	**84.** 1.72)35
5. 6)322.6	**25.** 53)65.23	**45.** 9.5)4.1	**65.** 0.51)0.836	**85.** 29.8)538
6. 5)472.3	**26.** 81)31.06	**46.** 8.3)7.2	**66.** 0.98)0.505	**86.** 70.2)746
7. 8)8901	**27.** 98)83.54	**47.** 5.9)2.8	**67.** 0.73)0.641	**87.** 40.1)864
8. 9)7132	**28.** 23)709.41	**48.** 4.1)98.2	**68.** 0.62)0.103	**88.** 93.2)601
9. 7)6479	**29.** 77)471.29	**49.** 7.4)30.6	**69.** 3.24)41.72	**89.** 69.7)408
10. 6)9583	**30.** 46)239.75	**50.** 5.2)61.7	**70.** 9.38)57.35	**90.** 32.4)417
11. 12)4.37	**31.** 324)4078	**51.** 4.8)27.2	**71.** 2.98)31.82	**91.** 95.8)573
12. 55)3.72	**32.** 938)5735	**52.** 6.3)46.5	**72.** 6.07)23.79	**92.** 29.6)318
13. 86)5.64	**33.** 298)3182	**53.** 2.7)50.1	**73.** 1.69)53.05	**93.** 0.47)9.1
14. 31)3.78	**34.** 607)2379	**54.** 9.6)78.2	**74.** 8.43)70.24	**94.** 0.31)7.2
15. 67)52.4	**35.** 169)5305	**55.** 0.65)0.14	**75.** 7.36)95.01	**95.** 2.51)9.5
16. 74)17.6	**36.** 843)70.24	**56.** 0.24)0.39	**76.** 4.26)19.82	**96.** 8.46)8.7
17. 28)74.2	**37.** 736)90.51	**57.** 0.17)0.95	**77.** 3.13)57	**97.** 5.09)2.4
18. 93)50.8	**38.** 142)43.57	**58.** 0.41)0.28	**78.** 2.49)76	**98.** 3.77)8.6
19. 40)63.1	**39.** 305)68.72	**59.** 0.93)0.52	**79.** 1.93)93	**99.** 9.21)7.9
20. 17)27.4	**40.** 718)58.34	**60.** 0.57)0.21	**80.** 7.02)69	**100.** 7.62)3.1

Skills File

Comparing and renaming fractions and mixed numbers, pages 14–15

Compare. Replace ⬤ with <, >, or =.

1. $\frac{7}{8}$ ⬤ $\frac{5}{8}$

2. $\frac{2}{3}$ ⬤ $\frac{9}{12}$

3. $\frac{6}{16}$ ⬤ $\frac{3}{8}$

4. $\frac{11}{15}$ ⬤ $\frac{3}{5}$

5. $\frac{3}{7}$ ⬤ $\frac{1}{3}$

6. $\frac{1}{2}$ ⬤ $\frac{2}{5}$

7. $\frac{3}{4}$ ⬤ $\frac{6}{7}$

8. $\frac{2}{5}$ ⬤ $\frac{4}{9}$

9. $\frac{1}{9}$ ⬤ $\frac{1}{6}$

10. $\frac{5}{6}$ ⬤ $\frac{3}{4}$

11. $\frac{5}{8}$ ⬤ $\frac{7}{12}$

12. $\frac{3}{10}$ ⬤ $\frac{4}{15}$

13. $3\frac{4}{5}$ ⬤ $4\frac{1}{8}$

14. $7\frac{2}{3}$ ⬤ $8\frac{7}{8}$

15. $2\frac{3}{5}$ ⬤ $2\frac{3}{7}$

16. $1\frac{7}{8}$ ⬤ $1\frac{7}{9}$

17. $5\frac{1}{4}$ ⬤ $5\frac{1}{3}$

18. $6\frac{9}{10}$ ⬤ $6\frac{27}{30}$

Rename as a fraction.

46. $6\frac{3}{7}$

47. $1\frac{1}{4}$

48. $4\frac{1}{6}$

49. 7

50. $5\frac{1}{5}$

51. $2\frac{5}{8}$

52. $9\frac{2}{3}$

53. $8\frac{1}{10}$

54. $3\frac{1}{2}$

55. $8\frac{3}{5}$

56. $2\frac{9}{10}$

57. $4\frac{7}{8}$

58. $1\frac{4}{7}$

59. $6\frac{5}{6}$

60. 4

61. $3\frac{2}{9}$

62. $9\frac{7}{11}$

63. $5\frac{1}{12}$

64. $10\frac{3}{4}$

65. $8\frac{5}{8}$

66. 12

67. $7\frac{3}{11}$

68. $4\frac{7}{16}$

69. $6\frac{2}{15}$

70. $3\frac{5}{18}$

71. $11\frac{10}{11}$

72. $12\frac{13}{16}$

Rename in lowest terms.

19. $\frac{6}{10}$

20. $\frac{3}{15}$

21. $\frac{6}{18}$

22. $\frac{4}{14}$

23. $\frac{5}{35}$

24. $\frac{10}{12}$

25. $\frac{16}{24}$

26. $\frac{25}{100}$

27. $\frac{39}{42}$

28. $\frac{11}{88}$

29. $\frac{7}{14}$

30. $\frac{3}{24}$

31. $\frac{60}{100}$

32. $\frac{48}{54}$

33. $\frac{12}{72}$

34. $\frac{21}{27}$

35. $\frac{24}{30}$

36. $\frac{18}{63}$

37. $\frac{14}{63}$

38. $\frac{21}{48}$

39. $\frac{16}{80}$

40. $\frac{72}{81}$

41. $\frac{20}{90}$

42. $\frac{84}{100}$

43. $\frac{18}{81}$

44. $\frac{28}{42}$

45. $\frac{49}{56}$

Rename as a mixed number.

73. $\frac{5}{2}$

74. $\frac{9}{4}$

75. $\frac{7}{5}$

76. $\frac{25}{6}$

77. $\frac{19}{3}$

78. $\frac{27}{8}$

79. $\frac{42}{7}$

80. $\frac{13}{8}$

81. $\frac{73}{9}$

82. $\frac{38}{7}$

83. $\frac{33}{6}$

84. $\frac{45}{9}$

85. $\frac{29}{8}$

86. $\frac{18}{4}$

87. $\frac{25}{2}$

88. $\frac{53}{5}$

89. $\frac{51}{7}$

90. $\frac{40}{16}$

91. $\frac{50}{30}$

92. $\frac{78}{12}$

93. $\frac{56}{24}$

94. $\frac{63}{15}$

95. $\frac{45}{27}$

96. $\frac{64}{8}$

97. $\frac{121}{10}$

98. $\frac{84}{11}$

99. $\frac{143}{12}$

Skills File

Multiplying fractions and mixed numbers, pages 16–17

1. $\frac{1}{3} \times \frac{4}{5}$

2. $\frac{3}{5} \times \frac{1}{4}$

3. $\frac{1}{2} \times \frac{5}{6}$

4. $\frac{2}{7} \times \frac{2}{3}$

5. $\frac{1}{2} \times \frac{5}{8}$

6. $\frac{3}{7} \times \frac{1}{3}$

7. $\frac{4}{5} \times \frac{3}{4}$

8. $\frac{2}{3} \times \frac{7}{8}$

9. $\frac{6}{11} \times \frac{1}{3}$

10. $\frac{2}{9} \times \frac{9}{10}$

11. $\frac{5}{9} \times \frac{3}{5}$

12. $\frac{3}{8} \times \frac{4}{15}$

13. $\frac{5}{6} \times \frac{4}{5}$

14. $\frac{2}{9} \times \frac{8}{9}$

15. $\frac{3}{4} \times \frac{8}{9}$

16. $\frac{5}{6} \times \frac{7}{10}$

17. $\frac{5}{12} \times \frac{7}{12}$

18. $\frac{5}{8} \times \frac{16}{25}$

19. $\frac{3}{14} \times \frac{7}{18}$

20. $\frac{22}{25} \times \frac{10}{11}$

21. $\frac{8}{9} \times \frac{15}{28}$

22. $\frac{1}{2} \times 5$

23. $\frac{2}{3} \times 7$

24. $\frac{3}{4} \times 8$

25. $\frac{1}{4} \times 12$

26. $4 \times \frac{1}{3}$

27. $24 \times \frac{1}{12}$

28. $20 \times \frac{3}{10}$

29. $6 \times \frac{2}{5}$

30. $\frac{3}{8} \times 16$

31. $42 \times \frac{2}{9}$

32. $56 \times \frac{6}{7}$

33. $\frac{1}{10} \times 36$

34. $\frac{2}{3} \times 51$

35. $\frac{4}{5} \times 35$

36. $72 \times \frac{1}{8}$

37. $100 \times \frac{7}{10}$

38. $\frac{5}{12} \times 28$

39. $14 \times \frac{2}{11}$

40. $22 \times \frac{3}{7}$

41. $\frac{8}{9} \times 30$

42. $\frac{7}{10} \times 64$

43. $\frac{4}{7} \times 1\frac{2}{5}$

44. $\frac{1}{2} \times 1\frac{1}{5}$

45. $4\frac{3}{8} \times \frac{2}{5}$

46. $3\frac{1}{2} \times \frac{6}{7}$

47. $\frac{2}{3} \times 1\frac{5}{16}$

48. $2\frac{5}{8} \times \frac{4}{7}$

49. $1\frac{3}{8} \times \frac{8}{11}$

50. $\frac{9}{10} \times 1\frac{1}{4}$

51. $\frac{5}{6} \times 2\frac{1}{3}$

52. $3\frac{1}{9} \times \frac{1}{2}$

53. $\frac{3}{5} \times 6\frac{2}{3}$

54. $5\frac{1}{4} \times \frac{1}{6}$

55. $4\frac{2}{7} \times \frac{3}{5}$

56. $\frac{5}{9} \times 15\frac{3}{4}$

57. $1\frac{1}{4} \times 8$

58. $3 \times 1\frac{1}{2}$

59. $12 \times 1\frac{1}{8}$

60. $9 \times 3\frac{2}{3}$

61. $1\frac{7}{8} \times 6$

62. $2\frac{1}{3} \times 7$

63. $4 \times 5\frac{1}{6}$

64. $5 \times 3\frac{3}{10}$

65. $4 \times 4\frac{1}{2}$

66. $1\frac{1}{6} \times 9$

67. $24 \times 4\frac{1}{3}$

68. $1\frac{1}{12} \times 8$

69. $4 \times 7\frac{2}{3}$

70. $5\frac{5}{12} \times 6$

71. $2\frac{1}{2} \times 3\frac{1}{3}$

72. $3\frac{3}{4} \times 1\frac{1}{3}$

73. $1\frac{1}{2} \times 2\frac{1}{6}$

74. $5\frac{1}{3} \times 1\frac{1}{8}$

75. $3\frac{1}{2} \times 2\frac{1}{3}$

76. $2\frac{2}{3} \times 1\frac{3}{4}$

77. $3\frac{8}{9} \times 2\frac{2}{5}$

78. $2\frac{1}{3} \times 1\frac{2}{7}$

79. $5\frac{1}{4} \times 1\frac{2}{3}$

80. $3\frac{3}{5} \times 4\frac{4}{9}$

81. $1\frac{3}{7} \times 8\frac{3}{4}$

82. $2\frac{2}{15} \times 2\frac{1}{12}$

83. $6\frac{3}{5} \times 2\frac{7}{9}$

84. $4\frac{4}{15} \times 5\frac{5}{16}$

85. $\frac{1}{2} \times \frac{2}{5} \times \frac{1}{3}$

86. $\frac{2}{3} \times \frac{1}{2} \times \frac{5}{8}$

87. $\frac{1}{4} \times \frac{4}{5} \times \frac{3}{8}$

88. $\frac{1}{2} \times \frac{5}{6} \times 3\frac{3}{5}$

89. $\frac{1}{6} \times 3 \times \frac{5}{8}$

90. $2 \times \frac{5}{8} \times \frac{6}{7}$

91. $1\frac{2}{3} \times \frac{4}{5} \times 9$

92. $\frac{1}{2} \times 4\frac{1}{2} \times 3\frac{1}{2}$

93. $\frac{2}{3} \times \frac{3}{8} \times 7$

94. $\frac{5}{6} \times 3 \times \frac{4}{15}$

95. $2\frac{1}{4} \times 5\frac{1}{3} \times \frac{7}{8}$

96. $3\frac{1}{5} \times \frac{1}{2} \times 1\frac{3}{4}$

97. $4\frac{1}{8} \times 1\frac{3}{5} \times \frac{2}{3}$

98. $2\frac{1}{2} \times 3\frac{1}{3} \times 2\frac{1}{4}$

99. $1\frac{5}{16} \times \frac{2}{3} \times 2\frac{2}{3}$

100. $10 \times \frac{4}{5} \times 3\frac{1}{12}$

101. $2\frac{1}{4} \times \frac{3}{5} \times 8$

102. $2\frac{2}{3} \times 1\frac{3}{4} \times 5$

103. $4 \times 2\frac{1}{5} \times 3\frac{1}{8}$

104. $6\frac{1}{4} \times 5\frac{1}{2} \times 8$

105. $3\frac{3}{4} \times 4\frac{4}{5} \times 5\frac{5}{6}$

Skills File

Dividing fractions and mixed numbers, pages 16–17

1. $\frac{3}{4} \div \frac{1}{2}$

2. $\frac{1}{4} \div \frac{2}{3}$

3. $\frac{3}{5} \div \frac{7}{8}$

4. $\frac{1}{2} \div \frac{5}{8}$

5. $\frac{2}{3} \div \frac{1}{6}$

6. $\frac{7}{8} \div \frac{2}{5}$

7. $\frac{4}{9} \div \frac{2}{7}$

8. $\frac{1}{10} \div \frac{2}{3}$

9. $\frac{12}{25} \div \frac{4}{15}$

10. $\frac{1}{2} \div 3$

11. $\frac{3}{5} \div 9$

12. $\frac{1}{8} \div 2$

13. $\frac{4}{5} \div 3$

14. $\frac{4}{15} \div 8$

15. $\frac{15}{16} \div 3$

16. $\frac{4}{5} \div 10$

17. $\frac{8}{9} \div 12$

18. $\frac{7}{12} \div 4$

19. $5 \div \frac{2}{3}$

20. $6 \div \frac{3}{8}$

21. $6 \div \frac{3}{4}$

22. $10 \div \frac{5}{8}$

23. $7 \div \frac{3}{4}$

24. $5 \div \frac{2}{3}$

25. $1 \div \frac{3}{4}$

26. $2 \div \frac{4}{5}$

27. $9 \div \frac{6}{7}$

28. $\frac{2}{3} \div 1\frac{1}{2}$

29. $\frac{3}{10} \div 1\frac{1}{5}$

30. $\frac{3}{8} \div 2\frac{1}{3}$

31. $\frac{1}{3} \div 1\frac{1}{9}$

32. $\frac{1}{2} \div 1\frac{1}{4}$

33. $\frac{3}{4} \div 7\frac{1}{2}$

34. $\frac{2}{5} \div 2\frac{3}{5}$

35. $\frac{3}{8} \div 3\frac{1}{2}$

36. $\frac{7}{10} \div 2\frac{4}{5}$

37. $3\frac{3}{4} \div \frac{3}{5}$

38. $2\frac{1}{4} \div \frac{9}{10}$

39. $5\frac{3}{5} \div \frac{4}{5}$

40. $7\frac{1}{2} \div \frac{1}{2}$

41. $1\frac{1}{8} \div \frac{5}{6}$

42. $3\frac{3}{4} \div \frac{3}{8}$

43. $8\frac{1}{3} \div \frac{1}{6}$

44. $6\frac{2}{3} \div \frac{15}{16}$

45. $5\frac{1}{4} \div \frac{7}{10}$

46. $5\frac{1}{3} \div 3$

47. $5\frac{7}{8} \div 2$

48. $1\frac{4}{5} \div 15$

49. $8\frac{1}{4} \div 3$

50. $2\frac{2}{3} \div 3$

51. $5\frac{1}{4} \div 7$

52. $3\frac{1}{5} \div 8$

53. $9\frac{1}{3} \div 7$

54. $8\frac{3}{4} \div 14$

55. $8 \div 1\frac{1}{3}$

56. $9 \div 1\frac{5}{7}$

57. $12 \div 3\frac{3}{4}$

58. $4 \div 1\frac{2}{3}$

59. $6 \div 1\frac{1}{8}$

60. $10 \div 4\frac{3}{8}$

61. $25 \div 3\frac{1}{3}$

62. $7 \div 2\frac{1}{2}$

63. $40 \div 1\frac{3}{5}$

64. $2\frac{7}{8} \div 1\frac{7}{8}$

65. $9\frac{1}{4} \div 2\frac{3}{4}$

66. $4\frac{1}{6} \div 5\frac{2}{3}$

67. $2\frac{3}{4} \div 3\frac{2}{3}$

68. $7\frac{4}{5} \div 1\frac{6}{7}$

69. $8\frac{5}{9} \div 3\frac{2}{3}$

70. $1\frac{1}{8} \div 1\frac{5}{16}$

71. $3\frac{3}{5} \div 2\frac{1}{4}$

72. $2\frac{7}{10} \div 1\frac{3}{5}$

73. $9\frac{3}{8} \div 1\frac{7}{8}$

74. $7\frac{1}{4} \div 2\frac{1}{2}$

75. $5\frac{5}{8} \div 5\frac{5}{6}$

76. $1\frac{3}{5} \div 2\frac{2}{3}$

77. $1\frac{7}{8} \div 3\frac{1}{3}$

78. $7\frac{1}{2} \div 1\frac{1}{2}$

79. $3\frac{7}{8} \div 1\frac{1}{4}$

80. $8\frac{1}{6} \div 1\frac{2}{5}$

81. $4\frac{1}{2} \div 2\frac{2}{5}$

82. $6\frac{1}{4} \div 2\frac{1}{2}$

83. $6\frac{2}{3} \div 7\frac{1}{2}$

84. $3\frac{3}{5} \div 4\frac{1}{5}$

85. $3\frac{3}{5} \div 2\frac{1}{4}$

86. $8\frac{2}{3} \div 2\frac{1}{6}$

87. $3\frac{1}{3} \div 2\frac{1}{12}$

88. $2\frac{7}{10} \div 1\frac{5}{8}$

89. $6\frac{7}{8} \div 1\frac{5}{6}$

90. $4\frac{1}{6} \div 3\frac{3}{4}$

91. $10\frac{1}{2} \div 1\frac{3}{4}$

92. $2\frac{3}{5} \div 3\frac{9}{10}$

93. $2\frac{2}{7} \div 5\frac{1}{3}$

94. $2\frac{4}{5} \div 1\frac{3}{4}$

95. $1\frac{1}{4} \div 7\frac{1}{2}$

96. $1\frac{5}{7} \div 5\frac{1}{4}$

97. $4\frac{2}{3} \div 1\frac{1}{6}$

98. $4\frac{1}{2} \div 2\frac{1}{4}$

99. $8\frac{2}{3} \div 2\frac{3}{5}$

100. $2\frac{3}{8} \div 1\frac{1}{2}$

101. $3\frac{3}{10} \div 4\frac{2}{5}$

102. $10\frac{1}{2} \div 2\frac{1}{3}$

103. $5\frac{5}{6} \div 1\frac{5}{9}$

104. $13\frac{3}{4} \div 1\frac{2}{3}$

105. $16\frac{2}{3} \div 2\frac{3}{11}$

Skills File

Adding fractions and mixed numbers, pages 18–19

1. $\frac{1}{3}$
$+ \frac{3}{4}$

2. $\frac{1}{10}$
$+ \frac{3}{5}$

3. $\frac{5}{6}$
$+ \frac{1}{2}$

4. $\frac{3}{5}$
$+ \frac{2}{15}$

5. $\frac{1}{2}$
$+ \frac{5}{7}$

6. $\frac{7}{10}$
$+ \frac{1}{2}$

7. $\frac{7}{9}$
$+ \frac{7}{12}$

8. $\frac{3}{4}$
$+ \frac{2}{3}$

9. $\frac{1}{6}$
$+ \frac{8}{9}$

10. $\frac{3}{4}$
$+ \frac{5}{6}$

11. $\frac{9}{10}$
$+ \frac{1}{2}$

12. $\frac{5}{16}$
$+ \frac{1}{4}$

13. $\frac{4}{5}$
$+ \frac{7}{10}$

14. $\frac{7}{8}$
$+ \frac{1}{3}$

15. $\frac{7}{8}$
$+ \frac{1}{6}$

16. $\frac{7}{12}$
$+ \frac{2}{3}$

17. $\frac{1}{10}$
$+ \frac{1}{6}$

18. $\frac{5}{6}$
$+ \frac{2}{9}$

19. $\frac{2}{5}$
$+ \frac{7}{8}$

20. $\frac{9}{16}$
$+ \frac{3}{4}$

21. $\frac{5}{8}$
$+ \frac{2}{3}$

22. $\frac{8}{15}$
$+ \frac{4}{5}$

23. $\frac{11}{18}$
$+ \frac{5}{6}$

24. $\frac{4}{9}$
$+ \frac{7}{12}$

25. $5\frac{1}{6}$
$+ \frac{7}{8}$

26. $3\frac{5}{6}$
$+ \frac{7}{10}$

27. $4\frac{7}{9}$
$+ \frac{1}{4}$

28. $2\frac{3}{8}$
$+ \frac{5}{24}$

29. $3\frac{5}{8}$
$+ \frac{2}{3}$

30. $1\frac{9}{10}$
$+ \frac{1}{5}$

31. $5\frac{3}{8}$
$+ \frac{1}{24}$

32. $7\frac{1}{2}$
$+ \frac{3}{10}$

33. $3\frac{2}{5}$
$+ \frac{2}{3}$

34. $3\frac{15}{16}$
$+ \frac{7}{8}$

35. $12\frac{1}{10}$
$+ \frac{4}{5}$

36. $16\frac{4}{5}$
$+ \frac{1}{6}$

37. $3\frac{8}{15}$
$+ 4\frac{4}{5}$

38. $6\frac{2}{3}$
$+ 4\frac{7}{12}$

39. $2\frac{2}{9}$
$+ 3\frac{7}{18}$

40. $3\frac{1}{2}$
$+ 1\frac{5}{8}$

41. $2\frac{3}{5}$
$+ 6\frac{5}{8}$

42. $5\frac{1}{2}$
$+ 3\frac{1}{4}$

43. $7\frac{5}{8}$
$+ 1\frac{1}{6}$

44. $2\frac{3}{4}$
$+ 1\frac{7}{12}$

45. $4\frac{2}{3}$
$+ 8\frac{1}{5}$

46. $3\frac{1}{8}$
$+ 7\frac{2}{3}$

47. $1\frac{4}{5}$
$+ 5\frac{1}{3}$

48. $8\frac{3}{5}$
$+ 9\frac{2}{5}$

49. $12\frac{1}{4}$
$+ 8\frac{7}{12}$

50. $2\frac{7}{8}$
$+ 3\frac{5}{6}$

51. $2\frac{2}{5}$
$+ 7\frac{7}{15}$

52. $6\frac{1}{4}$
$+ 2\frac{4}{5}$

53. $5\frac{1}{6}$
$+ 9\frac{3}{10}$

54. $8\frac{5}{12}$
$+ 7\frac{3}{4}$

55. $8\frac{7}{10}$
$+ 5\frac{2}{3}$

56. $4\frac{11}{12}$
$+ 3\frac{1}{4}$

57. $7\frac{1}{2}$
$+ 2\frac{2}{3}$

58. $5\frac{1}{7}$
$+ 3\frac{2}{3}$

59. $16\frac{1}{3}$
$+ 2\frac{1}{6}$

60. $15\frac{3}{8}$
$+ 9\frac{3}{16}$

61. $\frac{1}{2}$
$\frac{2}{3}$
$+ \frac{1}{4}$

62. $\frac{1}{3}$
$\frac{5}{8}$
$+ \frac{5}{6}$

63. $1\frac{1}{2}$
$\frac{4}{5}$
$+ 2\frac{1}{3}$

64. $3\frac{3}{8}$
$4\frac{1}{2}$
$+ \frac{1}{6}$

65. $2\frac{5}{12}$
$2\frac{2}{3}$
$+ 1\frac{1}{4}$

66. $4\frac{1}{6}$
$1\frac{2}{5}$
$+ 3\frac{2}{3}$

67. $1\frac{3}{8}$
$1\frac{1}{3}$
$+ 1\frac{5}{6}$

68. $3\frac{3}{4}$
$4\frac{2}{5}$
$+ 3\frac{1}{2}$

Skills File

Subtracting fractions and mixed numbers, pages 18–19

1. $\dfrac{5}{6} - \dfrac{1}{3}$

2. $\dfrac{3}{4} - \dfrac{1}{2}$

3. $\dfrac{7}{8} - \dfrac{1}{4}$

4. $\dfrac{4}{5} - \dfrac{1}{3}$

5. $\dfrac{7}{8} - \dfrac{1}{6}$

6. $\dfrac{5}{6} - \dfrac{2}{3}$

7. $\dfrac{1}{2} - \dfrac{2}{7}$

8. $\dfrac{3}{4} - \dfrac{3}{10}$

9. $\dfrac{4}{5} - \dfrac{3}{10}$

10. $\dfrac{5}{8} - \dfrac{1}{6}$

11. $\dfrac{17}{18} - \dfrac{7}{9}$

12. $\dfrac{4}{15} - \dfrac{1}{10}$

13. $\dfrac{4}{5} - \dfrac{2}{3}$

14. $\dfrac{5}{6} - \dfrac{1}{8}$

15. $\dfrac{9}{10} - \dfrac{5}{6}$

16. $\dfrac{2}{3} - \dfrac{4}{7}$

17. $\dfrac{8}{15} - \dfrac{2}{5}$

18. $\dfrac{13}{16} - \dfrac{3}{4}$

19. $\dfrac{5}{7} - \dfrac{1}{2}$

20. $\dfrac{5}{8} - \dfrac{1}{6}$

21. $\dfrac{7}{10} - \dfrac{2}{15}$

22. $\dfrac{11}{15} - \dfrac{5}{9}$

23. $\dfrac{5}{6} - \dfrac{7}{10}$

24. $\dfrac{11}{12} - \dfrac{1}{8}$

25. $2 - \dfrac{5}{8}$

26. $8 - \dfrac{2}{5}$

27. $9 - \dfrac{1}{3}$

28. $13 - \dfrac{4}{7}$

29. $3 - \dfrac{7}{8}$

30. $15 - \dfrac{3}{10}$

31. $10 - \dfrac{6}{7}$

32. $6 - \dfrac{1}{4}$

33. $10 - 4\dfrac{2}{3}$

34. $7 - 6\dfrac{7}{10}$

35. $18 - 8\dfrac{3}{5}$

36. $9 - 5\dfrac{2}{3}$

37. $3 - 1\dfrac{5}{7}$

38. $12 - 6\dfrac{5}{6}$

39. $16 - 9\dfrac{3}{8}$

40. $6 - 5\dfrac{1}{16}$

41. $3\dfrac{1}{2} - \dfrac{2}{5}$

42. $4\dfrac{7}{8} - \dfrac{3}{16}$

43. $5\dfrac{1}{10} - \dfrac{3}{5}$

44. $4\dfrac{4}{9} - \dfrac{5}{6}$

45. $9\dfrac{1}{3} - 6$

46. $15\dfrac{4}{9} - 7$

47. $21\dfrac{7}{8} - 17$

48. $12\dfrac{3}{10} - 11$

49. $14\dfrac{5}{6} - 8\dfrac{1}{2}$

50. $10\dfrac{4}{5} - 8\dfrac{3}{4}$

51. $7\dfrac{3}{4} - 2\dfrac{3}{16}$

52. $2\dfrac{7}{12} - 2\dfrac{3}{8}$

53. $5\dfrac{7}{8} - 5\dfrac{5}{12}$

54. $8\dfrac{3}{4} - 2\dfrac{1}{3}$

55. $9\dfrac{3}{10} - 5\dfrac{1}{5}$

56. $8\dfrac{5}{8} - 4\dfrac{3}{16}$

57. $3\dfrac{4}{5} - 1\dfrac{3}{20}$

58. $9\dfrac{5}{6} - 2\dfrac{1}{3}$

59. $10\dfrac{7}{8} - 5\dfrac{5}{12}$

60. $12\dfrac{13}{15} - 9\dfrac{5}{6}$

61. $5\dfrac{1}{4} - 2\dfrac{3}{4}$

62. $8\dfrac{3}{8} - 4\dfrac{5}{8}$

63. $9\dfrac{1}{6} - 4\dfrac{5}{9}$

64. $7\dfrac{5}{6} - 4\dfrac{8}{9}$

65. $10\dfrac{1}{3} - 3\dfrac{4}{5}$

66. $5\dfrac{1}{4} - 2\dfrac{7}{10}$

67. $6\dfrac{3}{4} - 4\dfrac{4}{5}$

68. $11\dfrac{3}{8} - 9\dfrac{2}{3}$

69. $18\dfrac{5}{6} - 13\dfrac{11}{12}$

70. $14\dfrac{4}{9} - 7\dfrac{3}{4}$

71. $13\dfrac{7}{12} - 9\dfrac{5}{8}$

72. $16\dfrac{1}{10} - 15\dfrac{7}{15}$

Skills File

Ratio and proportion, pages 30–31

Find the cross-products. Tell whether the ratios are equal.

1. $\frac{6}{30}$ $\frac{4}{20}$

2. $\frac{3}{13}$ $\frac{5}{15}$

3. $\frac{10}{12}$ $\frac{12}{14}$

4. $\frac{7}{6}$ $\frac{21}{18}$

5. $\frac{40}{8}$ $\frac{160}{30}$

6. $\frac{5}{12}$ $\frac{15}{36}$

7. $\frac{5}{9}$ $\frac{11}{18}$

8. $\frac{2}{15}$ $\frac{6}{45}$

9. $\frac{15}{24}$ $\frac{5}{8}$

10. $\frac{7}{12}$ $\frac{28}{48}$

11. $\frac{4}{5}$ $\frac{12}{16}$

12. $\frac{6}{14}$ $\frac{15}{35}$

13. $\frac{5}{13}$ $\frac{4}{12}$

14. $\frac{8}{5}$ $\frac{28}{15}$

15. $\frac{14}{38}$ $\frac{21}{57}$

16. $\frac{42}{28}$ $\frac{63}{42}$

17. $\frac{12}{15}$ $\frac{26}{30}$

18. $\frac{17}{35}$ $\frac{27}{54}$

19. $\frac{2.1}{0.7}$ $\frac{6}{2}$

20. $\frac{18}{4.5}$ $\frac{100}{25}$

21. $\frac{8.4}{12}$ $\frac{12}{14}$

22. $\frac{6}{1.8}$ $\frac{3}{0.9}$

23. $\frac{30.6}{100}$ $\frac{1.8}{6}$

24. $\frac{0.16}{0.06}$ $\frac{0.55}{0.4}$

25. $\frac{3}{3.98}$ $\frac{5}{5.98}$

26. $\frac{11}{15}$ $\frac{0.99}{1.35}$

27. $\frac{8}{12}$ $\frac{2.4}{3.2}$

28. $\frac{1.8}{2.7}$ $\frac{42}{63}$

29. $\frac{2}{0.3}$ $\frac{42}{6.3}$

30. $\frac{0.8}{3}$ $\frac{2.7}{10}$

31. $\frac{7.9}{4}$ $\frac{16.1}{8.6}$

32. $\frac{2.8}{4.5}$ $\frac{2.1}{3.5}$

33. $\frac{25.5}{15.3}$ $\frac{0.5}{0.3}$

34. $\frac{1.8}{16.5}$ $\frac{0.6}{5.5}$

35. $\frac{0.9}{2.1}$ $\frac{0.25}{0.5}$

Solve and check.

36. $\frac{4}{3} = \frac{s}{27}$

37. $\frac{25}{n} = \frac{5}{20}$

38. $\frac{24}{8} = \frac{9}{x}$

39. $\frac{a}{42} = \frac{5}{14}$

40. $\frac{x}{45} = \frac{7}{9}$

41. $\frac{5}{7} = \frac{b}{42}$

42. $\frac{36}{w} = \frac{12}{21}$

43. $\frac{65}{10} = \frac{13}{d}$

44. $\frac{34}{72} = \frac{17}{m}$

45. $\frac{c}{21} = \frac{19}{57}$

46. $\frac{4}{30} = \frac{t}{36}$

47. $\frac{3}{y} = \frac{10}{15}$

48. $\frac{4}{f} = \frac{24}{9}$

49. $\frac{18}{15} = \frac{s}{18}$

50. $\frac{r}{6} = \frac{4}{5}$

51. $\frac{16}{3} = \frac{8}{h}$

52. $\frac{9}{5} = \frac{v}{8}$

53. $\frac{5}{k} = \frac{4}{3}$

54. $\frac{0.07}{0.56} = \frac{2}{w}$

55. $\frac{d}{1.6} = \frac{2.4}{3.2}$

56. $\frac{18}{y} = \frac{2.4}{2.8}$

57. $\frac{0.07}{0.02} = \frac{3.5}{b}$

58. $\frac{g}{8} = \frac{23.7}{3}$

59. $\frac{1.5}{0.6} = \frac{d}{0.36}$

60. $\frac{0.4}{0.14} = \frac{18}{y}$

61. $\frac{n}{1.26} = \frac{4}{0.72}$

62. $\frac{10.6}{5} = \frac{a}{2.5}$

63. $\frac{0.9}{g} = \frac{0.4}{4.8}$

64. $\frac{0.08}{0.6} = \frac{c}{3.3}$

65. $\frac{0.03}{0.27} = \frac{9}{v}$

66. $\frac{0.8}{n} = \frac{4.8}{9}$

67. $\frac{a}{21} = \frac{7.8}{63}$

68. $\frac{0.18}{0.29} = \frac{2.88}{t}$

69. $\frac{9.6}{4.7} = \frac{m}{2.35}$

70. $\frac{4.9}{h} = \frac{2.1}{1.2}$

Skills File

Writing percents, decimals, and fractions, pages 32–33

Write as a percent.

1. 0.39
2. 0.62
3. 0.04
4. 0.08
5. 0.7
6. 0.5
7. 0.727
8. 0.345
9. 0.802
10. 0.109
11. 0.061
12. 0.557

13. 0.2946
14. 0.4372
15. 0.7708
16. 0.9021
17. 0.1008
18. 0.0566
19. 3.62
20. 4.78
21. 9.01
22. 2.149
23. 7.681
24. 5.023

Write as a decimal.

52. 17%
53. 82%
54. 30%
55. 90%
56. 75%
57. 46%
58. 5%
59. 8%
60. 51.3%
61. 20.7%
62. 19.6%
63. 7.42%

64. 3.08%
65. 5.91%
66. $8\frac{3}{4}$%
67. $4\frac{1}{2}$%
68. $1\frac{1}{4}$%
69. $23\frac{1}{4}$%
70. $50\frac{1}{2}$%
71. $47\frac{3}{8}$%
72. 172%
73. 206%
74. 270%
75. 159%

Write as a percent.

25. $\frac{1}{2}$
26. $\frac{3}{4}$
27. $\frac{2}{5}$
28. $\frac{1}{4}$
29. $\frac{2}{25}$
30. $\frac{6}{20}$
31. $\frac{21}{50}$
32. $\frac{8}{25}$
33. $\frac{7}{10}$

34. $\frac{9}{10}$
35. $\frac{1}{20}$
36. $\frac{37}{50}$
37. $\frac{18}{25}$
38. $\frac{1}{8}$
39. $\frac{15}{32}$
40. $\frac{3}{16}$
41. $\frac{15}{16}$
42. $\frac{5}{8}$

43. $\frac{5}{32}$
44. $\frac{29}{32}$
45. $\frac{3}{8}$
46. $\frac{9}{16}$
47. $\frac{7}{8}$
48. $\frac{3}{2}$
49. $\frac{13}{4}$
50. $\frac{19}{5}$
51. $\frac{27}{20}$

Write as a fraction in lowest terms.

76. 10%
77. 80%
78. 30%
79. 90%
80. 25%
81. 75%
82. 45%
83. 95%
84. 5%
85. 8%
86. 3%
87. 1%

88. 41%
89. 24%
90. 68%
91. 79%
92. 86%
93. 13%
94. 51%
95. 34%
96. 160%
97. 172%
98. 103%
99. 250%

Skills File

Using percent, pages 34–37

1. 25% of 60 is ___.
2. 90% of 50 is ___.
3. 7% of 82 is ___.
4. 14.8% of 45 is ___.
5. 5.3% of 94 is ___.
6. 32.6% of 72 is ___.
7. $4\frac{1}{2}$% of 25 is ___.
8. $18\frac{3}{4}$% of 30 is ___.
9. Find 41% of 17.
10. Find 89% of 52.
11. Find 1.9% of 200.
12. Find 8.5% of 350.
13. Find $5\frac{1}{2}$% of 63.
14. Find $6\frac{5}{8}$% of 100.
15. Find 108% of 80.
16. Find 150% of 35.
17. 7% of 81 is what number?
18. 23% of 57 is what number?
19. 52% of 90 is what number?
20. 7.2% of 18 is what number?
21. What number is 9.6% of 54?
22. What number is $3\frac{1}{2}$% of 100?
23. What number is $9\frac{3}{4}$% of 270?

24. ___% of 25 is 17.
25. ___% of 50 is 4.
26. ___% of 35 is 7.
27. ___% of 64 is 16.
28. ___% of 60 is 45.
29. ___% of 40 is 1.2.
30. ___% of 66 is 36.3.
31. ___% of 82 is 11.48.
32. ___% of 75 is 45.75.
33. ___% of 44 is 15.4.
34. ___% of 27 is 10.8.
35. ___% of 50 is 44.5.
36. What percent of 90 is 18?
37. What percent of 40 is 6?
38. What percent of 48 is 18?
39. What percent of 56 is 35?
40. What percent of 50 is 47?
41. 42 is what percent of 48?
42. 70 is what percent of 80?
43. 18.4 is what percent of 23?
44. 12 is what percent of 32?

45. 40% of ___ is 30.
46. 5% of ___ is 2.
47. 14% of ___ is 21.
48. 25% of ___ is 1.8.
49. 2% of ___ is 0.56.
50. 5% of ___ is 0.41.
51. 75% of ___ is 5.4.
52. $82\frac{1}{2}$% of ___ is 33.
53. $6\frac{1}{4}$% of ___ is 12.5.
54. $3\frac{3}{4}$% of ___ is 7.5.
55. 12.5% of ___ is 6.
56. 7.3% of ___ is 0.73.
57. 60% of what number is 18?
58. 8% of what number is 10?
59. 17% of what number is 14.45?
60. $37\frac{1}{2}$% of what number is 26.25?
61. 54.8% of what number is 8.22?
62. 6.3 is 20% of what number?
63. 1.12 is 32% of what number?
64. 8.4 is 70% of what number?
65. 27.2 is 85% of what number?

COMPUTER LITERACY

The PRINT and END Statements

A computer is a very fast and accurate machine. A computer does not think. It needs instructions from a human. A computer **program** is a set of instructions. BASIC is a common programming language. In BASIC, numbers are written as decimals or decimal approximations. The data that is put into the program is called **input**. The computer executes the program, and what it prints out is called the **output**.

The computer recognizes these symbols of operation:

✱ (multiply)   + (add)
/ (divide)   − (subtract)

The instructions to a computer are called statements. The PRINT statement causes the computer to print what is between quotation marks or answers to calculations.

The END statement stops the program. It should be the last statement in a program.

Program A

Input   Output

```
10 PRINT "HELLO"        HELLO
20 PRINT "MY NAME"      MY NAME
30 PRINT "IS"           IS
40 PRINT "HAL."         HAL.
50 END
```

Every statement of a program is given a line number. Although the statements do not have to be typed in order, the computer always executes them in numerical order. Many people number the statements by tens so that statements can be added to the program if necessary.

Program B

Input   Output

```
10 PRINT 6+2       8
20 PRINT 6-2       4
30 PRINT 6*2       12
40 PRINT 6/2       3
50 END
```

A semicolon separates items in a PRINT statement.

Program C

Input   Output

```
10 PRINT "9/3=";9/3        9/3= 3
20 PRINT "10/4=";10/4      10/4= 2.5
30 PRINT "8/3=";8/3        8/3= 2.666666667
40 END
```

Give the output for each program.

1. ```
   10 PRINT "THIS IS"
   20 PRINT "A BASIC"
   30 PRINT "PROGRAM."
   40 END
   ```

2. ```
   10 PRINT 3+4
   20 PRINT 7-2
   30 PRINT 5*8
   40 PRINT 24/4
   50 END
   ```

3. ```
   10 PRINT "2+4=";2+4
   20 PRINT "9-7=";9-7
   30 PRINT 8*4;"=8*4"
   40 PRINT 9/5;"=9/5"
   50 END
   ```

4. Give the output for Program A if the following statement is added after line 50.

   `35 PRINT "NOT"`

5. Write a program to print your name, your age, and the name of your school.

6. Write a program to compute 12 + 5, 9 − 4, 6 × 18, and 15 ÷ 3.
   ```

COMPUTER LITERACY

The LET and INPUT Statements

A computer has thousands of memory locations. Each location can hold exactly one value at a time. When a memory location is used, it is given a name. A name can be either a single letter or a single letter followed by a single digit. C and B3 are examples of names that can be used.

In BASIC, the LET statement is used to put a value in a memory location. In Program A, lines 10 and 20 assign values into memory locations. In line 30, the values for R and S are retrieved from the memory, the computation is performed, and the resulting value is stored in another memory location (T).

Program A

Input | Output
```
10 LET R=6          54
20 LET S=R+3
30 LET T=R*S
40 PRINT T
50 END
```

The INPUT statement is another way to put a value into a memory location. When the computer gets to an INPUT statement in a program, it prints a question mark and waits for a number to be typed in. In Program B, the user typed 5 for X and 8 for Y.

Program B

Input | Output
```
10 INPUT X          ? 5
20 INPUT Y          ? 8
30 PRINT 2*(X+Y)-3    23
40 END
```

The INPUT statement allows you, the user, to run the same program more than once, using a different value each time. Use commas between names in INPUT statements.

A letter followed by $ can be used to put letters and/or numbers into a memory location. This is called a string variable and is often used for names and addresses. In a LET statement, quotation marks must be used to show where the string begins and ends.

Program C

Input | Output
```
10 INPUT N$              ? B.HUFFMAN
20 LET T$="TEST AVERAGE="  ? 97,95,96
30 INPUT S1,S2,S3        B.HUFFMAN
40 LET A=(S1+S2+S3)/3    TEST AVERAGE= 96
50 PRINT N$
60 PRINT T$;A
70 END
```

Give the output for Program B when

1. X is 7; Y is 15. **2.** X is 20; Y is 35.

3. Give the output for Program C when N$ is your name, S1 is 88, S2 is 95, and S3 is 90.

Give the output for each program. Use 7 for B and 8 for H.

4.
```
10 PRINT "DISTANCE"
20 LET R=80
30 LET T=3
40 PRINT R*T
50 END
```
5.
```
10 INPUT B
20 INPUT H
30 LET A=B*H
40 PRINT A
50 END
```

6. Use INPUT statements to write a program to find the area of a triangle.

COMPUTER LITERACY

The GO TO and IF . . . THEN Statements

A computer executes a program in the order of the line numbers unless the program tells the computer to go to a specific statement. The GO TO statement tells the computer to skip ahead or to go back to a specified line. It is often used to repeat a set of statements.

Program A

Input	Output
10 INPUT X	? 4
20 PRINT 3*X	12
30 GO TO 10	? 9
40 END	27
	?

In Program A, line 30 sends the computer to line 10 where another value for X is to be entered. The user first typed 4 for X, then 9. The computer will keep asking for values for X until the program is stopped by the user.

The IF . . . THEN statement compares two values. If the comparison is true, the statement sends the computer to a specified line. If the statement is false, the computer will go to the next higher statement number.

BASIC recognizes these comparisons:

= (equal)	<> (not equal)
< (less than)	<= (less than or equal)
> (greater than)	>= (greater than or equal)

In Program B, when the user types YES for line 30, line 40 sends the computer back to line 10. If the user types anything other than YES for line 30, the computer will go to line 50.

Program B

Input	Output
10 INPUT A,B	? 6,8
20 PRINT "A+B=";A+B	A+B= 14
30 INPUT Q$	? YES
40 IF Q$="YES" THEN 10	? 15,23
50 PRINT "DONE"	A+B= 38
60 END	? NO
	DONE

Give the output for Program A when

1. X is 20, 34, 56, and 128.

Give the output for Program B when

2. A is 34; B is 57; Q$ is YES.

3. A is 66; B is 75; Q$ is NO.

4. Give the output. Enter 7, 2, 3, 12, 17, 9, 999, and 0.

```
10 INPUT A,B
20 IF A=999 THEN 50
30 PRINT A;"*";B;"=";A*B
40 GO TO 10
50 PRINT "NO MORE DATA"
60 END
```

5. Give the output. Enter your name for N$ and 7, 25, and 130 for A.

```
10 INPUT N$
20 INPUT A
30 IF A>99 THEN 60
40 PRINT 3*A+14
50 GO TO 20
60 PRINT "THAT'S ALL ";N$
70 END
```

6. Rewrite Program A so that it will end if you put in a number greater than 244.

COMPUTER LITERACY

The READ, DATA, and REM Statements

The LET and INPUT statements are used to put values into a program. Another way to tell the computer the values of A and B is to use the READ and DATA statements. As the computer executes the READ statement, it looks for a DATA statement in the program. The word DATA is followed by the values, each value separated from the next by a comma.

In Program A, the first time the computer reads L and W, it uses 4 for L and 2.5 for W. The second time, it uses 18 for L and 11 for W. The computer keeps track of where it is in the data line. On the third pass through Program A, the computer will type a message that it is out of data and stop.

Program A

Input

```
10 READ L,W
20 LET P=2*L+2*W
30 PRINT "PERIMETER =";P
40 GO TO 10
50 DATA 4,2.5,18,11
60 END
```

Output

```
PERIMETER = 13
PERIMETER = 58
OUT OF DATA AT
LINE 10
```

The REM statement is ignored by the computer. REM stands for remark. This statement is used to supply information to someone looking at the program.

Program B

Input

```
10 REM  FINDING INTEREST
20 READ P,R,T
30 PRINT "INTEREST =";P*R*T
40 GO TO 20
50 DATA 1000,.08,2,1800,
   .065,1.75
60 END
```

Output

```
INTEREST = 160
INTEREST = 204.75
OUT OF DATA AT
LINE 20
```

1. Give the output for Program A when this statement is added to the program.

   ```
   55 DATA 12,5,7,2,1.4,1.1,23,14
   ```

2. Give the output for Program B when this statement is added to the program.

   ```
   52 DATA 2200,.07,1.75,2575,
      .065,4
   ```

Give the output for each program.

3. ```
   10 READ R
   20 REM   CIRCUMFERENCE
   30 LET C=3.14*2*R
   40 PRINT "R =";R;" C =";C
   50 GO TO 10
   60 DATA 5,10,17
   70 END
   ```

4. ```
   10 READ P
   20 REM  20% DISCOUNT
   30 LET S=.8*P
   40 PRINT "REGULAR PRICE IS";P
   50 PRINT "SALE PRICE IS    ";S
   60 GO TO 10
   70 DATA 15,22,27.50,30,42.75
   80 END
   ```

5. ```
   10 REM   GROSS PAY
   20 READ N$,R,H
   30 IF H>40 THEN 70
   40 LET P=R*H
   50 PRINT N$;"  PAY =";P
   60 GO TO 20
   70 LET P=40*R+(H-40)*1.5*R
   80 GO TO 50
   90 DATA ANDERSON,10.50,35,
   JENSEN,11.75,42
   100 DATA RIEDELL,12,45,
   BRETZLAUF,10.75,38
   110 END
   ```

6. Given the regular price and the sale price for several items, write a program to find the amount of discount and the rate of discount.
   ```

COMPUTER LITERACY

The FOR and NEXT Statements

A loop is a set of statements that are executed over and over again. When the number of times a loop is to be executed is known, the FOR and NEXT statements can be used. The FOR statement specifies the first and last values to use. The NEXT statement decides whether the loop is to be executed again. The statements that are repeated are placed between the FOR and NEXT statements.

In Program A, line 10 tells the computer to go through the loop using 1 as the first value for X. Line 30 sends the computer back to line 10 and the computer goes through the loop using 2 as the value for X. Each time the loop is executed, the value for X increases by 1. The loop is completed after the last value of X (4) that is indicated in the FOR statement is used, and the computer goes to the line following the NEXT statement.

Program A

Input	Output
``` 10 FOR X=1 TO 4 20 PRINT X 30 NEXT X 40 END ```	1 2 3 4

In Program B, STEP 3 tells the computer to increase the value of Y by 3 each time the loop is executed. If no step is given, the value increases by 1.

Program B

Input	Output
``` 10 FOR Y=6 TO 15 STEP 3 20 PRINT Y 30 NEXT Y 40 END ```	6 9 12 15

Program C adds the even numbers from 2 to 10, printing each sum as it goes. Notice that in line 30, a different value is assigned to S each time the loop is executed.

Program C

Input	Output
``` 10 LET S=0 20 FOR N=2 TO 10 STEP 2 30 LET S=S+N 40 PRINT S 50 NEXT N 60 END ```	2 6 12 20 30

Give the output for each program.

1.
```
10 FOR N=3 TO 8
20 PRINT N
30 NEXT N
40 END
```

2.
```
10 FOR M=12 TO 20 STEP 4
20 PRINT M
30 NEXT M
40 END
```

3.
```
10 REM  COST OF 6 ITEMS
20 FOR N=1 TO 6
30 LET C=19.95*N
40 PRINT "NUMBER:";N;"COST:";C
50 NEXT N
60 END
```

4.
```
10 REM   ANNUAL COMPOUND INTEREST
20 REM  $100 AT 8%
30 LET P=100
40 FOR T=1 TO 5
50 LET P=P+I
60 LET I=P*.08
70 PRINT "YEAR:";T;"INTEREST: $";I
80 NEXT T
90 END
```

5. Write a program to find the amount earned by working from 1 to 8 hours at a rate of $4.50 an hour.

COMPUTER LITERACY

The INT and TAB Functions

INT(X) is the greatest integer function. The computer will determine the greatest integer that is less than or equal to the number specified in parentheses following INT. Some examples are:

INT(8) = 8   INT(0.07) = 0
INT(3.87) = 3   INT(9/2) = 4

An important use for INT is to determine whether one number is divisible by another number. If so, the quotient will be the same as the INT of the quotient. Program A uses the INT function to determine the even integers between 1 and 10.

Program A

Input	Output
10 FOR N=1 TO 10	2
20 IF INT(N/2)=N/2 THEN 50	4
30 NEXT N	6
40 GO TO 70	8
50 PRINT N	10
60 GO TO 30	
70 END	

The TAB function is used only in PRINT statements. It moves the computer across to a specified position. It is used to place output below headings.

Program B

Input	Output	
10 PRINT "RADIUS AREA"	RADIUS	AREA
20 INPUT R	? 5	
30 IF R=99 THEN 60	5	78.5
40 PRINT R;TAB(8);3.14*R*R	? 8	
50 GO TO 20	8	200.96
60 END	? 99	

Give the output for each program.

1.
```
10 FOR X=1 TO 60
20 IF INT(X/5)=X/5 THEN 50
30 NEXT X
40 GO TO 70
50 PRINT X
60 GO TO 30
70 END
```

2.
```
10 READ N
20 PRINT "DIVISORS OF";N;"ARE:"
30 FOR D=1 TO N
40 IF INT(N/D)<>N/D THEN 60
50 PRINT D
60 NEXT D
70 GO TO 10
80 DATA 24,36,56,59
90 END
```

3.
```
10 PRINT "PRICE  5% TAX  TOTAL"
20 READ P
30 PRINT P;TAB(8);.05*P;TAB(16);
P+.05*P
40 GO TO 20
50 DATA 1.20,6.80,12.60
60 END
```

4.
```
10 REM  CCM BANK SERVICE CHARGE
20 PRINT "ACCOUNT  SERVICE CHARGE"
30 READ A,B,N
40 REM  N IS NUMBER OF CHECKS
50 IF B>300 THEN 90
60 LET S=.1*N
70 PRINT "#";A;TAB(10);"$";S
80 GO TO 30
90 PRINT "#";A;TAB(10);"NO CHARGE"
100 GO TO 30
110 DATA 1519,85.72,16,1520,
234.87,15
120 DATA 1521,328.41,23,1522,
261.35,19
130 END
```

5. Write a program that will test if a number is divisible by 3.

Tables

Metric System

Length

10 millimeters (mm) = 1 centimeter (cm)

$\left.\begin{array}{r}\text{10 centimeters}\\\text{100 millimeters}\end{array}\right\}$ = 1 decimeter (dm)

$\left.\begin{array}{r}\text{10 decimeters}\\\text{100 centimeters}\end{array}\right\}$ = 1 meter (m)

1000 meters = 1 kilometer (km)

Area

100 square millimeters (mm²) = 1 square centimeter (cm²)

10,000 square centimeters = 1 square meter (m²)

100 square meters = 1 are (a)

10,000 square meters = 1 hectare (ha)

Volume

1000 cubic millimeters (mm³) = 1 cubic centimeter (cm³)

1000 cubic centimeters = 1 cubic decimeter (dm³)

1,000,000 cubic centimeters = 1 cubic meter (m³)

Mass

1000 milligrams (mg) = 1 gram (g)

1000 grams = 1 kilogram (kg)

1000 kilograms = 1 metric ton (t)

Capacity

1000 milliliters (mL) = 1 liter (L)

1000 liters = 1 kiloliter (kL)

United States Customary System

Length

12 inches (in.) = 1 foot (ft.)

$\left.\begin{array}{r}\text{3 feet}\\\text{36 inches}\end{array}\right\}$ = 1 yard (yd.)

$\left.\begin{array}{r}\text{1760 yards}\\\text{5280 feet}\end{array}\right\}$ = 1 mile (mi.)

6076 feet = 1 nautical mile

Area

144 square inches (sq. in.) = 1 square foot (sq. ft.)

9 square feet = 1 square yard (sq. yd.)

4840 square yards = 1 acre (A.)

Volume

1728 cubic inches (cu. in.) = 1 cubic foot (cu. ft.)

27 cubic feet = 1 cubic yard (cu. yd.)

Weight

16 ounces (oz.) = 1 pound (lb.)

2000 pounds = 1 ton (T.)

Capacity

8 fluid ounces (fl. oz.) = 1 cup (c.)

2 cups = 1 pint (pt.)

2 pints = 1 quart (qt.)

4 quarts = 1 gallon (gal.)

Symbols

$\approx$	approximately equal to
$\overline{AB}$	segment AB
$\angle G$	angle G
45°	45 degrees
⌐	right angle
$\sqrt{25}$	square root of 25

Geometric Formulas

Perimeter

rectangle $\quad P = 2l + 2w$

Circumference

circle $\quad C = \pi d$ or $C = 2\pi r$

Area

rectangle $\quad A = lw$

square $\quad A = s^2$

parallelogram

$\quad A = bh$

triangle $\quad A = \frac{1}{2}bh$

trapezoid $\quad A = \frac{1}{2}h(a + b)$

circle $\quad A = \pi r^2$

Surface area

rectangular prism

$\quad A = 2lw + 2lh + 2wh$

cube $\quad A = 6s^2$

cylinder $\quad A = 2\pi rh + 2\pi r^2$

Volume

rectangular prism

$\quad V = lwh$

cube $\quad V = s^3$

cylinder $\quad V = \pi r^2 h$

rectangular pyramid

$\quad V = \frac{1}{3}lwh$

cone $\quad V = \frac{1}{3}\pi r^2 h$

sphere $\quad V = \frac{4}{3}\pi r^3$

Monthly Payment per $1 Borrowed						
	Number of equal monthly payments					
Annual rate	6	12	18	24	30	36
12%	0.17255	0.08885	0.06098	0.04707	0.03875	0.03321
13%	0.17304	0.08932	0.06145	0.04754	0.03922	0.03369
14%	0.17354	0.08979	0.06192	0.04801	0.03970	0.03418
15%	0.17403	0.09026	0.06238	0.04849	0.04019	0.03467
15.5%	0.17428	0.09049	0.06262	0.04872	0.04042	0.03491
16%	0.17453	0.09073	0.06286	0.04896	0.04066	0.03516
16.5%	0.17478	0.09097	0.06309	0.04920	0.04091	0.03540
17%	0.17503	0.09120	0.06333	0.04944	0.04115	0.03565
17.5%	0.17528	0.09144	0.06357	0.04968	0.04139	0.03590
18%	0.17553	0.09168	0.06381	0.04992	0.04164	0.03615
18.5%	0.17577	0.09192	0.06404	0.05017	0.04189	0.03640
19%	0.17602	0.09216	0.06428	0.05041	0.04213	0.03666
19.5%	0.17627	0.09240	0.06452	0.05065	0.04238	0.03691
20%	0.17652	0.09263	0.06476	0.05090	0.04263	0.03716
20.5%	0.17677	0.09287	0.06500	0.05114	0.04288	0.03742
21%	0.17702	0.09311	0.06524	0.05139	0.04313	0.03768
21.5%	0.17727	0.09335	0.06549	0.05163	0.04338	0.03793
22%	0.17752	0.09359	0.06573	0.05188	0.04363	0.03819
22.5%	0.17777	0.09384	0.06597	0.05213	0.04389	0.03845
23%	0.17802	0.09408	0.06621	0.05237	0.04414	0.03871
23.5%	0.17827	0.09432	0.06646	0.05262	0.04439	0.03897
24%	0.17853	0.09456	0.06670	0.05287	0.04465	0.03923

SINGLE Persons—WEEKLY Payroll Period

At least	But less than	0	1	2	3	4	5	6	7	8	9	10 or more
And the wages are—		Exemptions claimed										
		The amount of income tax to be withheld shall be—										
$0	$28	$0	$0	$0	$0	$0	$0	$0	$0	$0	$0	$0
28	29	.20	0	0	0	0	0	0	0	0	0	0
29	30	.30	0	0	0	0	0	0	0	0	0	0
30	31	.50	0	0	0	0	0	0	0	0	0	0
31	32	.60	0	0	0	0	0	0	0	0	0	0
32	33	.80	0	0	0	0	0	0	0	0	0	0
33	34	.90	0	0	0	0	0	0	0	0	0	0
34	35	1.10	0	0	0	0	0	0	0	0	0	0
35	36	1.20	0	0	0	0	0	0	0	0	0	0
36	37	1.40	0	0	0	0	0	0	0	0	0	0
37	38	1.50	0	0	0	0	0	0	0	0	0	0
38	39	1.70	0	0	0	0	0	0	0	0	0	0
39	40	1.80	0	0	0	0	0	0	0	0	0	0
40	41	2.00	0	0	0	0	0	0	0	0	0	0
41	42	2.10	0	0	0	0	0	0	0	0	0	0
42	43	2.30	0	0	0	0	0	0	0	0	0	0
43	44	2.40	0	0	0	0	0	0	0	0	0	0
44	45	2.60	0	0	0	0	0	0	0	0	0	0
45	46	2.70	0	0	0	0	0	0	0	0	0	0
46	47	2.90	0	0	0	0	0	0	0	0	0	0
47	48	3.00	.10	0	0	0	0	0	0	0	0	0
48	49	3.20	.30	0	0	0	0	0	0	0	0	0
49	50	3.30	.40	0	0	0	0	0	0	0	0	0
50	51	3.50	.60	0	0	0	0	0	0	0	0	0
51	52	3.60	.70	0	0	0	0	0	0	0	0	0
52	53	3.80	.90	0	0	0	0	0	0	0	0	0
53	54	3.90	1.00	0	0	0	0	0	0	0	0	0
54	55	4.10	1.20	0	0	0	0	0	0	0	0	0
55	56	4.20	1.30	0	0	0	0	0	0	0	0	0
56	57	4.40	1.50	0	0	0	0	0	0	0	0	0
57	58	4.50	1.60	0	0	0	0	0	0	0	0	0
58	59	4.70	1.80	0	0	0	0	0	0	0	0	0
59	60	4.80	1.90	0	0	0	0	0	0	0	0	0
60	62	5.10	2.20	0	0	0	0	0	0	0	0	0
62	64	5.40	2.50	0	0	0	0	0	0	0	0	0
64	66	5.70	2.80	0	0	0	0	0	0	0	0	0
66	68	6.10	3.10	.20	0	0	0	0	0	0	0	0
68	70	6.40	3.40	.50	0	0	0	0	0	0	0	0
70	72	6.80	3.70	.80	0	0	0	0	0	0	0	0
72	74	7.10	4.00	1.10	0	0	0	0	0	0	0	0
74	76	7.50	4.30	1.40	0	0	0	0	0	0	0	0
76	78	7.90	4.60	1.70	0	0	0	0	0	0	0	0
78	80	8.20	4.90	2.00	0	0	0	0	0	0	0	0
80	82	8.60	5.20	2.30	0	0	0	0	0	0	0	0
82	84	8.90	5.50	2.60	0	0	0	0	0	0	0	0
84	86	9.30	5.80	2.90	0	0	0	0	0	0	0	0
86	88	9.70	6.20	3.20	.30	0	0	0	0	0	0	0
88	90	10.00	6.60	3.50	.60	0	0	0	0	0	0	0
90	92	10.40	6.90	3.80	.90	0	0	0	0	0	0	0
92	94	10.70	7.30	4.10	1.20	0	0	0	0	0	0	0
94	96	11.10	7.60	4.40	1.50	0	0	0	0	0	0	0
96	98	11.50	8.00	4.70	1.80	0	0	0	0	0	0	0
98	100	11.80	8.40	5.00	2.10	0	0	0	0	0	0	0
100	105	12.50	9.00	5.50	2.60	0	0	0	0	0	0	0
105	110	13.40	9.90	6.40	3.40	.50	0	0	0	0	0	0
110	115	14.30	10.80	7.30	4.10	1.20	0	0	0	0	0	0
115	120	15.20	11.70	8.20	4.90	2.00	0	0	0	0	0	0
120	125	16.10	12.60	9.10	5.70	2.70	0	0	0	0	0	0
125	130	17.00	13.50	10.00	6.60	3.50	.60	0	0	0	0	0
130	135	17.90	14.40	10.90	7.50	4.20	1.40	0	0	0	0	0

SINGLE Persons—WEEKLY Payroll Period

And the wages are—		Exemptions claimed										
At least	But less than	0	1	2	3	4	5	6	7	8	9	10 or more
		The amount of income tax to be withheld shall be—										
$135	$140	$19.00	$15.30	$11.80	$8.40	$5.00	$2.10	$0	$0	$0	$0	$0
140	145	20.00	16.20	12.70	9.30	5.80	2.90	0	0	0	0	0
145	150	21.10	17.10	13.60	10.20	6.70	3.60	.70	0	0	0	0
150	160	22.60	18.60	15.00	11.50	8.10	4.70	1.80	0	0	0	0
160	170	24.70	20.70	16.80	13.30	9.90	6.40	3.30	.50	0	0	0
170	180	26.80	22.80	18.80	15.10	11.70	8.20	4.80	2.00	0	0	0
180	190	28.90	24.90	20.90	16.90	13.50	10.00	6.50	3.50	.60	0	0
190	200	31.00	27.00	23.00	18.90	15.30	11.80	8.30	5.00	2.10	0	0
200	210	33.60	29.10	25.10	21.00	17.10	13.60	10.10	6.70	3.60	.70	0
210	220	36.20	31.20	27.20	23.10	19.10	15.40	11.90	8.50	5.10	2.20	0
220	230	38.80	33.80	29.30	25.20	21.20	17.20	13.70	10.30	6.80	3.70	.80
230	240	41.40	36.40	31.40	27.30	23.30	19.20	15.50	12.10	8.60	5.20	2.30
240	250	44.00	39.00	34.00	29.40	25.40	21.30	17.30	13.90	10.40	6.90	3.80
250	260	46.60	41.60	36.60	31.60	27.50	23.40	19.40	15.70	12.20	8.70	5.30
260	270	49.20	44.20	39.20	34.20	29.60	25.50	21.50	17.50	14.00	10.50	7.10
270	280	51.80	46.80	41.80	36.80	31.80	27.60	23.60	19.60	15.80	12.30	8.90
280	290	54.80	49.40	44.40	39.40	34.40	29.70	25.70	21.70	17.60	14.10	10.70
290	300	57.80	52.10	47.00	42.00	37.00	32.00	27.80	23.80	19.70	15.90	12.50
300	310	60.80	55.10	49.60	44.60	39.60	34.60	29.90	25.90	21.80	17.80	14.30
310	320	63.80	58.10	52.30	47.20	42.20	37.20	32.20	28.00	23.90	19.90	16.10
320	330	66.80	61.10	55.30	49.80	44.80	39.80	34.80	30.10	26.00	22.00	17.90
330	340	70.00	64.10	58.30	52.50	47.40	42.40	37.40	32.40	28.10	24.10	20.00
340	350	73.40	67.10	61.30	55.50	50.00	45.00	40.00	35.00	30.20	26.20	22.10
350	360	76.80	70.30	64.30	58.50	52.80	47.60	42.60	37.60	32.60	28.30	24.20
360	370	80.20	73.70	67.30	61.50	55.80	50.20	45.20	40.20	35.20	30.40	26.30
370	380	83.60	77.10	70.50	64.50	58.80	53.00	47.80	42.80	37.80	32.80	28.40
380	390	87.00	80.50	73.90	67.50	61.80	56.00	50.40	45.40	40.40	35.40	30.50
390	400	90.40	83.90	77.30	70.80	64.80	59.00	53.20	48.00	43.00	38.00	33.00
400	410	93.80	87.30	80.70	74.20	67.80	62.00	56.20	50.60	45.60	40.60	35.60
410	420	97.20	90.70	84.10	77.60	71.10	65.00	59.20	53.50	48.20	43.20	38.20
420	430	100.60	94.10	87.50	81.00	74.50	68.00	62.20	56.50	50.80	45.80	40.80
430	440	104.10	97.50	90.90	84.40	77.90	71.30	65.20	59.50	53.70	48.40	43.40
440	450	108.00	100.90	94.30	87.80	81.30	74.70	68.20	62.50	56.70	51.00	46.00
450	460	111.90	104.40	97.70	91.20	84.70	78.10	71.60	65.50	59.70	53.90	48.60
460	470	115.80	108.30	101.10	94.60	88.10	81.50	75.00	68.50	62.70	56.90	51.20
470	480	119.70	112.20	104.70	98.00	91.50	84.90	78.40	71.80	65.70	59.90	54.20
480	490	123.60	116.10	108.60	101.40	94.90	88.30	81.80	75.20	68.70	62.90	57.20
490	500	127.50	120.00	112.50	105.00	98.30	91.70	85.20	78.60	72.10	65.90	60.20
500	510	131.40	123.90	116.40	108.90	101.70	95.10	88.60	82.00	75.50	69.00	63.20
510	520	135.30	127.80	120.30	112.80	105.30	98.50	92.00	85.40	78.90	72.40	66.20
520	530	139.20	131.70	124.20	116.70	109.20	101.90	95.40	88.80	82.30	75.80	69.20
530	540	143.10	135.60	128.10	120.60	113.10	105.60	98.80	92.20	85.70	79.20	72.60
540	550	147.00	139.50	132.00	124.50	117.00	109.50	102.20	95.60	89.10	82.60	76.00
550	560	150.90	143.40	135.90	128.40	120.90	113.40	105.90	99.00	92.50	86.00	79.40
560	570	154.80	147.30	139.80	132.30	124.80	117.30	109.80	102.40	95.90	89.40	82.80
570	580	158.70	151.20	143.70	136.20	128.70	121.20	113.70	106.20	99.30	92.80	86.20
580	590	162.60	155.10	147.60	140.10	132.60	125.10	117.60	110.10	102.70	96.20	89.60
590	600	166.50	159.00	151.50	144.00	136.50	129.00	121.50	114.00	106.50	99.60	93.00
600	610	170.40	162.90	155.40	147.90	140.40	132.90	125.40	117.90	110.40	103.00	96.40
610	620	174.30	166.80	159.30	151.80	144.30	136.80	129.30	121.80	114.30	106.80	99.80
620	630	178.20	170.70	163.20	155.70	148.20	140.70	133.20	125.70	118.20	110.70	103.20
630	640	182.10	174.60	167.10	159.60	152.10	144.60	137.10	129.60	122.10	114.60	107.10
640	650	186.00	178.50	171.00	163.50	156.00	148.50	141.00	133.50	126.00	118.50	111.00
650	660	189.90	182.40	174.90	167.40	159.90	152.40	144.90	137.40	129.90	122.40	114.90
660	670	193.80	186.30	178.80	171.30	163.80	156.30	148.80	141.30	133.80	126.30	118.80
39 percent of the excess over $670 plus—												
$670 and over		195.80	188.30	180.80	173.30	165.80	158.30	150.80	143.30	135.80	128.30	120.80

403

MARRIED Persons—WEEKLY Payroll Period

And the wages are—		Exemptions claimed										
At least	But less than	0	1	2	3	4	5	6	7	8	9	10 or more
		The amount of income tax to be withheld shall be—										
$0	$46	$0	$0	$0	$0	$0	$0	$0	$0	$0	$0	$0
46	47	.10	0	0	0	0	0	0	0	0	0	0
47	48	.20	0	0	0	0	0	0	0	0	0	0
48	49	.40	0	0	0	0	0	0	0	0	0	0
49	50	.50	0	0	0	0	0	0	0	0	0	0
50	51	.70	0	0	0	0	0	0	0	0	0	0
51	52	.80	0	0	0	0	0	0	0	0	0	0
52	53	1.00	0	0	0	0	0	0	0	0	0	0
53	54	1.10	0	0	0	0	0	0	0	0	0	0
54	55	1.30	0	0	0	0	0	0	0	0	0	0
55	56	1.40	0	0	0	0	0	0	0	0	0	0
56	57	1.60	0	0	0	0	0	0	0	0	0	0
57	58	1.70	0	0	0	0	0	0	0	0	0	0
58	59	1.90	0	0	0	0	0	0	0	0	0	0
59	60	2.00	0	0	0	0	0	0	0	0	0	0
60	62	2.20	0	0	0	0	0	0	0	0	0	0
62	64	2.50	0	0	0	0	0	0	0	0	0	0
64	66	2.80	0	0	0	0	0	0	0	0	0	0
66	68	3.10	.20	0	0	0	0	0	0	0	0	0
68	70	3.40	.50	0	0	0	0	0	0	0	0	0
70	72	3.70	.80	0	0	0	0	0	0	0	0	0
72	74	4.00	1.10	0	0	0	0	0	0	0	0	0
74	76	4.30	1.40	0	0	0	0	0	0	0	0	0
76	78	4.60	1.70	0	0	0	0	0	0	0	0	0
78	80	4.90	2.00	0	0	0	0	0	0	0	0	0
80	82	5.20	2.30	0	0	0	0	0	0	0	0	0
82	84	5.50	2.60	0	0	0	0	0	0	0	0	0
84	86	5.80	2.90	.10	0	0	0	0	0	0	0	0
86	88	6.10	3.20	.40	0	0	0	0	0	0	0	0
88	90	6.40	3.50	.70	0	0	0	0	0	0	0	0
90	92	6.70	3.80	1.00	0	0	0	0	0	0	0	0
92	94	7.00	4.10	1.30	0	0	0	0	0	0	0	0
94	96	7.30	4.40	1.60	0	0	0	0	0	0	0	0
96	98	7.60	4.70	1.90	0	0	0	0	0	0	0	0
98	100	7.90	5.00	2.20	0	0	0	0	0	0	0	0
100	105	8.50	5.60	2.70	0	0	0	0	0	0	0	0
105	110	9.20	6.30	3.40	.50	0	0	0	0	0	0	0
110	115	10.00	7.10	4.20	1.30	0	0	0	0	0	0	0
115	120	10.70	7.80	4.90	2.00	0	0	0	0	0	0	0
120	125	11.50	8.60	5.70	2.80	0	0	0	0	0	0	0
125	130	12.20	9.30	6.40	3.50	.70	0	0	0	0	0	0
130	135	13.10	10.10	7.20	4.30	1.40	0	0	0	0	0	0
135	140	14.00	10.80	7.90	5.00	2.20	0	0	0	0	0	0
140	145	14.90	11.60	8.70	5.80	2.90	0	0	0	0	0	0
145	150	15.80	12.40	9.40	6.50	3.70	.80	0	0	0	0	0
150	160	17.20	13.70	10.60	7.70	4.80	1.90	0	0	0	0	0
160	170	19.00	15.50	12.10	9.20	6.30	3.40	.50	0	0	0	0
170	180	20.80	17.30	13.80	10.70	7.80	4.90	2.00	0	0	0	0
180	190	22.60	19.10	15.60	12.20	9.30	6.40	3.50	.60	0	0	0
190	200	24.40	20.90	17.40	14.00	10.80	7.90	5.00	2.10	0	0	0
200	210	26.20	22.70	19.20	15.80	12.30	9.40	6.50	3.60	.80	0	0
210	220	28.10	24.50	21.00	17.60	14.10	10.90	8.00	5.10	2.30	0	0
220	230	30.20	26.30	22.80	19.40	15.90	12.50	9.50	6.60	3.80	.90	0
230	240	32.30	28.30	24.60	21.20	17.70	14.30	11.00	8.10	5.30	2.40	0
240	250	34.40	30.40	26.40	23.00	19.50	16.10	12.60	9.60	6.80	3.90	1.00
250	260	36.50	32.50	28.50	24.80	21.30	17.90	14.40	11.10	8.30	5.40	2.50
260	270	38.60	34.60	30.60	26.60	23.10	19.70	16.20	12.70	9.80	6.90	4.00
270	280	40.70	36.70	32.70	28.60	24.90	21.50	18.00	14.50	11.30	8.40	5.50
280	290	42.80	38.80	34.80	30.70	26.70	23.30	19.80	16.30	12.90	9.90	7.00
290	300	45.10	40.90	36.90	32.80	28.80	25.10	21.60	18.10	14.70	11.40	8.50

MARRIED Persons—WEEKLY Payroll Period

And the wages are—		Exemptions claimed										
At least	But less than	0	1	2	3	4	5	6	7	8	9	10 or more
		The amount of income tax to be withheld shall be—										
$300	$310	$47.50	$43.00	$39.00	$34.90	$30.90	$26.90	$23.40	$19.90	$16.50	$13.00	$10.00
310	320	49.90	45.30	41.10	37.00	33.00	28.90	25.20	21.70	18.30	14.80	11.50
320	330	52.30	47.70	43.20	39.10	35.10	31.00	27.00	23.50	20.10	16.60	13.20
330	340	54.70	50.10	45.50	41.20	37.20	33.10	29.10	25.30	21.90	18.40	15.00
340	350	57.10	52.50	47.90	43.30	39.30	35.20	31.20	27.20	23.70	20.20	16.80
350	360	59.50	54.90	50.30	45.70	41.40	37.30	33.30	29.30	25.50	22.00	18.60
360	370	61.90	57.30	52.70	48.10	43.50	39.40	35.40	31.40	27.30	23.80	20.40
370	380	64.60	59.70	55.10	50.50	45.90	41.50	37.50	33.50	29.40	25.60	22.20
380	390	67.40	62.10	57.50	52.90	48.30	43.70	39.60	35.60	31.50	27.50	24.00
390	400	70.20	64.80	59.90	55.30	50.70	46.10	41.70	37.70	33.60	29.60	25.80
400	410	73.00	67.60	62.30	57.70	53.10	48.50	43.80	39.80	35.70	31.70	27.60
410	420	75.80	70.40	65.00	60.10	55.50	50.90	46.20	41.90	37.80	33.80	29.70
420	430	78.60	73.20	67.80	62.50	57.90	53.30	48.60	44.00	39.90	35.90	31.80
430	440	81.40	76.00	70.60	65.20	60.30	55.70	51.00	46.40	42.00	38.00	33.90
440	450	84.20	78.80	73.40	68.00	62.70	58.10	53.40	48.80	44.20	40.10	36.00
450	460	87.00	81.60	76.20	70.80	65.40	60.50	55.80	51.20	46.60	42.20	38.10
460	470	90.20	84.40	79.00	73.60	68.20	62.90	58.20	53.60	49.00	44.40	40.20
470	480	93.40	87.30	81.80	76.40	71.00	65.60	60.60	56.00	51.40	46.80	42.30
480	490	96.60	90.50	84.60	79.20	73.80	68.40	63.10	58.40	53.80	49.20	44.60
490	500	99.80	93.70	87.50	82.00	76.60	71.20	65.90	60.80	56.20	51.60	47.00
500	510	103.00	96.90	90.70	84.80	79.40	74.00	68.70	63.30	58.60	54.00	49.40
510	520	106.20	100.10	93.90	87.70	82.20	76.80	71.50	66.10	61.00	56.40	51.80
520	530	109.40	103.30	97.10	90.90	85.00	79.60	74.30	68.90	63.50	58.80	54.20
530	540	112.60	106.50	100.30	94.10	88.00	82.40	77.10	71.70	66.30	61.20	56.60
540	550	115.80	109.70	103.50	97.30	91.20	85.20	79.90	74.50	69.10	63.70	59.00
550	560	119.00	112.90	106.70	100.50	94.40	88.20	82.70	77.30	71.90	66.50	61.40
560	570	122.70	116.10	109.90	103.70	97.60	91.40	85.50	80.10	74.70	69.30	63.90
570	580	126.40	119.30	113.10	106.90	100.80	94.60	88.50	82.90	77.50	72.10	66.70
580	590	130.10	123.00	116.30	110.10	104.00	97.80	91.70	85.70	80.30	74.90	69.50
590	600	133.80	126.70	119.50	113.30	107.20	101.00	94.90	88.70	83.10	77.70	72.30
600	610	137.50	130.40	123.20	116.50	110.40	104.20	98.10	91.90	85.90	80.50	75.10
610	620	141.20	134.10	126.90	119.80	113.60	107.40	101.30	95.10	89.00	83.30	77.90
620	630	144.90	137.80	130.60	123.50	116.80	110.60	104.50	98.30	92.20	86.10	80.70
630	640	148.60	141.50	134.30	127.20	120.10	113.80	107.70	101.50	95.40	89.20	83.50
640	650	152.30	145.20	138.00	130.90	123.80	117.00	110.90	104.70	98.60	92.40	86.30
650	660	156.00	148.90	141.70	134.60	127.50	120.40	114.10	107.90	101.80	95.60	89.50
660	670	159.70	152.60	145.40	138.30	131.20	124.10	117.30	111.10	105.00	98.80	92.70
670	680	163.40	156.30	149.10	142.00	134.90	127.80	120.70	114.30	108.20	102.00	95.90
680	690	167.10	160.00	152.80	145.70	138.60	131.50	124.40	117.50	111.40	105.20	99.10
690	700	170.80	163.70	156.50	149.40	142.30	135.20	128.10	121.00	114.60	108.40	102.30
700	710	174.50	167.40	160.20	153.10	146.00	138.90	131.80	124.70	117.80	111.60	105.50
710	720	178.20	171.10	163.90	156.80	149.70	142.60	135.50	128.40	121.20	114.80	108.70
720	730	181.90	174.80	167.60	160.50	153.40	146.30	139.20	132.10	124.90	118.00	111.90
730	740	185.60	178.50	171.30	164.20	157.10	150.00	142.90	135.80	128.60	121.50	115.10
740	750	189.30	182.20	175.00	167.90	160.80	153.70	146.60	139.50	132.30	125.20	118.30
750	760	193.00	185.90	178.70	171.60	164.50	157.40	150.30	143.20	136.00	128.90	121.80
760	770	196.70	189.60	182.40	175.30	168.20	161.10	154.00	146.90	139.70	132.60	125.50
770	780	200.40	193.30	186.10	179.00	171.90	164.80	157.70	150.60	143.40	136.30	129.20
780	790	204.10	197.00	189.80	182.70	175.60	168.50	161.40	154.30	147.10	140.00	132.90
790	800	207.80	200.70	193.50	186.40	179.30	172.20	165.10	158.00	150.80	143.70	136.60
800	810	211.50	204.40	197.20	190.10	183.00	175.90	168.80	161.70	154.50	147.40	140.30
810	820	215.20	208.10	200.90	193.80	186.70	179.60	172.50	165.40	158.20	151.10	144.00
820	830	218.90	211.80	204.60	197.50	190.40	183.30	176.20	169.10	161.90	154.80	147.70
830	840	222.60	215.50	208.30	201.20	194.10	187.00	179.90	172.80	165.60	158.50	151.40
840	850	226.30	219.20	212.00	204.90	197.80	190.70	183.60	176.50	169.30	162.20	155.10
		37 percent of the excess over $850 plus—										
$850 and over		228.10	221.00	213.90	206.80	199.70	192.50	185.40	178.30	171.20	164.10	157.00

1980 Tax Table A/Single (Filing Status Box 1)

If line 11, Form 1040A, or line 34, Form 1040, is—		And the total number of exemptions claimed on line 6 is—		
Over	But not over	1	2	3
		Your tax is—		
11,100	11,150	1,413	1,203	1,001
11,150	11,200	1,424	1,214	1,010
11,200	11,250	1,434	1,224	1,020
11,250	11,300	1,445	1,235	1,029
11,300	11,350	1,455	1,245	1,039
11,350	11,400	1,466	1,256	1,048
11,400	11,450	1,476	1,266	1,058
11,450	11,500	1,487	1,277	1,067
11,500	11,550	1,497	1,287	1,077
11,550	11,600	1,508	1,298	1,088
11,600	11,650	1,518	1,308	1,098
11,650	11,700	1,529	1,319	1,109
11,700	11,750	1,539	1,329	1,119
11,750	11,800	1,550	1,340	1,130
11,800	11,850	1,561	1,350	1,140
11,850	11,900	1,573	1,361	1,151
11,900	11,950	1,585	1,371	1,161
11,950	12,000	1,597	1,382	1,172
12,000	12,050	1,609	1,392	1,182
12,050	12,100	1,621	1,403	1,193
12,100	12,150	1,633	1,413	1,203
12,150	12,200	1,645	1,424	1,214
12,200	12,250	1,657	1,434	1,224
12,250	12,300	1,669	1,445	1,235
12,300	12,350	1,681	1,455	1,245
12,350	12,400	1,693	1,466	1,256
12,400	12,450	1,705	1,476	1,266
12,450	12,500	1,717	1,487	1,277
12,500	12,550	1,729	1,497	1,287
12,550	12,600	1,741	1,508	1,298
12,600	12,650	1,753	1,518	1,308
12,650	12,700	1,765	1,529	1,319
12,700	12,750	1,777	1,539	1,329
12,750	12,800	1,789	1,550	1,340
12,800	12,850	1,801	1,561	1,350
12,850	12,900	1,813	1,573	1,361
12,900	12,950	1,825	1,585	1,371
12,950	13,000	1,837	1,597	1,382
13,000	13,050	1,849	1,609	1,392
13,050	13,100	1,861	1,621	1,403
13,100	13,150	1,873	1,633	1,413
13,150	13,200	1,885	1,645	1,424
13,200	13,250	1,897	1,657	1,434
13,250	13,300	1,909	1,669	1,445
13,300	13,350	1,921	1,681	1,455
13,350	13,400	1,933	1,693	1,466
13,400	13,450	1,945	1,705	1,476
13,450	13,500	1,957	1,717	1,487
13,500	13,550	1,969	1,729	1,497
13,550	13,600	1,981	1,741	1,508
13,600	13,650	1,993	1,753	1,518
13,650	13,700	2,005	1,765	1,529
13,700	13,750	2,017	1,777	1,539
13,750	13,800	2,029	1,789	1,550
13,800	13,850	2,041	1,801	1,561
13,850	13,900	2,053	1,813	1,573
13,900	13,950	2,066	1,825	1,585
13,950	14,000	2,079	1,837	1,597
14,000	14,050	2,092	1,849	1,609
14,050	14,100	2,105	1,861	1,621

Continued next column

If line 11, Form 1040A, or line 34, Form 1040, is—		And the total number of exemptions claimed on line 6 is—		
Over	But not over	1	2	3
		Your tax is—		
14,100	14,150	2,118	1,873	1,633
14,150	14,200	2,131	1,885	1,645
14,200	14,250	2,144	1,897	1,657
14,250	14,300	2,157	1,909	1,669
14,300	14,350	2,170	1,921	1,681
14,350	14,400	2,183	1,933	1,693
14,400	14,450	2,196	1,945	1,705
14,450	14,500	2,209	1,957	1,717
14,500	14,550	2,222	1,969	1,729
14,550	14,600	2,235	1,981	1,741
14,600	14,650	2,248	1,993	1,753
14,650	14,700	2,261	2,005	1,765
14,700	14,750	2,274	2,017	1,777
14,750	14,800	2,287	2,029	1,789
14,800	14,850	2,300	2,041	1,801
14,850	14,900	2,313	2,053	1,813
14,900	14,950	2,326	2,066	1,825
14,950	15,000	2,339	2,079	1,837
15,000	15,050	2,352	2,092	1,849
15,050	15,100	2,365	2,105	1,861
15,100	15,150	2,378	2,118	1,873
15,150	15,200	2,391	2,131	1,885
15,200	15,250	2,404	2,144	1,897
15,250	15,300	2,417	2,157	1,909
15,300	15,350	2,430	2,170	1,921
15,350	15,400	2,443	2,183	1,933
15,400	15,450	2,456	2,196	1,945
15,450	15,500	2,469	2,209	1,957
15,500	15,550	2,482	2,222	1,969
15,550	15,600	2,495	2,235	1,981
15,600	15,650	2,508	2,248	1,993
15,650	15,700	2,521	2,261	2,005
15,700	15,750	2,534	2,274	2,017
15,750	15,800	2,547	2,287	2,029
15,800	15,850	2,560	2,300	2,041
15,850	15,900	2,573	2,313	2,053
15,900	15,950	2,586	2,326	2,066
15,950	16,000	2,599	2,339	2,079
16,000	16,050	2,613	2,352	2,092
16,050	16,100	2,628	2,365	2,105
16,100	16,150	2,643	2,378	2,118
16,150	16,200	2,658	2,391	2,131
16,200	16,250	2,673	2,404	2,144
16,250	16,300	2,688	2,417	2,157
16,300	16,350	2,703	2,430	2,170
16,350	16,400	2,718	2,443	2,183
16,400	16,450	2,733	2,456	2,196
16,450	16,500	2,748	2,469	2,209
16,500	16,550	2,763	2,482	2,222
16,550	16,600	2,778	2,495	2,235
16,600	16,650	2,793	2,508	2,248
16,650	16,700	2,808	2,521	2,261
16,700	16,750	2,823	2,534	2,274
16,750	16,800	2,838	2,547	2,287
16,800	16,850	2,853	2,560	2,300
16,850	16,900	2,868	2,573	2,313
16,900	16,950	2,883	2,586	2,326
16,950	17,000	2,898	2,599	2,339
17,000	17,050	2,913	2,613	2,352
17,050	17,100	2,928	2,628	2,365

Continued next column

If line 11, Form 1040A, or line 34, Form 1040, is—		And the total number of exemptions claimed on line 6 is—		
Over	But not over	1	2	3
		Your tax is—		
17,100	17,150	2,943	2,643	2,378
17,150	17,200	2,958	2,658	2,391
17,200	17,250	2,973	2,673	2,404
17,250	17,300	2,988	2,688	2,417
17,300	17,350	3,003	2,703	2,430
17,350	17,400	3,018	2,718	2,443
17,400	17,450	3,033	2,733	2,456
17,450	17,500	3,048	2,748	2,469
17,500	17,550	3,063	2,763	2,482
17,550	17,600	3,078	2,778	2,495
17,600	17,650	3,093	2,793	2,508
17,650	17,700	3,108	2,808	2,521
17,700	17,750	3,123	2,823	2,534
17,750	17,800	3,138	2,838	2,547
17,800	17,850	3,153	2,853	2,560
17,850	17,900	3,168	2,868	2,573
17,900	17,950	3,183	2,883	2,586
17,950	18,000	3,198	2,898	2,599
18,000	18,050	3,213	2,913	2,613
18,050	18,100	3,228	2,928	2,628
18,100	18,150	3,243	2,943	2,643
18,150	18,200	3,258	2,958	2,658
18,200	18,250	3,273	2,973	2,673
18,250	18,300	3,288	2,988	2,688
18,300	18,350	3,303	3,003	2,703
18,350	18,400	3,318	3,018	2,718
18,400	18,450	3,333	3,033	2,733
18,450	18,500	3,348	3,048	2,748
18,500	18,550	3,363	3,063	2,763
18,550	18,600	3,378	3,078	2,778
18,600	18,650	3,393	3,093	2,793
18,650	18,700	3,408	3,108	2,808
18,700	18,750	3,423	3,123	2,823
18,750	18,800	3,438	3,138	2,838
18,800	18,850	3,453	3,153	2,853
18,850	18,900	3,468	3,168	2,868
18,900	18,950	3,483	3,183	2,883
18,950	19,000	3,498	3,198	2,898
19,000	19,050	3,513	3,213	2,913
19,050	19,100	3,528	3,228	2,928
19,100	19,150	3,543	3,243	2,943
19,150	19,200	3,558	3,258	2,958
19,200	19,250	3,574	3,273	2,973
19,250	19,300	3,591	3,288	2,988
19,300	19,350	3,608	3,303	3,003
19,350	19,400	3,625	3,318	3,018
19,400	19,450	3,642	3,333	3,033
19,450	19,500	3,659	3,348	3,048
19,500	19,550	3,676	3,363	3,063
19,550	19,600	3,693	3,378	3,078
19,600	19,650	3,710	3,393	3,093
19,650	19,700	3,727	3,408	3,108
19,700	19,750	3,744	3,423	3,123
19,750	19,800	3,761	3,438	3,138
19,800	19,850	3,778	3,453	3,153
19,850	19,900	3,795	3,468	3,168
19,900	19,950	3,812	3,483	3,183
19,950	20,000	3,829	3,498	3,198

1980 Tax Table B/Married Filing Joint Return (Filing Status Box 2)

If line 11, Form 1040A, or line 34, Form 1040, is— Over	But not over	And the total number of exemptions claimed on line 6 is— 2	3	4	5	6	7	8	9
		Your tax is—							
18,400	18,450	2,367	2,144	1,934	1,724	1,514	1,319	1,139	959
18,450	18,500	2,379	2,155	1,945	1,735	1,525	1,328	1,148	968
18,500	18,550	2,391	2,165	1,955	1,745	1,535	1,337	1,157	977
18,550	18,600	2,403	2,176	1,966	1,756	1,546	1,346	1,166	986
18,600	18,650	2,415	2,186	1,976	1,766	1,556	1,355	1,175	995
18,650	18,700	2,427	2,197	1,987	1,777	1,567	1,364	1,184	1,004
18,700	18,750	2,439	2,207	1,997	1,787	1,577	1,373	1,193	1,013
18,750	18,800	2,451	2,218	2,008	1,798	1,588	1,382	1,202	1,022
18,800	18,850	2,463	2,228	2,018	1,808	1,598	1,391	1,211	1,031
18,850	18,900	2,475	2,239	2,029	1,819	1,609	1,400	1,220	1,040
18,900	18,950	2,487	2,249	2,039	1,829	1,619	1,409	1,229	1,049
18,950	19,000	2,499	2,260	2,050	1,840	1,630	1,420	1,238	1,058
19,000	19,050	2,511	2,271	2,060	1,850	1,640	1,430	1,247	1,067
19,050	19,100	2,523	2,283	2,071	1,861	1,651	1,441	1,256	1,076
19,100	19,150	2,535	2,295	2,081	1,871	1,661	1,451	1,265	1,085
19,150	19,200	2,547	2,307	2,092	1,882	1,672	1,462	1,274	1,094
19,200	19,250	2,559	2,319	2,102	1,892	1,682	1,472	1,283	1,103
19,250	19,300	2,571	2,331	2,113	1,903	1,693	1,483	1,292	1,112
19,300	19,350	2,583	2,343	2,123	1,913	1,703	1,493	1,301	1,121
19,350	19,400	2,595	2,355	2,134	1,924	1,714	1,504	1,310	1,130
19,400	19,450	2,607	2,367	2,144	1,934	1,724	1,514	1,319	1,139
19,450	19,500	2,619	2,379	2,155	1,945	1,735	1,525	1,328	1,148
19,500	19,550	2,631	2,391	2,165	1,955	1,745	1,535	1,337	1,157
19,550	19,600	2,643	2,403	2,176	1,966	1,756	1,546	1,346	1,166
19,600	19,650	2,655	2,415	2,186	1,976	1,766	1,556	1,355	1,175
19,650	19,700	2,667	2,427	2,197	1,987	1,777	1,567	1,364	1,184
19,700	19,750	2,679	2,439	2,207	1,997	1,787	1,577	1,373	1,193
19,750	19,800	2,691	2,451	2,218	2,008	1,798	1,588	1,382	1,202
19,800	19,850	2,703	2,463	2,228	2,018	1,808	1,598	1,391	1,211
19,850	19,900	2,715	2,475	2,239	2,029	1,819	1,609	1,400	1,220
19,900	19,950	2,727	2,487	2,249	2,039	1,829	1,619	1,409	1,229
19,950	20,000	2,739	2,499	2,260	2,050	1,840	1,630	1,420	1,238
20,000	20,050	2,751	2,511	2,271	2,060	1,850	1,640	1,430	1,247
20,050	20,100	2,763	2,523	2,283	2,071	1,861	1,651	1,441	1,256
20,100	20,150	2,775	2,535	2,295	2,081	1,871	1,661	1,451	1,265
20,150	20,200	2,787	2,547	2,307	2,092	1,882	1,672	1,462	1,274
20,200	20,250	2,799	2,559	2,319	2,102	1,892	1,682	1,472	1,283
20,250	20,300	2,811	2,571	2,331	2,113	1,903	1,693	1,483	1,292
20,300	20,350	2,823	2,583	2,343	2,123	1,913	1,703	1,493	1,301
20,350	20,400	2,835	2,595	2,355	2,134	1,924	1,714	1,504	1,310
20,400	20,450	2,847	2,607	2,367	2,144	1,934	1,724	1,514	1,319
20,450	20,500	2,859	2,619	2,379	2,155	1,945	1,735	1,525	1,328
20,500	20,550	2,871	2,631	2,391	2,165	1,955	1,745	1,535	1,337
20,550	20,600	2,883	2,643	2,403	2,176	1,966	1,756	1,546	1,346
20,600	20,650	2,895	2,655	2,415	2,186	1,976	1,766	1,556	1,355
20,650	20,700	2,907	2,667	2,427	2,197	1,987	1,777	1,567	1,364
20,700	20,750	2,919	2,679	2,439	2,207	1,997	1,787	1,577	1,373
20,750	20,800	2,931	2,691	2,451	2,218	2,008	1,798	1,588	1,382
20,800	20,850	2,943	2,703	2,463	2,228	2,018	1,808	1,598	1,391
20,850	20,900	2,955	2,715	2,475	2,239	2,029	1,819	1,609	1,400
20,900	20,950	2,967	2,727	2,487	2,249	2,039	1,829	1,619	1,409
20,950	21,000	2,979	2,739	2,499	2,260	2,050	1,840	1,630	1,420
21,000	21,050	2,991	2,751	2,511	2,271	2,060	1,850	1,640	1,430
21,050	21,100	3,003	2,763	2,523	2,283	2,071	1,861	1,651	1,441
21,100	21,150	3,015	2,775	2,535	2,295	2,081	1,871	1,661	1,451
21,150	21,200	3,027	2,787	2,547	2,307	2,092	1,882	1,672	1,462
21,200	21,250	3,039	2,799	2,559	2,319	2,102	1,892	1,682	1,472
21,250	21,300	3,051	2,811	2,571	2,331	2,113	1,903	1,693	1,483
21,300	21,350	3,063	2,823	2,583	2,343	2,123	1,913	1,703	1,493
21,350	21,400	3,075	2,835	2,595	2,355	2,134	1,924	1,714	1,504
21,400	21,450	3,087	2,847	2,607	2,367	2,144	1,934	1,724	1,514
21,450	21,500	3,099	2,859	2,619	2,379	2,155	1,945	1,735	1,525
21,500	21,550	3,111	2,871	2,631	2,391	2,165	1,955	1,745	1,535
21,550	21,600	3,123	2,883	2,643	2,403	2,176	1,966	1,756	1,546
21,600	21,650	3,135	2,895	2,655	2,415	2,186	1,976	1,766	1,556
21,650	21,700	3,147	2,907	2,667	2,427	2,197	1,987	1,777	1,567
21,700	21,750	3,159	2,919	2,679	2,439	2,207	1,997	1,787	1,577
21,750	21,800	3,171	2,931	2,691	2,451	2,218	2,008	1,798	1,588
21,800	21,850	3,183	2,943	2,703	2,463	2,228	2,018	1,808	1,598
21,850	21,900	3,195	2,955	2,715	2,475	2,239	2,029	1,819	1,609
21,900	21,950	3,207	2,967	2,727	2,487	2,249	2,039	1,829	1,619
21,950	22,000	3,219	2,979	2,739	2,499	2,260	2,050	1,840	1,630

1980 Tax Table B/Married Filing Joint Return (Filing Status Box 2)

If line 11, Form 1040A, or line 34, Form 1040, is— Over	But not over	And the total number of exemptions claimed on line 6 is— 2	3	4	5	6	7	8	9
		Your tax is—							
25,600	25,650	4,232	3,952	3,672	3,392	3,135	2,895	2,655	2,415
25,650	25,700	4,246	3,966	3,686	3,406	3,147	2,907	2,667	2,427
25,700	25,750	4,260	3,980	3,700	3,420	3,159	2,919	2,679	2,439
25,750	25,800	4,274	3,994	3,714	3,434	3,171	2,931	2,691	2,451
25,800	25,850	4,288	4,008	3,728	3,448	3,183	2,943	2,703	2,463
25,850	25,900	4,302	4,022	3,742	3,462	3,195	2,955	2,715	2,475
25,900	25,950	4,316	4,036	3,756	3,476	3,207	2,967	2,727	2,487
25,950	26,000	4,330	4,050	3,770	3,490	3,219	2,979	2,739	2,499
26,000	26,050	4,344	4,064	3,784	3,504	3,231	2,991	2,751	2,511
26,050	26,100	4,358	4,078	3,798	3,518	3,243	3,003	2,763	2,523
26,100	26,150	4,372	4,092	3,812	3,532	3,255	3,015	2,775	2,535
26,150	26,200	4,386	4,106	3,826	3,546	3,267	3,027	2,787	2,547
26,200	26,250	4,400	4,120	3,840	3,560	3,280	3,039	2,799	2,559
26,250	26,300	4,414	4,134	3,854	3,574	3,294	3,051	2,811	2,571
26,300	26,350	4,428	4,148	3,868	3,588	3,308	3,063	2,823	2,583
26,350	26,400	4,442	4,162	3,882	3,602	3,322	3,075	2,835	2,595
26,400	26,450	4,456	4,176	3,896	3,616	3,336	3,087	2,847	2,607
26,450	26,500	4,470	4,190	3,910	3,630	3,350	3,099	2,859	2,619
26,500	26,550	4,484	4,204	3,924	3,644	3,364	3,111	2,871	2,631
26,550	26,600	4,498	4,218	3,938	3,658	3,378	3,123	2,883	2,643
26,600	26,650	4,513	4,232	3,952	3,672	3,392	3,135	2,895	2,655
26,650	26,700	4,529	4,246	3,966	3,686	3,406	3,147	2,907	2,667
26,700	26,750	4,545	4,260	3,980	3,700	3,420	3,159	2,919	2,679
26,750	26,800	4,561	4,274	3,994	3,714	3,434	3,171	2,931	2,691
26,800	26,850	4,577	4,288	4,008	3,728	3,448	3,183	2,943	2,703
26,850	26,900	4,593	4,302	4,022	3,742	3,462	3,195	2,955	2,715
26,900	26,950	4,609	4,316	4,036	3,756	3,476	3,207	2,967	2,727
26,950	27,000	4,625	4,330	4,050	3,770	3,490	3,219	2,979	2,739
27,000	27,050	4,641	4,344	4,064	3,784	3,504	3,231	2,991	2,751
27,050	27,100	4,657	4,358	4,078	3,798	3,518	3,243	3,003	2,763
27,100	27,150	4,673	4,372	4,092	3,812	3,532	3,255	3,015	2,775
27,150	27,200	4,689	4,386	4,106	3,826	3,546	3,267	3,027	2,787
27,200	27,250	4,705	4,400	4,120	3,840	3,560	3,280	3,039	2,799
27,250	27,300	4,721	4,414	4,134	3,854	3,574	3,294	3,051	2,811
27,300	27,350	4,737	4,428	4,148	3,868	3,588	3,308	3,063	2,823
27,350	27,400	4,753	4,442	4,162	3,882	3,602	3,322	3,075	2,835
27,400	27,450	4,769	4,456	4,176	3,896	3,616	3,336	3,087	2,847
27,450	27,500	4,785	4,470	4,190	3,910	3,630	3,350	3,099	2,859
27,500	27,550	4,801	4,484	4,204	3,924	3,644	3,364	3,111	2,871
27,550	27,600	4,817	4,498	4,218	3,938	3,658	3,378	3,123	2,883
27,600	27,650	4,833	4,513	4,232	3,952	3,672	3,392	3,135	2,895
27,650	27,700	4,849	4,529	4,246	3,966	3,686	3,406	3,147	2,907
27,700	27,750	4,865	4,545	4,260	3,980	3,700	3,420	3,159	2,919
27,750	27,800	4,881	4,561	4,274	3,994	3,714	3,434	3,171	2,931
27,800	27,850	4,897	4,577	4,288	4,008	3,728	3,448	3,183	2,943
27,850	27,900	4,913	4,593	4,302	4,022	3,742	3,462	3,195	2,955
27,900	27,950	4,929	4,609	4,316	4,036	3,756	3,476	3,207	2,967
27,950	28,000	4,945	4,625	4,330	4,050	3,770	3,490	3,219	2,979
28,000	28,050	4,961	4,641	4,344	4,064	3,784	3,504	3,231	2,991
28,050	28,100	4,977	4,657	4,358	4,078	3,798	3,518	3,243	3,003
28,100	28,150	4,993	4,673	4,372	4,092	3,812	3,532	3,255	3,015
28,150	28,200	5,009	4,689	4,386	4,106	3,826	3,546	3,267	3,027
28,200	28,250	5,025	4,705	4,400	4,120	3,840	3,560	3,280	3,039
28,250	28,300	5,041	4,721	4,414	4,134	3,854	3,574	3,294	3,051
28,300	28,350	5,057	4,737	4,428	4,148	3,868	3,588	3,308	3,063
28,350	28,400	5,073	4,753	4,442	4,162	3,882	3,602	3,322	3,075
28,400	28,450	5,089	4,769	4,456	4,176	3,896	3,616	3,336	3,087
28,450	28,500	5,105	4,785	4,470	4,190	3,910	3,630	3,350	3,099
28,500	28,550	5,121	4,801	4,484	4,204	3,924	3,644	3,364	3,111
28,550	28,600	5,137	4,817	4,498	4,218	3,938	3,658	3,378	3,123
28,600	28,650	5,153	4,833	4,513	4,232	3,952	3,672	3,392	3,135
28,650	28,700	5,169	4,849	4,529	4,246	3,966	3,686	3,406	3,147
28,700	28,750	5,185	4,865	4,545	4,260	3,980	3,700	3,420	3,159
28,750	28,800	5,201	4,881	4,561	4,274	3,994	3,714	3,434	3,171
28,800	28,850	5,217	4,897	4,577	4,288	4,008	3,728	3,448	3,183
28,850	28,900	5,233	4,913	4,593	4,302	4,022	3,742	3,462	3,195
28,900	28,950	5,249	4,929	4,609	4,316	4,036	3,756	3,476	3,207
28,950	29,000	5,265	4,945	4,625	4,330	4,050	3,770	3,490	3,219
29,000	29,050	5,281	4,961	4,641	4,344	4,064	3,784	3,504	3,231
29,050	29,100	5,297	4,977	4,657	4,358	4,078	3,798	3,518	3,243
29,100	29,150	5,313	4,993	4,673	4,372	4,092	3,812	3,532	3,255
29,150	29,200	5,329	5,009	4,689	4,386	4,106	3,826	3,546	3,267

1980 Tax Table C/Married Filing Separate Return (Filing Status Box 3)

If line 11, Form 1040A, or line 34, Form 1040, is—		And the total number of exemptions claimed on line 6 is—		
Over	But not over	1	2	3
		Your tax is—		
10,800	10,850	1,571	1,331	1,096
10,850	10,900	1,583	1,343	1,106
10,900	10,950	1,595	1,355	1,117
10,950	11,000	1,607	1,367	1,127
11,000	11,050	1,619	1,379	1,139
11,050	11,100	1,631	1,391	1,151
11,100	11,150	1,644	1,403	1,163
11,150	11,200	1,658	1,415	1,175
11,200	11,250	1,672	1,427	1,187
11,250	11,300	1,686	1,439	1,199
11,300	11,350	1,700	1,451	1,211
11,350	11,400	1,714	1,463	1,223
11,400	11,450	1,728	1,475	1,235
11,450	11,500	1,742	1,487	1,247
11,500	11,550	1,756	1,499	1,259
11,550	11,600	1,770	1,511	1,271
11,600	11,650	1,784	1,523	1,283
11,650	11,700	1,798	1,535	1,295
11,700	11,750	1,812	1,547	1,307
11,750	11,800	1,826	1,559	1,319
11,800	11,850	1,840	1,571	1,331
11,850	11,900	1,854	1,583	1,343
11,900	11,950	1,868	1,595	1,355
11,950	12,000	1,882	1,607	1,367
12,000	12,050	1,896	1,619	1,379
12,050	12,100	1,910	1,631	1,391
12,100	12,150	1,924	1,644	1,403
12,150	12,200	1,938	1,658	1,415
12,200	12,250	1,952	1,672	1,427
12,250	12,300	1,966	1,686	1,439
12,300	12,350	1,980	1,700	1,451
12,350	12,400	1,994	1,714	1,463
12,400	12,450	2,008	1,728	1,475
12,450	12,500	2,022	1,742	1,487
12,500	12,550	2,036	1,756	1,499
12,550	12,600	2,050	1,770	1,511
12,600	12,650	2,064	1,784	1,523
12,650	12,700	2,078	1,798	1,535
12,700	12,750	2,092	1,812	1,547
12,750	12,800	2,106	1,826	1,559
12,800	12,850	2,120	1,840	1,571
12,850	12,900	2,134	1,854	1,583
12,900	12,950	2,148	1,868	1,595
12,950	13,000	2,162	1,882	1,607
13,000	13,050	2,176	1,896	1,619
13,050	13,100	2,190	1,910	1,631
13,100	13,150	2,204	1,924	1,644
13,150	13,200	2,218	1,938	1,658
13,200	13,250	2,232	1,952	1,672
13,250	13,300	2,246	1,966	1,686
13,300	13,350	2,261	1,980	1,700
13,350	13,400	2,277	1,994	1,714
13,400	13,450	2,293	2,008	1,728
13,450	13,500	2,309	2,022	1,742
13,500	13,550	2,325	2,036	1,756
13,550	13,600	2,341	2,050	1,770
13,600	13,650	2,357	2,064	1,784
13,650	13,700	2,373	2,078	1,798
13,700	13,750	2,389	2,092	1,812
13,750	13,800	2,405	2,106	1,826

Continued next column

If line 11, Form 1040A, or line 34, Form 1040, is—		And the total number of exemptions claimed on line 6 is—		
Over	But not over	1	2	3
		Your tax is—		
13,800	13,850	2,421	2,120	1,840
13,850	13,900	2,437	2,134	1,854
13,900	13,950	2,453	2,148	1,868
13,950	14,000	2,469	2,162	1,882
14,000	14,050	2,485	2,176	1,896
14,050	14,100	2,501	2,190	1,910
14,100	14,150	2,517	2,204	1,924
14,150	14,200	2,533	2,218	1,938
14,200	14,250	2,549	2,232	1,952
14,250	14,300	2,565	2,246	1,966
14,300	14,350	2,581	2,261	1,980
14,350	14,400	2,597	2,277	1,994
14,400	14,450	2,613	2,293	2,008
14,450	14,500	2,629	2,309	2,022
14,500	14,550	2,645	2,325	2,036
14,550	14,600	2,661	2,341	2,050
14,600	14,650	2,677	2,357	2,064
14,650	14,700	2,693	2,373	2,078
14,700	14,750	2,709	2,389	2,092
14,750	14,800	2,725	2,405	2,106
14,800	14,850	2,741	2,421	2,120
14,850	14,900	2,757	2,437	2,134
14,900	14,950	2,773	2,453	2,148
14,950	15,000	2,789	2,469	2,162
15,000	15,050	2,805	2,485	2,176
15,050	15,100	2,821	2,501	2,190
15,100	15,150	2,837	2,517	2,204
15,150	15,200	2,853	2,533	2,218
15,200	15,250	2,869	2,549	2,232
15,250	15,300	2,885	2,565	2,246
15,300	15,350	2,901	2,581	2,261
15,350	15,400	2,917	2,597	2,277
15,400	15,450	2,933	2,613	2,293
15,450	15,500	2,949	2,629	2,309
15,500	15,550	2,965	2,645	2,325
15,550	15,600	2,981	2,661	2,341
15,600	15,650	2,997	2,677	2,357
15,650	15,700	3,013	2,693	2,373
15,700	15,750	3,029	2,709	2,389
15,750	15,800	3,045	2,725	2,405
15,800	15,850	3,061	2,741	2,421
15,850	15,900	3,077	2,757	2,437
15,900	15,950	3,093	2,773	2,453
15,950	16,000	3,110	2,789	2,469
16,000	16,050	3,128	2,805	2,485
16,050	16,100	3,147	2,821	2,501
16,100	16,150	3,165	2,837	2,517
16,150	16,200	3,184	2,853	2,533
16,200	16,250	3,202	2,869	2,549
16,250	16,300	3,221	2,885	2,565
16,300	16,350	3,239	2,901	2,581
16,350	16,400	3,258	2,917	2,597
16,400	16,450	3,276	2,933	2,613
16,450	16,500	3,295	2,949	2,629
16,500	16,550	3,313	2,965	2,645
16,550	16,600	3,332	2,981	2,661
16,600	16,650	3,350	2,997	2,677
16,650	16,700	3,369	3,013	2,693
16,700	16,750	3,387	3,029	2,709
16,750	16,800	3,406	3,045	2,725

Continued next column

If line 11, Form 1040A, or line 34, Form 1040, is—		And the total number of exemptions claimed on line 6 is—		
Over	But not over	1	2	3
		Your tax is—		
16,800	16,850	3,424	3,061	2,741
16,850	16,900	3,443	3,077	2,757
16,900	16,950	3,461	3,093	2,773
16,950	17,000	3,480	3,110	2,789
17,000	17,050	3,498	3,128	2,805
17,050	17,100	3,517	3,147	2,821
17,100	17,150	3,535	3,165	2,837
17,150	17,200	3,554	3,184	2,853
17,200	17,250	3,572	3,202	2,869
17,250	17,300	3,591	3,221	2,885
17,300	17,350	3,609	3,239	2,901
17,350	17,400	3,628	3,258	2,917
17,400	17,450	3,646	3,276	2,933
17,450	17,500	3,665	3,295	2,949
17,500	17,550	3,683	3,313	2,965
17,550	17,600	3,702	3,332	2,981
17,600	17,650	3,720	3,350	2,997
17,650	17,700	3,739	3,369	3,013
17,700	17,750	3,757	3,387	3,029
17,750	17,800	3,776	3,406	3,045
17,800	17,850	3,794	3,424	3,061
17,850	17,900	3,813	3,443	3,077
17,900	17,950	3,831	3,461	3,093
17,950	18,000	3,850	3,480	3,110
18,000	18,050	3,868	3,498	3,128
18,050	18,100	3,887	3,517	3,147
18,100	18,150	3,905	3,535	3,165
18,150	18,200	3,924	3,554	3,184
18,200	18,250	3,942	3,572	3,202
18,250	18,300	3,961	3,591	3,221
18,300	18,350	3,979	3,609	3,239
18,350	18,400	3,998	3,628	3,258
18,400	18,450	4,016	3,646	3,276
18,450	18,500	4,035	3,665	3,295
18,500	18,550	4,053	3,683	3,313
18,550	18,600	4,072	3,702	3,332
18,600	18,650	4,092	3,720	3,350
18,650	18,700	4,113	3,739	3,369
18,700	18,750	4,135	3,757	3,387
18,750	18,800	4,156	3,776	3,406
18,800	18,850	4,178	3,794	3,424
18,850	18,900	4,199	3,813	3,443
18,900	18,950	4,221	3,831	3,461
18,950	19,000	4,242	3,850	3,480
19,000	19,050	4,264	3,868	3,498
19,050	19,100	4,285	3,887	3,517
19,100	19,150	4,307	3,905	3,535
19,150	19,200	4,328	3,924	3,554
19,200	19,250	4,350	3,942	3,572
19,250	19,300	4,371	3,961	3,591
19,300	19,350	4,393	3,979	3,609
19,350	19,400	4,414	3,998	3,628
19,400	19,450	4,436	4,016	3,646
19,450	19,500	4,457	4,035	3,665
19,500	19,550	4,479	4,053	3,683
19,550	19,600	4,500	4,072	3,702
19,600	19,650	4,522	4,092	3,720
19,650	19,700	4,543	4,113	3,739
19,700	19,750	4,565	4,135	3,757
19,750	19,800	4,586	4,156	3,776
19,800	19,850	4,608	4,178	3,794
19,850	19,900	4,629	4,199	3,813
19,900	19,950	4,651	4,221	3,831
19,950	20,000	4,672	4,242	3,850

1980 Tax Rate Schedules

If you cannot use one of the Tax Tables, figure your tax on the amount on Schedule TC, Part I, line 3, by using the appropriate Tax Rate Schedule on this page. Enter the tax on Schedule TC, Part I, line 4.
Note: Your zero bracket amount has been built into these Tax Rate Schedules.

SCHEDULE X—Single Taxpayers

Use this schedule if you checked Filing Status Box 1 on Form 1040—

If the amount on Schedule TC, Part I, line 3, is: Enter on Schedule TC, Part I, line 4:

Not over $2,300 ...... -0-

Over—	But not over—		of the amount over—
$2,300	$3,400	14%	$2,300
$3,400	$4,400	$154+16%	$3,400
$4,400	$6,500	$314+18%	$4,400
$6,500	$8,500	$692+19%	$6,500
$8,500	$10,800	$1,072+21%	$8,500
$10,800	$12,900	$1,555+24%	$10,800
$12,900	$15,000	$2,059+26%	$12,900
$15,000	$18,200	$2,605+30%	$15,000
$18,200	$23,500	$3,565+34%	$18,200
$23,500	$28,800	$5,367+39%	$23,500
$28,800	$34,100	$7,434+44%	$28,800
$34,100	$41,500	$9,766+49%	$34,100
$41,500	$55,300	$13,392+55%	$41,500
$55,300	$81,800	$20,982+63%	$55,300
$81,800	$108,300	$37,677+68%	$81,800
$108,300	....	$55,697+70%	$108,300

SCHEDULE Y—Married Taxpayers and Qualifying Widows and Widowers

Married Filing Joint Returns and Qualifying Widows and Widowers

Use this schedule if you checked Filing Status Box 2 or 5 on Form 1040—

If the amount on Schedule TC, Part I, line 3, is: Enter on Schedule TC, Part I, line 4:

Not over $3,400 ...... -0-

Over—	But not over—		of the amount over—
$3,400	$5,500	14%	$3,400
$5,500	$7,600	$294+16%	$5,500
$7,600	$11,900	$630+18%	$7,600
$11,900	$16,000	$1,404+21%	$11,900
$16,000	$20,200	$2,265+24%	$16,000
$20,200	$24,600	$3,273+28%	$20,200
$24,600	$29,900	$4,505+32%	$24,600
$29,900	$35,200	$6,201+37%	$29,900
$35,200	$45,800	$8,162+43%	$35,200
$45,800	$60,000	$12,720+49%	$45,800
$60,000	$85,600	$19,678+54%	$60,000
$85,600	$109,400	$33,502+59%	$85,600
$109,400	$162,400	$47,544+64%	$109,400
$162,400	$215,400	$81,464+68%	$162,400
$215,400	....	$117,504+70%	$215,400

Married Filing Separate Returns

Use this schedule if you checked Filing Status Box 3 on Form 1040—

If the amount on Schedule TC, Part I, line 3, is: Enter on Schedule TC, Part I, line 4:

Not over $1,700 ...... -0-

Over—	But not over—		of the amount over—
$1,700	$2,750	14%	$1,700
$2,750	$3,800	$147.00+16%	$2,750
$3,800	$5,950	$315.00+18%	$3,800
$5,950	$8,000	$702.00+21%	$5,950
$8,000	$10,100	$1,132.50+24%	$8,000
$10,100	$12,300	$1,636.50+28%	$10,100
$12,300	$14,950	$2,252.50+32%	$12,300
$14,950	$17,600	$3,100.50+37%	$14,950
$17,600	$22,900	$4,081.00+43%	$17,600
$22,900	$30,000	$6,360.00+49%	$22,900
$30,000	$42,800	$9,839.00+54%	$30,000
$42,800	$54,700	$16,751.00+59%	$42,800
$54,700	$81,200	$23,772.00+64%	$54,700
$81,200	$107,700	$40,732.00+68%	$81,200
$107,700	....	$58,752.00+70%	$107,700

Careers Chart

This four-page chart gives information about selected careers in eight career clusters: Trades, Technology, Science, Health, Arts, Social Service, Business Contact, and Business Detail.* Information given includes training qualifications of most workers, estimated employment in 1978, and projected average annual openings to 1990 due to growth and replacement needs.

The following code is used under the heading "Qualifications."

C 4 years or more of college required
S Special training required (technical or vocational school, junior college, or apprenticeship)
— No college or special training required

Trades	Qualifications	Estimated employment in 1978	Average annual openings to 1990
Air-conditioning, refrigeration, or heating mechanic	S	210,000	8200
Aircraft mechanic	S	132,000	3500
Appliance repairer	—	145,000	6900
Assembler	—	1,164,000	77,000
Automobile mechanic	—	860,000	37,000
Bricklayer	S	205,000	6200
Carpenter	S	1,253,000	58,000
Electrician (construction)	S	290,000	12,900
Industrial machinery repairer	S	655,000	58,000
Inspector (manufacturing)	—	771,000	35,000
Instrument maker (mechanical)	S	6000	300
Machine tool operator	—	542,000	19,600
Machinist	S	484,000	22,500
Maintenance electrician	S	300,000	15,500
Meatcutter	S	204,000	5200
Millwright	S	95,000	4700
Painter or paperhanger	—	504,000	27,000
Plumber or pipefitter	S	428,000	20,000
Power truck operator	—	363,000	14,000
Supervisor	S	1,671,000	69,000
Television or radio service technician	S	131,000	6100
Tool and die maker	S	170,000	8600
Truck and bus mechanic	—	165,000	6800
Welder	—	679,000	35,000

*Cluster titles are based on interest areas measured by the Vocational Interest Profile used in The American College Testing Career Planning Program. Reprinted by permission. Information about qualifications and employment is from *Occupational Projections and Training Data, 1980 Edition.*

Technology	Qualifications	Estimated employment in 1978	Average annual openings to 1990
Aerospace engineer	C	60,000	1900
Air traffic controller	C	21,000	700
Chemical engineer	C	53,000	1800
Civil engineer	C	155,000	7800
Drafter	S	296,000	11,000
Electrical engineer	C	300,000	10,500
Engineering and science technician	S	600,000	23,000
Forester	C	31,200	1400
Mechanical engineer	C	195,000	7500
Pilot or copilot	S	76,000	3800
Surveyor or surveying technician	S	62,000	2300

Science

	Qualifications	Estimated employment in 1978	Average annual openings to 1990
Chemist	C	143,000	6100
Economist	C	130,000	7800
Geologist	C	31,000	1700
Life scientist	C	215,000	11,200
Mathematician	C	33,500	1000
Meteorologist	C	7300	300
Physicist	C	44,000	1000

Health

	Qualifications	Estimated employment in 1978	Average annual openings to 1990
Dental assistant	—	150,000	11,000
Dental hygienist	S	35,000	6000
Dentist	C	120,000	5500
Dietitian	C	35,000	3300
Hospital attendant or nursing aide	—	1,037,000	94,000
Licensed practical nurse	S	518,000	60,000
Medical laboratory worker	S,C	210,000	14,800
Pharmacist	C	135,000	7800
Physician	C	405,000	19,000
Radiologic technologist	S	100,000	9000
Registered nurse	S,C	1,060,000	85,000
Surgical technician	S	35,000	2600
Veterinarian	C	33,500	1700

Arts

Arts	Qualifications	Estimated employment in 1978	Average annual openings to 1990
Actor or actress	S	13,400	850
Architect	C	54,000	4000
Dancer	S	8000	550
Display worker	—	44,000	3300
Interior designer	S	79,000	3600
Musician or music teacher	S,C	127,000	8900
Newspaper reporter	C	45,000	2400
Photographer	—	93,000	3800
Radio or television announcer	—	27,000	850
Singer or singing teacher	S,C	22,000	1600

Social Service

Social Service	Qualifications	Estimated employment in 1978	Average annual openings to 1990
Barber	S	121,000	9700
Building custodian	—	2,251,000	176,000
College or university teacher	C	673,000	11,000
Cook or chef	—	1,186,000	86,000
Cosmetologist	S	542,000	29,000
Firefighter	—	220,000	7500
Flight attendant	S	48,000	4800
Gasoline service station attendant	—	340,000	5200
Guard	—	550,000	70,000
Kindergarten or elementary school teacher	C	1,322,000	86,000
Lawyer	C	487,000	37,000
Librarian	C	142,000	8000
Mail carrier	—	245,000	7000
Mortician	S	45,000	2200
Personnel or labor relations worker	C	405,000	17,000
Police officer (municipal)	—	450,000	16,500
Private household worker	—	1,162,000	45,000
School counselor	C	45,000	1700
Secondary school teacher	C	1,087,000	7200
Social service aide	—	134,000	7500
Social worker	C	385,000	22,000
State police officer	—	47,000	1800
Teacher aide	—	342,000	26,000
Telephone operator	—	311,000	9900
Waiter or waitress	—	1,383,000	70,000

Business Contact

	Qualifications	Estimated employment in 1978	Average annual openings to 1990
Airline passenger agent	—	56,000	2200
Automobile parts clerk	—	97,000	4200
Automobile sales agent	—	158,000	10,400
Bank officer or manager	C	330,000	28,000
Bank teller	—	410,000	17,000
Conductor (railroad)	—	37,000	1700
Hotel manager or assistant	C	168,000	8900
Local truckdriver	—	1,720,000	64,000
Long-distance truckdriver	—	584,000	21,500
Manufacturers' sales representative	C	402,000	21,700
Postal clerk	—	260,000	2000
Public relations worker	C	185,000	7500
Purchasing agent	C	185,000	13,400
Real estate sales agent or broker	S	555,000	50,000
Retail sales worker	—	2,851,000	226,000
Securities sales worker	S	109,000	5500
Taxi driver	—	94,000	4300
Wholesale trade salesworker	—	840,000	40,000

Business Detail

	Qualifications	Estimated employment in 1978	Average annual openings to 1990
Accountant	C	985,000	61,000
Bank clerk	—	505,000	45,000
Bookkeeping worker	—	1,830,000	96,000
Cashier	—	1,400,000	119,000
Computer operator	—	666,000	12,500
File clerk	—	273,000	16,500
Front office clerk (hotel)	—	79,000	5400
Insurance actuary	C	9000	500
Office machine operator	—	160,000	9700
Programmer	S,C	247,000	9200
Receptionist	—	588,000	41,000
Shipping and receiving clerk	—	461,000	22,000
Stenographer or secretary	—	3,684,000	305,000
Stock clerk	—	507,000	23,000
Systems analyst	C	182,000	7900
Typist	—	1,044,000	59,000

Glossary

Brief descriptions of certain important terms are listed in this glossary. These descriptions need not be considered formal, complete definitions.

amortization table
Table showing amount of each payment of a loan and sometimes the breakdown of each payment into interest and principal.

annual
For one year, or 12 months.

annual yield
Percent of interest earned for 1 year; the rule is

$$\frac{\text{amount earned in 1 year}}{\text{amount invested}} \cdot$$

The answer is expressed as a percent.

area
Measure of an amount of surface, given in square units, inside a closed, plane figure.

assessed valuation
Value of property, usually a percentage of actual market value, upon which the property tax is based.

average daily balance
Average of the daily unpaid amounts in an account; used to determine the finance charge.

bank statement
Record from a bank showing deposits, canceled checks, and other information concerning an account.

bearings
Position or direction of boundaries, used in making a scale drawing of a piece of property.

beneficiary
Person named in an insurance policy to receive benefits if the insured person dies.

bodily injury insurance
Type of liability insurance that protects a car owner financially if someone is injured by the car.

bond
Type of investment in which a person lends money to a company or a government agency that will repay the amount of the loan with interest.

broker
Person who buys and sells for others; stocks, bonds, and real estate are often handled by brokers.

budget
Organized spending plan.

calorie
Unit of heat used to express the fuel value of food.

canceled checks
Checks, written on an account, that have been paid by the bank, marked "paid," and returned to the depositor with the bank statement.

capacity
Greatest number of units a container can hold.

cash on delivery
Amount paid at the time of delivery of a purchase.

cash value
Amount of money that can be borrowed from a life insurance policy by the insured; the policy can be traded in for this amount.

CD
Certificate of deposit.

certificate of deposit
Savings account of a specified size (often a multiple of $1000) that earns interest at a rate higher than that of a regular savings account.

charge account
Allows a customer to buy goods or services and pay at a later date or on an installment plan.

check
Written order to a bank directing the bank to pay out money from a depositor's account.

checking account
Bank account into which money is deposited; the money is withdrawn by using forms called checks.

check register
Depositor's record that a check has been written; gives the same information as a check stub.

check stub
Depositor's record that a check has been written; gives the same information as a check register.

classified ads
Short advertisements placed in a special section of newspapers or magazines; the ads concern such things as jobs available, jobs wanted, and property for rent or for sale; also called wants ads.

closing costs
Various fees and taxes that must be paid to complete the purchase of real estate.

collision insurance
Type of insurance that pays for repair of damage to the insured person's car caused by an accident.

commission
Straight commission: a percentage of total sales that is paid to a salesperson as wages. Graduated commission: wages in which the rate of commission varies, depending on the total sales.

common stock
Share of a business bought as an investment.

compound interest
Interest computed on the principal and on the interest previously earned.

comprehensive insurance
Type of insurance that pays for repair or replacement of a car in case of fire, theft, vandalism, or acts of nature.

consumer
A person who buys or rents goods and services offered to the public.

cross-products
The cross-products for the ratios below are 3×8 and 4×6; two ratios are equal if their cross-products are equal.
$\frac{3}{4} = \frac{6}{8}$ because $3 \times 8 = 4 \times 6$.

data
Information such as scores, values, and measurement.

deductible amount
Amount subtracted from an insured loss and not replaced by the insurance; $50 and $100 are common deductible amounts.

deductions
Money withheld from a person's pay for taxes, insurance, social security, and so on; also, amounts a person may subtract from gross income when computing income tax.

deferred-payment price
Sum of the down payment and total paid in monthly installments.

denominator
In the fraction $\frac{5}{6}$, the denominator is 6.

deposit
Money given to a bank to open or to add to a checking or a savings account; also, an amount paid when a person orders an item.

depreciation
Decrease in value of a piece of property because of age and wear; for automobiles, the greatest depreciation usually occurs in the first two years.

discount
Amount deducted from list price to obtain sale price; a percent of the list price.

dividend
In $820 \div 20 = 41$, the dividend is 820.

dividends (stock)
Part of a company's profits that is paid periodically to stockholders.

divisor
In $820 \div 20 = 41$, the divisor is 20.

down payment
Amount paid at the time of an installment purchase to reduce the amount of loan needed.

equation
Mathematical sentence that uses the equal sign; examples are $5 + 6 = 11$ and $4n = 28$.

exemptions
Persons claimed by a taxpayer as legally dependent on the taxpayer for support.

face value
Value stated on a bond, note, insurance policy, etc.

factor
Number used in multiplication; in $18 \times 4 = 72$, the numbers 18 and 4 are factors.

Federal Insurance Contributions Act (FICA)
Commonly called social security; provides retirement income, medical payments, and survivors' benefits to those who qualify.

FICA deduction
Amount withheld from a person's pay for social security.

finance charge
Amount charged for buying an item on credit or on an installment plan.

financing
Purchasing goods or services through installment buying.

fixed monthly expenses
Costs that require the same amount to be paid every month, such as rent.

fuel economy rate
Quotient of the distance traveled divided by the amount of fuel consumed; usually expressed as kilometers per liter or as miles per gallon.

graph
Picture used to show data; the picture could be a bar, line, or circle graph, or a pictograph. A graph might also be points on a grid matched with given ordered pairs of numbers.

gross income
Income before any deductions are made.

gross pay
Wages or salary before any deductions are made.

hourly rate
Dollar amount paid for each hour worked or fraction thereof.

income tax return
Form that must be completed to determine one's tax liability; depending on circumstances, a taxpayer may use the short form (1040A) or the long form (1040).

installment
Part of a sum of money or debt to be paid at certain stated times.

insurance
Provides protection against financial loss; common types of insurance are health, life (term, straight, limited payment, endowment), automobile, homeowner's, and personal property.

insured
Person covered by an insurance policy.

interest
Amount paid for the use of money; usually a percent of the amount invested, loaned, or borrowed.

investment
Expenditure of money for something that is expected to produce a profit.

itemized deductions
Expenses a taxpayer may list on which no tax is paid; used only if the total exceeds the zero bracket amount.

landlord
Person who owns buildings or land that is rented to others.

lease
Right to use real estate or other property for a given length of time with a payment of rent.

level-payment loan
Loan that is repaid in equal monthly installments.

liability insurance
Automobile insurance that includes bodily injury insurance and property damage insurance.

list price
Original price or regular price before discounts, fees, or commissions are subtracted.

loan
Amount of money that is borrowed for a certain period of time and upon which interest is usually paid.

mean
Average; the sum of a set of numbers divided by the number of addends.

median
Middle number in a set of numbers arranged in order.

minimum payment
Least amount that can be paid on a monthly bill for credit card expenses.

mode
Number occurring most often in a set of numbers.

mortgage loan
Money borrowed to buy a home.

mutual fund
Investment company that sells shares and combines the investors' money in order to buy a large variety of stocks and bonds.

net deposit
Amount deposited in an account, less cash received.

net pay
Amount left after all deductions have been subtracted from gross pay; sometimes called take-home pay.

numerator
In the fraction $\frac{5}{6}$, the numerator is 5.

overtime
Time worked beyond the regular hours; an increase in the hourly rate is often given for this time.

percent
Word that indicates "hundredths" or "out of 100"; 4 percent (4%) means 0.04, or $\frac{4}{100}$.

perimeter
Measure of the distance around a closed figure.

policy (insurance)
Written agreement between the person being insured and the insurer.

premium
Cost of an insurance policy; premiums can be paid monthly, semiannually, or annually.

principal
Amount of money upon which interest is computed.

product
Answer in a multiplication problem; in $8 \times 12 = 96$, the product is 96.

promissory note
Written statement that is signed by a borrower and tells to whom, how much, and when payment will be made.

property damage insurance
Type of liability insurance that protects the car owner financially if the car damages the property of others.

proportion
Statement that two ratios are equal; an example is $\frac{3}{8} = \frac{9}{24}$.

protractor
Instrument used to draw or measure angles.

quarterly
Every 3 months, or 4 times a year.

quotient
Answer in a division problem; in $48 \div 6 = 8$, the quotient is 8.

real estate tax
Tax based upon the value of real estate owned.

reconciling a bank statement
Procedure used to see that the checkbook balance and the bank statement agree; this verifies the balance left in the account.

remainder
When 15 is divided by 6, the remainder is 3.

$$6\overline{)15} \quad \text{2 R3}$$

salary
Fixed amount paid to an employee at regular intervals for regular hours of work; usually paid every week, every 2 weeks, or every month.

sales tax
Tax imposed by state or local government on the retail price of certain goods and services.

savings account
Account at a bank or other savings institution into which money is deposited to earn interest.

scale drawing
Drawing in which all distances are measured and are in a constant ratio to the actual distances.

semiannual
Every 6 months, or twice a year.

service charge
Amount charged by a bank for handling an account; the service charge is printed on the bank statement.

share of stock
One unit of ownership in a company or corporation.

simple interest formula
Basic method of computing interest; the interest (I) equals the principal (p) times the rate (r) times the time (t) expressed in years.

$$I = p \times r \times t$$

social security
See Federal Insurance Contributions Act.

statistics
Collection of data, usually numbers, relating to any topic.

sticker price
Quoted price of a car, including the suggested retail price and the price of optional equipment.

surveyor
Person who accurately determines boundaries, measures distances, and makes scale drawings of land.

time and a half
Overtime rate of pay; 1.5 times the regular hourly rate.

tip
Small amount of money in excess of regular charges paid by a customer for a service, such as a tip paid to a waiter or a waitress for serving a meal.

trade-in allowance
Amount of money allowed for a used article as part of the purchase price of a new item.

unit price
Price per unit of measure of an item.

utilities
Public-service items, such as gas electricity, water, or telephone service, that are usually paid for by the individual consumer.

variable monthly expenses
Costs that change from month to month; most of a person's expenses are variable to some extent.

volume
Measure of an amount of space, given in cubic units.

wage and tax statement
Form W-2; a form, issued by an employer to an employee, that states the income earned and taxes withheld for the employee during the calendar year.

want ads
See classified ads.

zero bracket amount
The minimum deduction allowed a taxpayer when a federal income tax return is filed.

Selected Answers

page 5
Set A   **1.** 2000; 1500; 1540   **3.** 5000; 4900; 4870   **5.** 1000; 900; 930
    7. 6000; 6000; 6010   **9.** 7000; 7000; 7000
Set B   **11.** 13; 12.7; 12.68   **13.** 14; 13.9; 13.88   **15.** 48; 48.0; 47.97
    17. 321; 320.7; 320.71   **19.** 100; 100.1; 100.08
Related Problems   **21.** 4,000,000   **23.** $28.10; $28   **25.** $30.20; $30

page 7
Set A   **1.** 110; 109   **3.** 100; 104   **5.** 430; 434   **7.** 140; 136   **9.** 1200; 1165
Set B   **11.** 45; 44.95   **13.** 7; 7.19   **15.** 18; 18.46   **17.** 3; 2.73
Set C   **19.** 40; 44   **21.** 80; 84   **23.** 200; 204
Set D   **25.** 88; 87.69   **27.** 5; 4.733   **29.** 9; 9.31   **31.** 15; 14.55   **33.** 31; 30.614
Related Problems   **35.** $12.08

page 9
Set A   **1.** 4500   **3.** 14,000   **5.** 480,000   **7.** 5,400,000   **9.** 40,000   **11.** 1800
    13. 81,000   **15.** 2400
Set B   **17.** 1500; 1484   **19.** 1000; 1026   **21.** 14,000; 13,616   **23.** 18,000; 17,632
    25. 100,000; 108,072   **27.** 60,000; 64,414   **29.** 50,000; 54,135
    31. 720,000; 716,374   **33.** 1,600,000; 1,560,780   **35.** 2,000,000; 2,127,224
Mixed Practice   **37.** 320,000   **39.** 353,792   **41.** 29,852   **43.** 246,000
    45. 48,600,000   **47.** 6071   **49.** 3120   **51.** 34,486   **53.** 66,000   **55.** 3298
    57. 16,000   **59.** 364,000
Related Problems   **61.** 6000 bushels   **63.** 4200 pounds

page 11
Set A   **1.** 0.08   **3.** 0.064   **5.** 0.0036   **7.** 0.0056   **9.** 2.5   **11.** 0.081
    13. 4000   **15.** 0.02   **17.** 150   **19.** 5.4
Set B   **21.** 180; 179.2   **23.** 0.04; 0.04108   **25.** 24; 23.994   **27.** 0.1; 0.13412
    29. 18; 18.4968   **31.** 500; 504.45   **33.** 0.18; 0.176902   **35.** 24; 23.9328
    37. 360; 359.6899   **39.** 18; 17.98563
Mixed Practice   **41.** 0.032   **43.** 14.11   **45.** 0.0024   **47.** 3.6   **49.** 2.2715
    51. 1239.92   **53.** 48.5007   **55.** 0.7
Related Problems   **57.** $82.81   **59.** $288.61

page 13
Set A   **1.** 394   **3.** 36 R2   **5.** 49 R53   **7.** 471 R1   **9.** 175 R115
Set B   **11.** 29.86   **13.** 2.19   **15.** 0.20   **17.** 2.12   **19.** 4.83
Set C   **21.** 8   **23.** 4   **25.** 5   **27.** 3   **29.** 9
Related Problems   **31.** 89.3 feet

page 15
Set A   **1.** $>$ **3.** $<$ **5.** $>$ **7.** $>$ **9.** $>$

Set B   **11.** $\frac{3}{4}$ **13.** $\frac{2}{5}$ **15.** $\frac{3}{4}$ **17.** $\frac{1}{3}$

Set C   **19.** $\frac{29}{3}$ **21.** $\frac{53}{12}$ **23.** $\frac{55}{8}$ **25.** $\frac{71}{10}$

Set D   **27.** $4\frac{2}{3}$ **29.** 9   **31.** $2\frac{2}{5}$ **33.** 3

Related Problems   **35.** No

page 17
Set A   **1.** $\frac{5}{12}$ **3.** $\frac{1}{2}$ **5.** $\frac{4}{5}$

Set B   **7.** 4; $4\frac{1}{5}$ **9.** 16; $15\frac{3}{5}$ **11.** 36; $35\frac{1}{2}$

Set C   **13.** $\frac{5}{6}$ **15.** $1\frac{4}{5}$ **17.** $3\frac{5}{7}$

Mixed Practice   **19.** $2\frac{1}{7}$ **21.** $1\frac{1}{2}$ **23.** $2\frac{3}{16}$ **25.** 4   **27.** $\frac{5}{24}$

Related Problems   **29.** 375 miles

page 19
Set A   **1.** $\frac{11}{24}$ **3.** $\frac{13}{14}$ **5.** $1\frac{3}{16}$ **7.** $\frac{29}{36}$ **9.** $1\frac{23}{24}$ **11.** 7; $7\frac{1}{6}$ **13.** 3; $2\frac{17}{20}$
15. 11; $10\frac{11}{12}$ **17.** 13; $13\frac{1}{24}$ **19.** 11; $10\frac{15}{16}$ **21.** 8; $7\frac{19}{20}$

Set B   **23.** $\frac{1}{8}$ **25.** $\frac{1}{4}$ **27.** $\frac{1}{24}$ **29.** $\frac{1}{24}$ **31.** $3\frac{2}{5}$ **33.** 3; $3\frac{1}{4}$
35. 12; $11\frac{5}{8}$ **37.** 5; $5\frac{2}{9}$ **39.** 14; $13\frac{13}{16}$ **41.** 8; $7\frac{17}{20}$ **43.** 5; $5\frac{11}{24}$

Related Problems   **45.** $16\frac{3}{8}$

page 20   **1.** 0.833   **3.** 0.846   **5.** 0.625   **7.** 0.389   **9.** 0.288   **11.** 1.071
13. 2.622   **15.** 7.600   **17.** 2.800   **19.** 14.417   **21.** 31.067   **23.** 2.182
25. 17.273   **27.** 53.444   **29.** 15.333   **31.** 6.354

page 21   **1.** 7000; 7500; 7480   **2.** 24; 23.7; 23.72   **3.** 141   **4.** 8.28   **5.** 34
6. 41.46   **7.** 21,000   **8.** 24,192   **9.** 3.5   **10.** 35.041   **11.** 582
12. 6.23   **13.** 350   **14.** $>$ **15.** $\frac{2}{3}$ **16.** $\frac{39}{8}$ **17.** $9\frac{1}{3}$ **18.** $\frac{5}{21}$ **19.** $3\frac{1}{9}$
20. $4\frac{1}{2}$ **21.** $2\frac{4}{5}$ **22.** $\frac{19}{20}$ **23.** $6\frac{5}{24}$ **24.** $\frac{19}{40}$ **25.** $3\frac{5}{9}$

page 25
Set A   **1.** $a = 15$ **3.** $f = 1.53$ **5.** $c = 6.3$ **7.** $y = 4.1$ **9.** $m = 21$
   11. $t = 8.9$ **13.** $m = 6$
Set B   **15.** $g = 23$ **17.** $h = 1.38$ **19.** $n = 24$ **21.** $k = 0.79$ **23.** $m = 147$
   25. $t = 35.8$ **27.** $x = 8.02$
Mixed Practice   **29.** $t = 27$ **31.** $m = 12$ **33.** $t = 0.93$ **35.** $s = 5.6$
   37. $w = 51.19$ **39.** $y = 53$ **41.** $p = 91$ **43.** $b = 2.76$ **45.** $z = 9.05$
   47. $g = 33.4$
Related Problems   **49.** $r - 1.25 = 11.85$; $13.10

page 27
Set A   **1.** $a = 47$ **3.** $c = 17$ **5.** $x = 0.9$
Set B   **7.** $f = 0.6$ **9.** $r = 15.2$
Set C   **11.** $a = 3$ **13.** $t = 9$ **15.** $x = 12$
Mixed Practice   **17.** $f = 0.096$ **19.** $y = 0$ **21.** $z = 90$ **23.** $s = 4$ **25.** $x = 0$
   27. $x = 50$ **29.** $k = 0$
Related Problems   **31.** $0.85g = 7.65$; 9 games   **33.** $15t = 135$; 9 teams

page 29
Set A   **1.** $a = 1$ **3.** $n = 9$ **5.** $b = 3.5$ **7.** $m = 5$ **9.** $n = 1$
Set B   **11.** $m = 6$ **13.** $t = 7$ **15.** $n = 36$ **17.** $b = 144$ **19.** $x = 81$
Mixed Practice   **21.** $z = 8$ **23.** $x = 18$ **25.** $m = 0.2$ **27.** $x = 2$ **29.** $b = 4$
Related Problems   **31.** $3r - 450 = 315$; $255

page 31
Set A   **1.** $84 = 84$ **3.** $210 \neq 222$ **5.** $192 = 192$ **7.** $528 = 528$ **9.** $2.4 = 2.4$
   11. $21.6 = 21.6$ **13.** $0.1 = 0.1$ **15.** $453.6 \neq 420$
Set B   **17.** $a = 15$ **19.** $d = 9$ **21.** $x = 3.75$ **23.** $h = 4.2$ **25.** $x = 40$
   27. $s = 200$ **29.** $t = 0.006$ **31.** $y = 0.5$
Related Problems   **33.** 18 meters

pages 32–33
Set A   **1.** 43%   **3.** 9%   **5.** 2.7%   **7.** 22.5%   **9.** 19.75%   **11.** 7.45%
   13. 125%   **15.** 246.5%
Set B   **17.** 50%   **19.** 80%   **21.** 68%   **23.** 5%   **25.** 62.5%   **27.** 37.5%
   29. 220%
Set C   **31.** 0.23   **33.** 0.02   **35.** 0.135   **37.** 0.0875   **39.** 0.035
   41. 0.3225   **43.** 1.35   **45.** 1.07
Set D   **47.** $\frac{7}{10}$ **49.** $\frac{1}{2}$ **51.** $\frac{3}{4}$ **53.** $\frac{7}{20}$ **55.** $\frac{47}{100}$ **57.** $\frac{61}{100}$ **59.** $1\frac{9}{100}$
Related Problems   **61.** 0.22   **63.** 75%

pages 35–37
Set A   **1.** 14   **3.** 2.5   **5.** 32.34   **7.** 21.25   **9.** 42   **11.** 0.7125
Set B   **13.** 60%   **15.** 88%   **17.** 75%   **19.** 8%   **21.** 15%   **23.** 67.5%
Set C   **25.** 40   **27.** 90   **29.** 450   **31.** 11   **33.** 30   **35.** 144
Mixed Practice   **37.** 17   **39.** 160   **41.** 350   **43.** 75%   **45.** 47%   **47.** 14.5
Related Problems   **49.** $0.36   **51.** $0.17   **53.** 21%   **55.** $2.90   **57.** $140
    59. $6.38; $14.88

page 38   **1.** $709.59   **3.** $636.23   **5.** $471.49   **7.** $1387.08   **9.** $2415.19
    11. $1011.95; $758.96; $762.75

page 39   **1.** $d = 4.5$ **2.** $m = 8.5$ **3.** $f = 7.99$ **4.** $g = 7.95$ **5.** $x = 53$
6. $t = 7$ **7.** $b = 2.16$ **8.** $a = 4$ **9.** $c = 5$ **10.** $y = 8$ **11.** $a = 68$
12. $x = 6$ **13.** $250 \neq 260$ **14.** $28.8 = 28.8$ **15.** $c = 24$ **16.** $t = 88$
17. 6%   **18.** 46.5%   **19.** 76%   **20.** 31.25%   **21.** 0.57   **22.** 0.0575
23. $\frac{41}{100}$ **24.** $\frac{19}{50}$ **25.** 31.62   **26.** 24   **27.** 15%   **28.** 87.5%   **29.** 45
30. 150

page 43
Set A   **1.** 3.87 km   **3.** 14 mm   **5.** 2130 km
Set B   **7.** 60 m   **9.** 4590 km
Related Problems   **11–15.** Answers will vary.

page 45
Set A   **1.** 392.0 mm²   **3.** 9.4 km²   **5.** 322.5 m²
Set B   **7.** 210.0 mm²   **9.** 36.4 m²
Set C   **11.** 8177.0 mm³   **13.** 104.5 cm³   **15.** 1131.5 cm³
Related Problems   **17.** 0.8 m³

page 47
Set A   **1.** 250 mL   **3.** 40 L   **5.** 150 mL
Set B   **7.** 85 g   **9.** 165 g
Related Problems   **11.** Liter   **13.** Milliliter   **15.** Gram

page 49
Set A   **1.** 500 cm   **3.** 93 mm   **5.** 1275 cm   **7.** 500 mL   **9.** 2100 mg
Set B   **11.** 0.935 km   **13.** 0.429 m   **15.** 6.7 cm   **17.** 0.084 L   **19.** 1.375 g
Mixed Practice   **21.** 23,000 m   **23.** 180 mm   **25.** 0.06 m   **27.** 0.25 L
    29. 1.296 g
Related Problems   **31.** 1000 grams   **33.** 500 milliliters

page 51   **1.** 0°C   **3.** 3°C   **5.** 125°C   **7.** 39.8°C   **9.** 10°C
Related Problems   **11.** ⁻28°C   **13.** ⁻10°C   **15.** 25 km/h

page 53
Set A   **1.** 8 hours 35 minutes   **3.** 8 hours 20 minutes
Set B   **5.** 11:35 A.M.   **7.** 6:25 A.M.
Set C   **9.** 3 hours 10 minutes   **11.** 6 hours 35 minutes
Related Problems   **13.** 8 hours 5 minutes   **15.** 4:15 P.M.

page 55
Set A   **1.**   **Set B**   **3.**

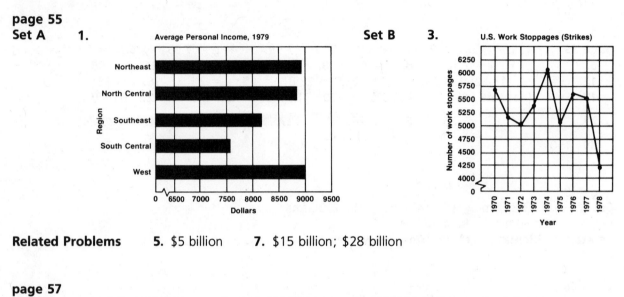

Related Problems   **5.** $5 billion   **7.** $15 billion; $28 billion

page 57
Set A   **1.** 1,443,600,000 t   **3.** 561,400,000 t   **5.** 320,800,000 t   **7.** $5250
         9. $1400   **11.** $1750
Set B   **13.** Land Owned by the Federal Government, 1979   **15.** Estimated Voting Population by Age, 1980

page 57 continued
Related Problems   **17.** 3,104,000 managers   **19.** 25.8%

page 59
Set A   **1.** 6   **3.** 38   **5.** 26   **7.** 121   **9.** 10.3
Set B   **11.** 7   **13.** 21   **15.** 25   **17.** 121   **19.** 10.3
Set C   **21.** 7   **23.** 21   **25.** 29   **27.** 116 and 132   **29.** 10.3
Related Problems   **31.** Bob 131, Matt 156; handicap: Bob 25
33. Bev 119, John 115; handicap: John 4

page 60   **1.** 600.5   **3.** 4567   **5.** 50,883.6   **7.** 68,802.1   **9.** 241.3
11. 1757 students   **13.** 56,501 people

page 61   **1.** 3 cm   **2.** 1 m   **3.** 33.6 m²   **4.** 51.7 cm²   **5.** 576.6 cm³
6. 13 L   **7.** 600 g   **8.** 7630 g   **9.** 0.34 m   **10.** 80°C
11. 10 hours 5 minutes   **12.** 8:05 P.M.   **13.** 3 hours 45 minutes
14.

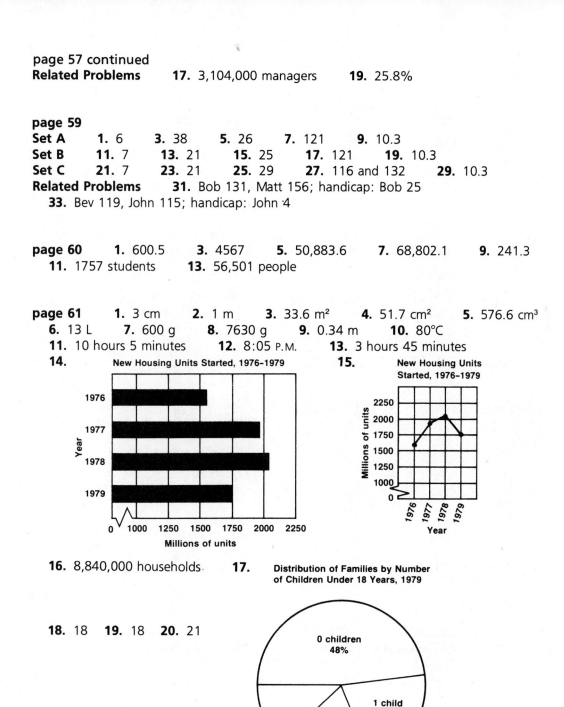

New Housing Units Started, 1976–1979

15. New Housing Units Started, 1976–1979

16. 8,840,000 households   **17.** Distribution of Families by Number of Children Under 18 Years, 1979

18. 18   **19.** 18   **20.** 21

0 children 48%

1 child 21%

2 children 19%

3 or more children 12%

page 65   **1.** 44   **3.** 55   **5.** 68   **7.** 69   **9.** 90

page 69   **1.** $404.00; $404.00   **3.** $260.00; $9.75; $48.75; $308.75
   5. $248.00; $9.30; $74.40; $322.40   **7.** $320.80; $12.03; $27.07; $347.87
   9. $341.20; $12.80; $44.80; $386.00   **11.** $321.20; $12.05; $63.26; $384.46

page 71   **1.** $410.00   **3.** $298.40   **5.** $428.20   **7.** $375.07   **9.** $550

page 73   **1.** $1.58   **3.** $1.29   **5.** $1.66   **7.** $0.82   **9.** $0.37
   11. $11.98; $4.79   **13.** $2.29; $0.92   **15.** $4.50; $1.80   **17.** $11.96; $4.78

page 75   **1.** $242.50   **3.** $336.50   **5.** $265.57   **7.** $318.92   **9.** $269
   11. $834

page 76   **1.** $1020.00   **3.** $1225.00   **5.** $1264.75

page 77   **1.** $9073.00; 14.0%   **3.** $10,692.97; 14.3%   **5.** $15,281.85; 11.5%
   7. $16,254.34; 10.2%   **9.** $16,680.94; 14.2%   **11.** $19,976.87; 9.3%

pages 79–81   **1.** $13.50   **3.** $18.80   **5.** $84.40   **7.** $65.20   **9.** $46.20
   11. $39.00   **13.** $10.70   **15.** $85.20   **17.** $6.29   **19.** $15.08   **21.** $12.07
   23. $102.88   **25.** None   **27.** $24.60; $15.69; $195.63
   29. $58.10; $20.69; $223.16   **31.** $80.50; $25.90; $267.68

page 83   **1.** M; $2432   **3.** G; $200   **5.** $16,125   **7.** $185.52   **9.** $24,612.50

page 84
Rounding whole numbers and decimals   **1.** 1000; 700; 670   **3.** 1000; 1200; 1250
   5. 5000; 5000; 5040   **7.** 65,000; 65,200; 65,190   **9.** 88,000; 87,900; 87,900
   11. 3; 3.3; 3.28   **13.** 75; 74.5; 74.52   **15.** 153; 152.8; 152.80
   17. 391; 391.5; 391.48   **19.** 85; 84.7; 84.67   **21.** 479; 479.0; 478.98
Subtracting whole numbers and decimals   **1.** 31   **3.** 66   **5.** 9   **7.** 12.5   **9.** 12.71
   11. 15.81   **13.** 3.482   **15.** 17.345   **17.** 0.353   **19.** 0.6   **21.** 5.103
   23. 71.4   **25.** 4.39   **27.** 12.516
Multiplying whole numbers   **1.** 1500   **3.** 42,000   **5.** 540,000   **7.** 180,000
   9. 301   **11.** 3,400,000   **13.** 7857   **15.** 2125   **17.** 3,570,000   **19.** 4032
   21. 34,408   **23.** 217,994   **25.** 8,113,050   **27.** 2,169,288

page 85   **1.** $194.40   **2.** $288   **3.** $155.82   **4.** $234   **5.** $240   **6.** $522.50   **7.** $30.70   **8.** $24.30   **9.** $208.00   **10.** B; $420

page 89   **1.** $514.65; $454.65   **3.** $70.31; $70.31   **5.** $419.18; $344.18   **7.** $182.07   **9.** $469.52

pages 90–91   **1.** Twenty-seven and $\frac{81}{100}$ **3.** Sixty and $\frac{00}{100}$ **5.** Fifteen and $\frac{00}{100}$ **7.** Three hundred ninety-five and $\frac{13}{100}$ **9.** One thousand two and $\frac{30}{100}$ **11.** $146.86; $97.91   **13.** $438.80

page 93   **1.** $282.22   **3.** $244.84   **5.** $528.87   **7.** $459.16   **9.** $373.54   **11.** $432.34   **13.** $304.66   **15.** $457.80

page 96   **1.** $71.29   **3.** $39.61   **5.** $174.72

page 97   **1.** $789.99   **3.** $1403.81   **5.** $745.99   **7.** $13.02   **9.** $221.88   **11.** $647.68   **13.** $534.50   **15.** $340.05

page 99   **1.** $1.25   **3.** $34.13   **5.** $23.93   **7.** $34.31   **9.** $72.52   **11.** $58.59   **13.** $918.13   **15.** $167.40

pages 100–101   **1.** $31.08   **3.** $101.46   **5.** $242.30   **7.** $28.74   **9.** $148.59   **11.** $136.48   **13.** $30.45

page 103   **1.** $26.25   **3.** $1629.15   **5.** $136.04   **7.** $787.69   **9.** $971.80   **11.** $872.10

page 104
Multiplying decimals   **1.** 0.35   **3.** 0.016   **5.** 0.0018   **7.** 0.00008   **9.** 140   **11.** 32   **13.** 2.1   **15.** 0.00002   **17.** 4.4   **19.** 34.944   **21.** 0.243   **23.** 153.51063   **25.** 1.574944   **27.** 1.701
Ratio and proportion   **1.** $120 = 120$ **3.** $140 \neq 144$ **5.** $0.064 \neq 0.033$ **7.** $n = 36$ **9.** $x = 15$ **11.** $d = 21$ **13.** $y = 81$

page 104 continued
Writing percents, decimals, and fractions   **1.** 0.17   **3.** 0.01   **5.** 0.96   **7.** 0.99
9. 0.0775   **11.** 0.125   **13.** 0.0675   **15.** 0.328   **17.** 0.0575   **19.** 1.03
21. 8.56   **23.** 0.0025   **25.** $\frac{1}{2}$ **27.** $\frac{7}{20}$ **29.** $\frac{3}{5}$ **31.** $\frac{6}{25}$ **33.** $\frac{1}{5}$ **35.** $\frac{9}{100}$
37. $\frac{33}{100}$ **39.** $\frac{9}{20}$ **41.** $\frac{19}{20}$ **43.** $\frac{3}{8}$ **45.** $1\frac{1}{10}$ **47.** $3\frac{1}{2}$

page 105   **1.** $81.18; $56.18   **2.** Thirty-eight and $\frac{72}{100}$ **3.** $206.62; $131.42
4. $419.44   **5.** $384.74   **6.** $109.11   **7.** $58.50   **8.** $98.88   **9.** $82.43
10. $137.56

page 109   **1.** $38.25   **3.** $17.64   **5.** $1.11   **7.** $115   **9.** $106.25
11. $108 interest; $1908 total due   **13.** $840 interest; $3240 total due

page 111   **1.** $47.16; $0.71; $47.87   **3.** $106.38; $1.60; $107.98
5. $22.33; $0.33; $47.32   **7.** $173.77; $2.61; $206.02   **9.** $0; $0; $20.94
11. $150.00; $2.25; $187.85

page 113   **1.** 10 days; $1471.90   **3.** $122.19; 19 days; $2321.61   **5.** $130.52
7. $122.19   **9.** $0.47; $42.47   **11.** $1.57; $83.30

page 114   **1.** $459.75   **3.** $409.75; 4 days; $1639.00   **5.** $422.06; 8 days; $3376.48
7. $441.05; 4 days; $1764.20   **9.** $456.84; 2 days; $913.68   **11.** $13,369.05; $431.26
13. Total of payments, $50.00; Balance after payments, $385.78; Total of purchases, $71.06;
Finance charge, $7.76; New balance, $464.60

page 115   **1.** $42.16; $54.70; $10.00   **3.** $107.36; $194.47; $20.00
5. $190.93; $193.79; $20.00   **7.** $9.68; $9.83; $9.83

page 117   **1.** $87.89   **3.** $122   **5.** $13.09   **7.** $46.51   **9.** $159.53
11. $3.36; $255.00; $202.64   **13.** $152.98; $2.04; $155.02; $102.66
15. $51.67; $0.69; $52.36; $0

page 119   **1.** $277.32; $27.82   **3.** $729.95; $891.60; $161.65
5. $174.20; $222.90; $48.70   **7.** $553.71; $740.88; $187.17
9. $202.77; $271.08; $68.31   **11.** $45.84; $550.08; $50.08
13. $18.08; $650.88; $150.88   **15.** $25.70; $616.80; $116.80
17. $25.82; $619.68; $119.68

page 121   **1.** $90.21   **3.** Ace Appliance Store   **5.** $72   **7.** $116.59
9. The 17% loan for 36 months in problem 8   **11.** $23.52   **13.** $16.44
15. The $100 a month at 2% per month in problem 14

page 122
Dividing whole numbers   **1.** 2604   **3.** 183   **5.** 1653 R2   **7.** 44 R57   **9.** 104 R43
11. 41 R10   **13.** 458   **15.** 209 R25   **17.** 45 R26   **19.** 679   **21.** 2274 R25
23. 3654 R13   **25.** 11,292 R57   **27.** 87 R96
Dividing decimals   **1.** 1.84   **3.** 0.66   **5.** 0.09   **7.** 5.42   **9.** 0.11   **11.** 6.39
13. 4.57   **15.** 280   **17.** 5.65   **19.** 0.78   **21.** 0.05   **23.** 1.39   **25.** 7.23

Multiplying fractions and mixed numbers   **1.** $\frac{2}{15}$ **3.** $\frac{1}{5}$ **5.** $\frac{1}{2}$ **7.** $6\frac{2}{3}$ **9.** $1\frac{4}{5}$
11. 5   **13.** $3\frac{1}{8}$ **15.** 6   **17.** $15\frac{3}{4}$ **19.** $\frac{5}{14}$ **21.** $16\frac{2}{3}$

page 123   **1.** $1567.50   **2.** $108.91   **3.** $80   **4.** $2.35   **5.** $211.83
6. $51.14   **7.** $50.29   **8.** $461.66   **9.** $68   **10.** Plan B

page 127   **1.** 74   **3.** 82   **5.** 65   **7.** 89   **9.** 66   **11.** 161   **13.** 121
15. 104   **17.** 174   **19.** 482   **21.** 512   **23.** 58   **25.** 126   **27.** 139

page 129   Program modifications may vary. Samples are given.

1.
MEYER'S DEPARTMENT STORE
CHARGE-ACCOUNT STATEMENT

BEGINNING OF AUGUST	
BALANCE	211.85
PAYMENTS DURING AUGUST	50
FINANCE CHARGE ON	
BALANCE OF $ 161.85	2.43
CHARGES DURING AUGUST	37.82
NEW BALANCE	202.1

3.
MEYER'S DEPARTMENT STORE
CHARGE-ACCOUNT STATEMENT

BEGINNING OF JANUARY	
BALANCE	37.42
PAYMENTS DURING JANUARY	37.42
FINANCE CHARGE ON	
BALANCE OF $ 0	0
CHARGES DURING JANUARY	23.51
NEW BALANCE	23.51

5.
MEYER'S DEPARTMENT STORE
CHARGE-ACCOUNT STATEMENT

BEGINNING OF JUNE	
BALANCE	83.92
PAYMENTS DURING JUNE	40
FINANCE CHARGE ON	
BALANCE OF $ 43.92	.66
CHARGES DURING JUNE	27.35
NEW BALANCE	71.93

7.
MEYER'S DEPARTMENT STORE
CHARGE-ACCOUNT STATEMENT

BEGINNING OF FEBRUARY	
BALANCE	287.93
PAYMENTS DURING FEBRUARY	35
FINANCE CHARGE ON	
BALANCE OF $ 252.93	3.79
CHARGES DURING FEBRUARY	29.68
NEW BALANCE	286.4

9.
MEYER'S DEPARTMENT STORE
CHARGE-ACCOUNT STATEMENT

BEGINNING OF OCTOBER	
BALANCE	87.21
PAYMENTS DURING OCTOBER	10
FINANCE CHARGE ON	
BALANCE OF $ 77.21	1.16
CHARGES DURING OCTOBER	19.58
NEW BALANCE	97.95

11. 182 IF P>0 THEN 190
183 IF B=0 THEN 190
184 PRINT "NO PAYMENT RECEIVED"
185 PRINT "IF PAYMENT IS IN MAIL, THANK YOU"

page 129 continued

13.
```
15 LET C=0
90 INPUT C1
91 IF C1=0 THEN 100
92 LET C=C+C1
93 GO TO 90
```
With this modification, zero must be entered for the last input for line 90 so the program can continue.

15.
```
75 PRINT "RETURNS";
76 INPUT R
101 IF R>U THEN 104
102 LET U=U−R
103 GO TO 110
104 LET A=0
105 LET A=R−U
106 LET F=0
107 GO TO 130
191 IF R=0 THEN 200
192 PRINT "$";R;"HAS BEEN CREDITED TO YOUR ACCOUNT"
225 IF A=0 THEN 230
226 PRINT "NEW BALANCE";TAB(30);"$";A;"CREDIT"
227 GO TO 240
```

17.
```
91 IF C1=0 THEN 97
97 PRINT "FINANCE CHARGE RATE";
98 INPUT Y
110 LET F=Y*U/100
```

page 133   **1.** $8160.49   **3.** $8771.49   **5.** $7989.49; yes   **7.** AM radio, $51; Sport-style mirrors, driver's remote, $53; Steel-belted, blackwall tires with 2.8-liter engine, $67   **9.** AM-FM stereo radio with 40 channel CB, $413; Sport-style mirrors, both remote, $80; Steel-belted, wide oval, billboard-lettered tires with 2.8-liter engine, $119

page 134   **1.** $8300   **3.** $8800   **5.** $7100   **7.** $8400   **9.** $6700

page 137   **1.** $41.25; $1036.75   **3.** $68.85; $2393.35   **5.** $129.15; $1998.15   **7.** $3738.95   **9.** $152.24; $3223.92   **11.** $28.14   **13.** $116.80   **15.** $3113.90   **17.** $9432.25   **19.** $741.75

page 139   **1.** $6125   **3.** $6165   **5.** $6805   **7.** $6708   **9.** $6698   **11.** $7342   **13.** $8539   **15.** $8445   **17.** $10,214   Subcompact model: Suburban, Ltd.   Compact model: Colonial Motors   Mid-sized model: Heritage, Ltd.   Full-sized model: Cass St. Motors   Luxury sedan: Prospect Sales   Sports car: Congress Motors   **19.** $8073   **21.** $8672.61

pages 141–142   **1.** $6000; $7258.80; $1258.80; $8998.80   **3.** $6853; $7870.68; $1017.68; $10,865.68   **5.** $6180; $6869.76; $689.76; $9344.76   **7.** $6853; $9662.88; $2809.88; $12,727.88   **9.** $4889; $5943.36; $1054.36; $9593.36

pages 141–142 continued

11.

SALE SUMMARY

Suggested Retail Price		**$6845.00**
Optional equipment	**$ 739.00**	
Destination charge	**$ 260.00**	
Sticker Price		**$7844.00**
Price reduction	**$ 500.00**	
Selling Price		**$7344.00**
Sales tax (__4%__)	**$ 293.76**	
License-plate fee	**$ 18.00**	
Title fee	**$ 5.00**	
Other charges	**$ ----**	
Total Cost		**$7660.76**
Trade-in allowance	**$ ----**	
Cash deposit	**$3060.76**	
Amount Financed		**$4600.00**
Finance charge	**$ 965.36**	
ANNUAL PERCENTAGE RATE ...	_____	
Number of payments	**24**	
Monthly payment	**$ 231.89**	
Total of payments	**$5565.36**	
Total Sale Price (deferred-payment price)		**$8626.12**

page 143　　**1.** 18.57%　　**3.** 20.92%　　**5.** 18.83%　　**7.** 21.03%

page 145　　**1.** $1813.50; $800; $2613.50　　**3.** $1752.50; $800; $2552.50
5. $1984.00; $1400; $3384.00　　**7.** $1350.00; $75; $1425.00
9. $1533.75; $350; $1883.75　　**11.** $902.50; $0; $902.50　　**13.** $400　　**15.** $1443.75
17. $1793.75

page 146
Subtracting whole numbers and decimals　　**1.** 34　　**3.** 24　　**5.** 67　　**7.** 21.1　　**9.** 18.2
11. 20.97　　**13.** 3.781　　**15.** 21.272　　**17.** 0.363　　**19.** 0.9　　**21.** 5.789
23. 26.6　　**25.** 1.96　　**27.** 47.504
Writing percents, decimals, and fractions　　**1.** 0.29　　**3.** 0.09　　**5.** 0.82　　**7.** 0.73
9. 0.1842　　**11.** 0.675　　**13.** 0.0825　　**15.** 0.184　　**17.** 0.0825　　**19.** 0.205
21. 4.05　　**23.** 2.5　　**25.** 56%　　**27.** 3%　　**29.** 50%　　**31.** 49%　　**33.** 5.3%
35. 33.9%　　**37.** 90.6%　　**39.** 1.25%　　**41.** 32.25%　　**43.** 90.54%　　**45.** 506%
47. 112.1%
Percent problems　　**1.** 4.9　　**3.** 39　　**5.** 207　　**7.** 6.6　　**9.** 12.5%　　**11.** 3%
13. 32%　　**15.** 44%　　**17.** 25　　**19.** 340　　**21.** 3　　**23.** 30

page 147   **1.** $9264   **2.** $6100   **3.** $98.75   **4.** $3096.65   **5.** $6675
6. $7488; $7598; $7522; Sayo Imports   **7.** $1089.74   **8.** $11,013.28   **9.** $1083
10. $2205

page 151   **1.** 1104.7 kilometers   **3.** 6.5 kilometers per liter   **5.** 5.9¢ per kilometer
7. 349.5 km; 6.1 km/L; 6.2¢   **9.** 242.0 km; 4.0 km/L; 9.5¢
11. 342.5 km; 4.5 km/L; 8.4¢

page 153   **1.** $4060; $3190; $2320; $2030; $1740; $4060
3. $4340; $3410; $2480; $2170; $1860; $4340
5. $4970; $3905; $2840; $2485; $2130; $4970
7. $5950; $4675; $3400; $2975; $2550; $5950
9. $6790; $5335; $3880; $3395; $2910; $6790

page 154   **1.** $3123   **3.** $1823   **5.** $3120   **7.** $3619   **9.** $4186   **11.** $2652
13. $2597   **15.** $5677   **17.** $2080   **19.** $3706   **21.** $2814   **23.** $5848

page 155   **1.** 8.586 km/L   **3.** 7.55 km/L   **5.** 7.736 km/L   **7.** 7.06 km/L
9. 10.45; 8.70; 1.75; 16.75%   **11.** 7.31; 6.85; 0.46; 6.29%

pages 157–159   **1.** $65.50   **3.** $6.70   **5.** $26.20   **7.** $9.06   **9.** $113.96
11. $27.50   **13.** $236.48

page 161   **1.** $250,000   **3.** $100,000   **5.** $217.81   **7.** $223.04   **9.** $342.47
11. $429.76   **13.** $372.68

page 163   **1.** $692.04; $81.60; $773.64   **3.** $280.32; $81.60; $361.92
5. $652.54; $55.60; $708.14   **7.** $264.32; $55.60; $319.92   **9.** $726.80; $76.20; $803.00

page 165   **1.** $4073.81   **3.** $6196.20   **5.** Depreciation; gas   **7.** $728.13
9. $2848.63   **11.** Radial tires

page 167   **1.** $71.60   **3.** $36   **5.** $42   **7.** $54   **9.** 2.7¢ per kilometer
11. $3792   **13.** $2340   **15.** $3096   **17.** $4440   **19.** $5220

page 168

Adding whole numbers and decimals **1.** 52 **3.** 157 **5.** 189 **7.** 232 **9.** 320
11. 1732 **13.** 1566 **15.** 12.85 **17.** 59.51 **19.** 18.87 **21.** 21.6
23. 1.44 **25.** 7.904 **27.** 154.07

Multiplying decimals **1.** 0.18 **3.** 0.036 **5.** 0.003 **7.** 0.00024 **9.** 320
11. 3.6 **13.** 5.6 **15.** 0.00003 **17.** 8.4 **19.** 34.452 **21.** 0.3588
23. 35.1568 **25.** 6.26824 **27.** 5.4846

Renaming fractions and mixed numbers **1.** $\frac{11}{8}$ **3.** $\frac{17}{6}$ **5.** $\frac{26}{5}$ **7.** $\frac{19}{2}$ **9.** $\frac{32}{9}$
11. $\frac{63}{10}$ **13.** $\frac{12}{1}$ **15.** $\frac{35}{16}$ **17.** $\frac{59}{10}$ **19.** $\frac{52}{11}$ **21.** $2\frac{1}{4}$ **23.** $1\frac{1}{2}$ **25.** $2\frac{1}{6}$
27. $4\frac{2}{3}$ **29.** $4\frac{1}{3}$ **31.** $1\frac{5}{16}$ **33.** $2\frac{3}{8}$ **35.** $1\frac{4}{5}$ **37.** $7\frac{4}{9}$

page 169 **1.** 6.8 kilometers per liter **2.** $3360 **3.** $2418 **4.** $71.75
5. $19.20 **6.** $372.68 **7.** $448.56 **8.** 27.5¢ per kilometer **9.** $59.10
10. $2340

page 173 **1.** 3600 kilometers **3.** 2108 kilometers **5.** 4274 kilometers
7. 4623 kilometers **9.** 5138 kilometers **11.** 142 kilometers **13.** 4434 kilometers

page 175 **1.** 167 kilometers; 2 hours **3.** 334 kilometers; 4 hours
5. 167 kilometers; 2 hours **7.** 338 kilometers; 4 hours **9.** 301 kilometers; 4 hours
11. 110 kilometers **13.** 80 kilometers **15.** 80 kilometers **17.** 132 km; 120 km
19. 160 km; 150 km **21.** 6 hours

page 177 **1.** $45.20 **3.** $671.80 **5.** $53.20

page 179 **1.** $184 **3.** $577.50 **5.** $1143.25 **7.** $497 **9.** $1000

page 180 **1.** $150 **3.** $149.60 **5.** $261.81 **7.** $138.14 **9.** $211.84

page 181 **1.** 828 km; $124.20; $175; $299.20 **3.** 544 km; $87.04; $112; $199.04
5. 379 km; $75.80; $96; $171.80 **7.** $206 **9.** $186 **11.** $129 **13.** $349
15. Compact Getaway Special; $135

page 183 **1.** $135 **3.** $212 **5.** $347.50 **7.** $585 **9.** $2356

page 184
Dividing decimals   **1.** 10.79   **3.** 0.08   **5.** 14.05   **7.** 0.81   **9.** 6.27   **11.** 11.94
13. 6   **15.** 6   **17.** 3   **19.** 8   **21.** 80   **23.** 32

Adding fractions and mixed numbers   **1.** $1\frac{1}{12}$ **3.** $1\frac{1}{3}$ **5.** $1\frac{1}{14}$ **7.** $1\frac{11}{36}$ **9.** $4\frac{1}{15}$
11. $8\frac{1}{3}$ **13.** $7\frac{5}{6}$ **15.** $6\frac{14}{15}$ **17.** $8\frac{3}{16}$ **19.** 19   **21.** $18\frac{17}{24}$

Subtracting fractions and mixed numbers   **1.** $\frac{1}{2}$ **3.** $\frac{3}{8}$ **5.** $\frac{17}{24}$ **7.** $\frac{1}{14}$ **9.** $2\frac{3}{8}$
11. $2\frac{1}{2}$ **13.** $4\frac{1}{3}$ **15.** $9\frac{9}{16}$ **17.** $6\frac{7}{15}$ **19.** $6\frac{1}{3}$ **21.** $7\frac{5}{12}$

page 185   **1.** 1214 kilometers   **2.** 269 kilometers   **3.** 100 kilometers   **4.** $81.20
5. $73   **6.** $508.75   **7.** $1880   **8.** $200.95   **9.** $606   **10.** $969

page 189   **1.** 44   **3.** 58   **5.** 37   **7.** 44   **9.** 29   **11.** 13   **13.** 36
15. 37   **17.** 65   **19.** 58   **21.** 107   **23.** 235   **25.** 219   **27.** 128

page 191   Program modifications may vary. A sample is given.

1.
```
AMOUNT TO FINANCE    $ 2500
ANNUAL INTEREST RATE  17  %
NUMBER OF MONTHS 18
MONTHLY PAYMENT    $  158.33
```

3.
```
AMOUNT TO FINANCE    $ 5250
ANNUAL INTEREST RATE  19  %
NUMBER OF MONTHS 24
MONTHLY PAYMENT    $  264.65
```

5.
```
AMOUNT TO FINANCE    $ 7185
ANNUAL INTEREST RATE  17.75  %
NUMBER OF MONTHS 36
MONTHLY PAYMENT    $  258.85
```

7.
```
AMOUNT TO FINANCE    $ 7210
ANNUAL INTEREST RATE  16.75  %
NUMBER OF MONTHS 36
MONTHLY PAYMENT    $  256.16
```

9.
```
AMOUNT TO FINANCE    $ 6820
ANNUAL INTEREST RATE  17.5  %
NUMBER OF MONTHS 18
MONTHLY PAYMENT    $  433.53
```

11.
```
AMOUNT TO FINANCE    $ 3000
ANNUAL INTEREST RATE  17.5  %
NUMBER OF MONTHS 24
MONTHLY PAYMENT    $  149.05
```
```
AMOUNT TO FINANCE    $ 3500
ANNUAL INTEREST RATE  18  %
NUMBER OF MONTHS 30
MONTHLY PAYMENT    $  145.74
```
$3500 at 18% annually for 30 months

13.
```
AMOUNT TO FINANCE    $ 4785
ANNUAL INTEREST RATE  18.5  %
NUMBER OF MONTHS 18
MONTHLY PAYMENT    $  306.45
```
```
AMOUNT TO FINANCE    $ 5000
ANNUAL INTEREST RATE  17  %
NUMBER OF MONTHS 24
MONTHLY PAYMENT    $  247.21
```
$5000 at 17% annually for 24 months

15.
```
20 PRINT "TOTAL COST";
30 INPUT T
32 PRINT "DOWN PAYMENT";
33 INPUT D
34 LET P=T−D
105 PRINT "TOTAL COST    $";T
106 PRINT "DOWN PAYMENT    $";D
```

17.
```
TOTAL COST    $ 8745
DOWN PAYMENT    $ 4000
AMOUNT TO FINANCE    $ 4745
ANNUAL INTEREST RATE  16.5  %
NUMBER OF MONTHS 28
MONTHLY PAYMENT    $  205.32
```
```
TOTAL COST    $ 9282
DOWN PAYMENT    $ 5000
AMOUNT TO FINANCE    $ 4282
ANNUAL INTEREST RATE  16.8  %
NUMBER OF MONTHS 24
MONTHLY PAYMENT    $  211.3
```
$8745 with a $4000 down payment at 16.5% annually for 28 months

page 191 continued

19.
TOTAL COST $ 8378
DOWN PAYMENT $ 3500
AMOUNT TO FINANCE $ 4878
ANNUAL INTEREST RATE 18.5 %
NUMBER OF MONTHS 24
COST OF FINANCING $ 995.04
MONTHLY PAYMENT $ 244.71

21.
TOTAL COST $ 10583
DOWN PAYMENT $ 4000
AMOUNT TO FINANCE $ 6583
ANNUAL INTEREST RATE 16.75 %
NUMBER OF MONTHS 30
COST OF FINANCING $ 1519.4
TOTAL SALE PRICE $ 12102.4
MONTHLY PAYMENT $ 270.08

pages 194–195   **1.** $252   **3.** $344   **5.** $290   **7.** $500   **9.** $208   **11.** $300
13. $229   **15.** $268   **17.** $365   **19.** $490   **21.** $472

page 197   **1.** $370   **3.** $410   **5.** $285   **7.** The Villas, $265; Colony Point, $285;
750 Nichols Road, $295; Summit, $370; Middletown Apartments, $380; Cranbrook Square, $410;
Meadow Green, $415   **9.** $205

page 199   **1.** 58915   **3.** 60279   **5.** 62750   **7.** 64431   **9.** Feb.–April 677;
April–June 643; June–Aug. 1828; Aug.–Oct. 1134; Oct.–Dec. 547

page 200   **1.** $0.90   **3.** $7.16   **5.** $18.05   **7.** $1.94   **9.** $22.13   **11.** $2.29
13. $22.78   **15.** $5.42   **17.** $0.90; $9.53; $7.22; $58.95; $18.21; $2.51; $1.96; $49.82;
$22.33; $61.46; $2.31; $13.14; $22.98; $4.31; $5.47; $0.10

page 203   **1.** 17.0 cm   **3.** 7.7 cm by 4.3 cm   **5.** 7.5 cm by 2.9 cm
7. 6.4 cm by 3.0 cm   **9.** 7.8 cm by 5.4 cm   **11.** 2.6 cm by 1.8 cm
13. 6.7 cm by 1.9 cm   **15.** Outline should be 14.4 cm by 13.8 cm

pages 204–205   For problems **1–5**,
answers are given in this order:
length, width, total.
1. 8; 5; 40   **3.** 15; 13; 195
5. 21; 17; 357   **7.** $162.50

11. 178 tiles   **13.** $216

9.

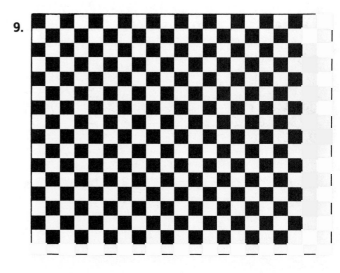

page 207   **1.** 400 sq. ft.; 154 sq. ft.; 554 sq. ft.; 2 gal.
   3. 176 sq. ft.; 30 sq. ft.; 206 sq. ft.; 1 gal.   **5.** 480 sq. ft.; 125 sq. ft.; 605 sq. ft.; 2 gal.

page 209   **1.** 480 sq. ft   **3.** 3 rolls   **5.** $110.37   **7.** 22 rolls   **9.** 19 rolls
   11. 3 rolls

page 211   **1.** $90.00   **3.** $57.20   **5.** $88.00   **7.** $131.25   **9.** $406.00
   11. $129.50   **13.** $273.00   **15.** $51.00

page 212
Dividing whole numbers   **1.** 511   **3.** 324 R4   **5.** 4742   **7.** 126 R28   **9.** 108 R21
   11. 121 R47   **13.** 44   **15.** 207   **17.** 80 R32   **19.** 1203 R3   **21.** 7814 R16
   23. 4285 R86   **25.** 204   **27.** 1646 R189
Multiplying fractions and mixed numbers   **1.** $\frac{5}{24}$ **3.** $\frac{2}{7}$ **5.** $\frac{1}{12}$ **7.** $3\frac{1}{2}$ **9.** $1\frac{1}{5}$
   11. $1\frac{1}{4}$ **13.** 27   **15.** 9   **17.** $24\frac{2}{5}$ **19.** $10\frac{1}{2}$
Ratio and proportion   **1.** $24 \neq 28$ **3.** $1200 \neq 1280$ **5.** $117.6 \neq 144$ **7.** $a = 30$
   9. $c \doteq 3$ **11.** $n = 5.3$ **13.** $n = 400$

page 213   **1.** $314   **2.** $238   **3.** $370   **4.** 40593   **5.** 22 cm
   6. 285 tiles   **7.** $65   **8.** 2 gallons   **9.** 15 rolls   **10.** $177.40

page 217   **1.** $36,000   **3.** $18,720   **5.** $29,120   **7.** $28,288   **9.** $22,880
   11. No   **13.** Yes

page 219   **1.** $10,000; $40,000; $458.00   **3.** $15,000; $60,000; $640.20
   5. $15,000; $45,000; $497.70   **7.** $21,000; $84,000; $895.44   **9.** $5000   **11.** $13
   13. $54,000   **15.** $44.10

pages 220–221   **1.** 300; $139,920; $99,920   **3.** 300; $144,480; $104,480
   5. $416.06; 240; $99,854.40; $64,354.40   **7.** $836.94; 360; $301,298.40; $245,798.40
   9. $51,216   **11.** $125,874   **13.** 4.3

page 222   **1.** $629.88   **3.** $53,980.08   **5.** $10.13   **7.** $629.65   **9.** $53,959.70

page 223   **1.** $449.82; $16.58; $39,967.02   **3.** $39,950.25; $449.44; $16.96; $39,933.29
5. $39,916.14; $449.06; $17.34; $39,898.80   **7.** $39,881.26; $448.66; $17.74; $39,863.52
9. $39,845.58; $448.26; $18.14; $39,827.44   **11.** $39,809.10; $447.85; $18.55; $39,790.55
13. $20,796.17; $233.96; $232.44; $20,563.73   **15.** $20,328.67; $228.70; $237.70; $20,090.97
17. 50%

page 225   **1.** $8.40   **3.** $2.07   **5.** $192.47   **7.** $2.76   **9.** $15.60   **11.** $6.60
13. $20.70   **15.** $181.85   **17.** $5.70   **19.** $7   **21.** $16.04   **23.** $13.56

page 227   **1.** $26,000; $715.00   **3.** $34,000; $1003.00   **5.** $36,000; $1490.40
7. $31,500; $1641.15   **9.** $19,350; $1465.96   **11.** $112.23

page 229   **1.** $116   **3.** $90   **5.** $1534   **7.** $520   **9.** $2209.50   **11.** $605
13. $187.50   **15.** $1785

pages 231–233   **1.** $69,200   **3.** $80,300   **5.** $106,500   **7.** $67,400   **9.** $1125
11. $82,305   **13.** $17,425   **15.** San Francisco-Oakland   **17.** Miami   **19.** $7290

page 234
Multiplying whole numbers   **1.** 3200   **3.** 3000   **5.** 280,000   **7.** 450,000
9. 17,696   **11.** 3180   **13.** 3,440,000   **15.** 816   **17.** 2037   **19.** 8,400,000
21. 216,544   **23.** 368,760   **25.** 1,285,309   **27.** 724,603

Renaming fractions and mixed numbers   **1.** $\frac{1}{4}$ **3.** $\frac{1}{2}$ **5.** $\frac{3}{4}$ **7.** $\frac{1}{2}$ **9.** $\frac{7}{8}$ **11.** $\frac{5}{6}$
13. $\frac{7}{10}$ **15.** $\frac{3}{4}$ **17.** $\frac{2}{21}$ **19.** $\frac{1}{3}$ **21.** $\frac{12}{5}$ **23.** $\frac{23}{10}$ **25.** $\frac{9}{5}$ **27.** $\frac{16}{5}$ **29.** $\frac{53}{8}$
31. $\frac{15}{4}$ **33.** $\frac{35}{8}$ **35.** $\frac{11}{10}$ **37.** $\frac{29}{12}$

Dividing fractions and mixed numbers   **1.** $1\frac{1}{2}$ **3.** $1\frac{1}{8}$ **5.** $\frac{24}{35}$ **7.** $7\frac{1}{2}$ **9.** 16
11. $6\frac{1}{4}$ **13.** $1\frac{7}{9}$ **15.** $1\frac{8}{15}$ **17.** $\frac{25}{34}$ **19.** $\frac{3}{4}$ **21.** $1\frac{7}{8}$

page 235   **1.** $30,992   **2.** $46,800   **3.** $506.85   **4.** $121,698   **5.** $416.25
6. $148.90   **7.** $1521.33   **8.** $412.50   **9.** $77,500   **10.** $23,400

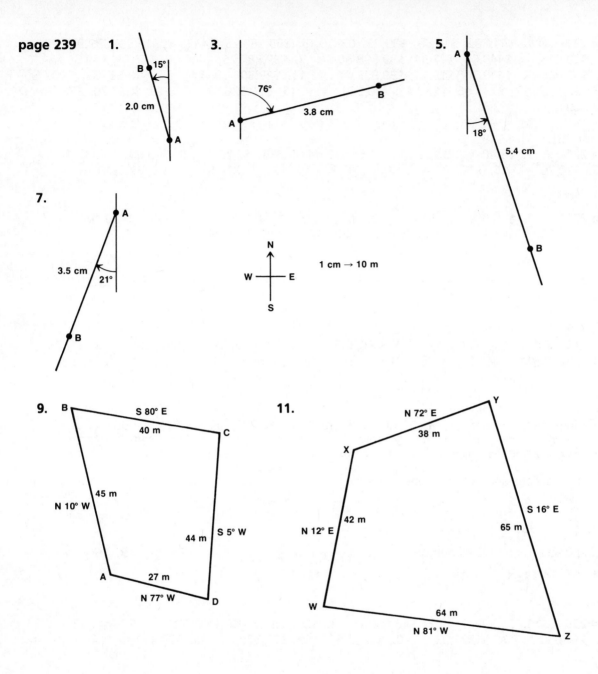

1.

B 15°

2.0 cm

A

3.

76°

A

3.8 cm

B

5.

A

18°

5.4 cm

B

7.

A

3.5 cm

21°

B

N

W —— E

S

1 cm → 10 m

9.

B

S 80° E

40 m

C

45 m

N 10° W

44 m

S 5° W

A

27 m

N 77° W

D

11.

Y

N 72° E

38 m

X

42 m

N 12° E

S 16° E

65 m

W

64 m

N 81° W

Z

pages 241–242   **1.** 750 square feet   **3.** 855 square feet   **5.** $70,832   **7.** $6149
9. 1884 square feet   **11.** 492 square feet   **13.** $81,018

page 243   **1.** $63,875.00; $7500.00; $71,375.00   **3.** $63,750.00; $4887.50; $68,637.50
5. $74,555.00; $7995.00; $82,550.00   **7.** $86,625.00; $8775.00; $95,400.00
9. $67,787.50; $8482.50; $76,270.00   **11.** $67,725.00; $6727.50; $74,452.50

page 245   **1.** 611 sq. ft.   **3.** $39\frac{3}{16}$ sq. ft.   **5.** $15\frac{3}{4}$ sq. ft.   **7.** $10\frac{1}{8}$ sq. ft.
9. 1532 sq. ft.

page 247   **1.** 480 square feet   **3.** 1680 square feet   **5.** 100 square feet
7. 269 square feet   **9.** 9877 bricks   **11.** 127 cubic feet

page 248
Multiplying fractions and mixed numbers   **1.** $\frac{7}{16}$ **3.** $\frac{2}{5}$ **5.** $\frac{3}{8}$ **7.** 8   **9.** $\frac{6}{8}$ **11.** $2\frac{2}{5}$
13. $38\frac{1}{3}$ **15.** $18\frac{6}{7}$ **17.** $22\frac{1}{4}$ **19.** $1\frac{1}{2}$
Adding fractions and mixed numbers   **1.** $\frac{3}{4}$ **3.** $1\frac{5}{12}$ **5.** $\frac{17}{18}$ **7.** $1\frac{1}{5}$ **9.** $2\frac{7}{12}$ **11.** $3\frac{1}{2}$
13. $9\frac{5}{24}$ **15.** $13\frac{13}{15}$ **17.** $10\frac{2}{15}$ **19.** 7
Subtracting fractions and mixed numbers   **1.** $\frac{1}{2}$ **3.** $\frac{1}{10}$ **5.** $\frac{1}{6}$ **7.** $\frac{3}{16}$ **9.** $8\frac{2}{3}$ **11.** $2\frac{2}{3}$
13. $2\frac{1}{8}$ **15.** $3\frac{11}{18}$ **17.** $2\frac{17}{18}$ **19.** $1\frac{5}{6}$

page 249   **1.**

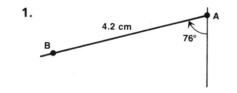

2. 1321 square feet   **3.** $51,519   **4.** $6037.50   **5.** $57,556.50
6. 230 square feet   **7.** $264.50   **8.** 99 square feet   **9.** 1365 bricks
10. 25 cubic feet

page 253   **1.** $3.16   **3.** $4.72   **5.** $3.36   **7.** $3.51   **9.** $7.96   **11.** $11.82
13. $14.75   **15.** $23.92   **17.** $6.27   **19.** $24.32   **21.** $20.15   **23.** $2.56
25. $4.38

1.

PAYMENT NUMBER	PRINCIPAL	AMOUNT OF INTEREST	AMOUNT PAID ON PRINCIPAL	'NEW' PRINCIPAL
1	2000	26.67	43.65	1956.35
2	1956.35	26.08	44.24	1912.11
3	1912.11	25.49	44.83	1867.28
4	1867.28	24.9	45.42	1821.86
5	1821.86	24.29	46.03	1775.83
6	1775.83	23.68	46.64	1729.19
7	1729.19	23.06	47.26	1681.93
8	1681.93	22.43	47.89	1634.04
9	1634.04	21.79	48.53	1585.51
10	1585.51	21.14	49.18	1536.33
11	1536.33	20.48	49.84	1486.49
12	1486.49	19.82	50.5	1435.99
13	1435.99	19.15	51.17	1384.82
14	1384.82	18.46	51.86	1332.96
15	1332.96	17.77	52.55	1280.41
16	1280.41	17.07	53.25	1227.16
17	1227.16	16.36	53.96	1173.2
18	1173.2	15.64	54.68	1117.52
19	1118.52	14.91	55.41	1063.11
20	1063.11	14.17	56.15	1006.96
21	1006.96	13.43	56.89	950.07
22	950.07	12.67	57.65	892.42
23	892.42	11.9	58.42	834
24	834	11.12	59.2	774.8
25	774.8	10.33	59.99	714.81
26	714.81	9.53	60.79	654.02
27	654.02	8.72	61.6	592.42
28	592.42	7.9	62.42	530
29	530	7.07	63.25	466.75
30	466.75	6.22	64.1	402.65
31	402.65	5.37	64.95	337.7
32	337.7	4.5	65.82	271.88
33	271.88	3.63	66.69	205.19
34	205.19	2.74	67.58	137.61
35	137.61	1.83	68.49	69.12
36	69.12	.92	69.12	0

3.

PAYMENT NUMBER	PRINCIPAL	AMOUNT OF INTEREST	AMOUNT PAID ON PRINCIPAL	'NEW' PRINCIPAL
1	4475	56.87	110.01	4364.99
2	4364.99	55.47	111.41	4253.58
.	.	.	.	.
.	.	.	.	.
.	.	.	.	.
33	164.4	2.09	164.4	0

5.

PAYMENT NUMBER	PRINCIPAL	AMOUNT OF INTEREST	AMOUNT PAID ON PRINCIPAL	'NEW' PRINCIPAL
1	5000	62.5	179.94	4820.06
2	4820.06	60.25	182.19	4637.87
.	.	.	.	.
.	.	.	.	.
.	.	.	.	.
24	239.25	2.99	239.25	0

7.

PAYMENT NUMBER	PRINCIPAL	AMOUNT OF INTEREST	AMOUNT PAID ON PRINCIPAL	'NEW' PRINCIPAL
1	3600	44.25	99.96	3500.04
2	3500.04	43.02	101.19	3398.85
.	.	.	.	.
.	.	.	.	.
.	.	.	.	.
30	142.43	1.75	142.43	0

9.

PAYMENT NUMBER	PRINCIPAL	AMOUNT OF INTEREST	AMOUNT PAID ON PRINCIPAL	'NEW' PRINCIPAL
1	4000	55.83	123.01	3876.99
2	3876.99	54.12	124.72	3752.27
.	.	.	.	.
.	.	.	.	.
.	.	.	.	.
27	176.18	2.46	176.18	0

11.

PAYMENT NUMBER	PRINCIPAL	AMOUNT OF INTEREST	AMOUNT PAID ON PRINCIPAL	'NEW' PRINCIPAL
1	9500	110.83	213.86	9286.14
2	9286.14	108.34	216.35	9069.79
.	.	.	.	.
.	.	.	.	.
.	.	.	.	.
36	320.83	3.74	320.83	0

13.
```
121 PRINT TAB(18);"MORTGAGE AMORTIZATION TABLE"
122 PRINT "PRINCIPAL AMOUNT";TAB(28);"$";P
123 PRINT "ANNUAL INTEREST RATE";TAB(29);Y;"%"
124 PRINT "TERM";TAB(29);N;"MONTHS"
125 PRINT "MONTHLY PAYMENT";TAB(28);"$";A
126 PRINT
```

15.
```
25 LET T1=0
26 LET T2=0
225 LET T1=T1+I
226 LET T2=T2+P1
241 PRINT
242 PRINT "TOTAL PAID TO INTEREST     $";FNR(T1)
243 PRINT "TOTAL PAID TO PRINCIPAL    $";FNR(T2)
244 PRINT TAB(28);"- - - - - - - -"
245 PRINT TAB(26);"$";FNR(T1+T2)
```

17.

MORTGAGE AMORTIZATION TABLE

PRINCIPAL AMOUNT	$ 2755
ANNUAL INTEREST RATE	17.5 %
TERM	6 MONTHS
MONTHLY PAYMENT	$ 482.89

PAYMENT NUMBER	PRINCIPAL	AMOUNT OF INTEREST	AMOUNT PAID ON PRINCIPAL	'NEW' PRINCIPAL
1	2755	40.18	442.71	2312.29
2	2312.29	33.72	449.17	1863.12
3	1863.12	27.17	455.72	1407.4
4	1407.4	20.52	462.37	945.03
5	945.03	13.78	469.11	475.92
6	475.92	6.94	475.92	0

Program continued on next page.

page 255 continued
   17. continued

   TOTAL PAID TO INTEREST $ 142.31
   TOTAL PAID TO PRINCIPAL $ 2755

                                $ 2897.31

page 259   **1.** $3546.55; yes   **3.** $6920.70; no   **5.** $7144.59; no   **7.** $4179.86; no
   9. $1424.99

page 262   **1.** $12,761; $1962   **3.** $18,365; $2604   **5.** $26,541; $2545

page 263   **1.** $1497   **3.** $2485   **5.** $3453   **7.** $4204   **9.** $3387   **11.** $2403

page 265   **1.** Refund: $101   **3.** Refund: $129   **5.** Balance due: $49
   7. Balance due: $242   **9.** Balance due: $125   **11.** Refund: $117

page 267   **1.** $15,015; $2500; $2092; $408 refund   **3.** $17,836; $3250; $3153; $97 refund
   5. $26,425; $3548; $3616; $68 balance due

pages 269–270   **1.** $4246; balance due: $360   **3.** $3033; refund: $117   **5.** $18,067
   7. $23,040   **9.** $88,502

page 271   **1.** $96.00   **3.** $148.90   **5.** $158.59

page 273   **1.** $134.75   **3.** $1344.55   **5.** $468.75   **7.** $204.84   **9.** $1895.20
   11. $793.36   **13.** $248   **15.** $4258

page 274
Rounding whole numbers and decimals   **1.** 1000; 800; 830   **3.** 1000; 600; 560
   5. 10,000; 9600; 9600   **7.** 1000; 1100; 1070   **9.** 60,000; 60,400; 60,380
   11. 85,000; 84,700; 84,660   **13.** 18; 18.2; 18.18   **15.** 79; 79.5; 79.46
   17. 258; 257.8; 257.77   **19.** 41; 41.0; 40.99   **21.** 602; 602.0; 602.02
Subtracting whole numbers and decimals   **1.** 52   **3.** 48   **5.** 5   **7.** 48.6   **9.** 66.2
   11. 69.42   **13.** 7.638   **15.** 11.089   **17.** 3.315   **19.** 0.8   **21.** 2.612   **23.** 2.5
   25. 25.58   **27.** 47.318

page 274 continued
Writing percents, decimals, and fractions   **1.** $\frac{3}{25}$ **3.** $\frac{11}{20}$ **5.** $\frac{47}{100}$ **7.** $\frac{31}{50}$ **9.** $\frac{4}{25}$
11. $\frac{7}{10}$ **13.** $\frac{27}{100}$ **15.** $\frac{13}{20}$ **17.** $2\frac{1}{4}$ **19.** $1\frac{3}{100}$ **21.** 50%   **23.** 10%
25. 60%   **27.** 70%   **29.** 38%   **31.** 36%   **33.** 37.5%   **35.** 56.25%
37. 22.5%   **39.** 425%   **41.** 760%

page 275   **1.** Yes   **2.** $15,278   **3.** $2197   **4.** $2534   **5.** Balance due: $165
6. Refund: $82   **7.** Refund: $150   **8.** $15,427   **9.** $759   **10.** $485

page 279   **1.** $632.00; $208.00   **3.** $4410.00; $690.00   **5.** $2210.00; $540.00
7. $3207.00; $1069.00   **9.** $1766.40; $213.60   **11.** $328.50   **13.** $482.60

page 281   **1.** $168   **3.** $395.25   **5.** $206.40   **7.** $340   **9.** $45,000; $531
11. $32,000

pages 283–285   **1.** $413.70   **3.** $1917   **5.** $221   **7.** $1099.53   **9.** $772.48
11. $303.16   **13.** $1004   **15.** $1684.80   **17.** $5454   **19.** $1290
21. $44,572.50   **23.** $1160   **25.** $8050

page 287   **1.** $29.97   **3.** $38.82   **5.** $236.03   **7.** $18.26   **9.** $1690.80
11. $1692

page 288   **1.** $15.09; $181.08; $8.59   **3.** $11.15; $133.80; $6.34
5. $13.02; $156.24; $7.47   **7.** $10.90; $130.80; $6.25   **9.** $40.93; $163.72; $6.30
11. $38.66; $154.64; $5.93   **13.** $51.34; $205.36; $7.91   **15.** $98.64; $197.28; $3.86
17. $158.97; $317.94; $6.23   **19.** $167.84; $335.68; $6.59

pages 290–291   **1.** $67,000; $16,147   **3.** $80,000; $18,240   **5.** $37,000; $9694
7. $40,000; $12,920   **9.** $68,000; $19,448   **11.** $17.06   **13.** $22,368.73

pages 294–295   **1.** $7043   **3.** $9945   **5.** $5352.00   **7.** $7636.80   **9.** $10,836.00
11. $4843.20   **13.** $5914.80   **15.** $463.20

page 296
Adding whole numbers and decimals   **1.** 55   **3.** 170   **5.** 108   **7.** 120   **9.** 231
11. 882   **13.** 1071   **15.** 1731   **17.** 21.94   **19.** 115.66   **21.** 16.05
23. 17.81   **25.** 1.44   **27.** 11.269

page 296 continued

Multiplying whole numbers   **1.** 2400   **3.** 60,000   **5.** 12,000,000   **7.** 1400
    9. 320,000   **11.** 420,000   **13.** 810,000   **15.** 1872   **17.** 2936   **19.** 29,488
    21. 329,280   **23.** 200,882   **25.** 643,405   **27.** 147,288
Percent problems   **1.** 9.4   **3.** 20   **5.** 1.78   **7.** 90   **9.** 95%   **11.** 85%
    13. 3.5%   **15.** 800   **17.** 40   **19.** 200   **21.** 125

page 297   **1.** $721.25   **2.** $185.25   **3.** $930.60   **4.** $17,700   **5.** $19.20
    6. $46,000   **7.** $18,481.60   **8.** $6847   **9.** $5215.20   **10.** $23,292

page 301   **1.** $25.00   **3.** $50.00; $150   **5.** $100.00; $600   **7.** $2500.00; $30,000
    9. $500.00; $10,000   **11.** $44.77   **13.** $505.50   **15.** $86.54   **17.** $614.80
    19. $14,540.00

pages 303–304   **1.** 0.07788; $77.88   **3.** 0.06096; $609.60   **5.** 0.03257; $130.28
    7. 0.01428; $35.70   **9.** $103.30   **11.** $226.02; 7.53%   **13.** $322.45; $322.45; 6.45%
    15. $28.56; $114.24; 5.71%   **17.** $1000 CD paying $61.83 each year

page 305   **1.** $217.65; $2919.08   **3.** $3154.27; $254.14; $3408.41
    5. $3683.03; $296.74; $3979.77   **7.** $4300.42; $346.48; $4646.90
    9. $5021.30; $404.57; $5425.87   **11.** $2014.30   **13.** 9 years

pages 307–309   **1.** $193.88   **3.** $585.63   **5.** $2202.13   **7.** $11,915.00
    9. $6278.50   **11.** $83.25; $33.00 loss   **13.** $767.50; $26.75 profit
    15. $5688.50; $261.65 loss   **17.** $310.25; $9.75 loss   **19.** $120.00; 5.71%
    21. $159.00; 3.98%   **23.** $361.20; 5.16%   **25.** $775.00; 13.48%

page 311   **1.** $19.91; $99.55   **3.** $14.26; $213.90   **5.** $4.50; $337.50
    7. $8.34; $100.08   **9.** $24.97; $399.52   **11.** $796.40   **13.** $1.13
    15. 41.6667 shares

page 312
Rounding whole numbers and decimals   **1.** 1000; 700; 720   **3.** 3000; 3500; 3490
    5. 9000; 9400; 9360   **7.** 56,000; 56,200; 56,200   **9.** 1000; 1000; 1000
    11. 6; 5.6; 5.63   **13.** 47; 47.5; 47.46   **15.** 376; 376.3; 376.29
    17. 765; 765.0; 764.97   **19.** 68; 68.0; 68.02   **21.** 347; 347.0; 347.00
Dividing decimals   **1.** 3.03   **3.** 0.90   **5.** 0.09   **7.** 0.02   **9.** 0.22   **11.** 2.77
    13. 3.64   **15.** 80.00   **17.** 4.68   **19.** 0.04   **21.** 0.02   **23.** 2.20   **25.** 244.21

page 312 continued

Ratio and proportion **1.** $9 \neq 10$ **3.** $36 \neq 14$ **5.** $183.6 \neq 180$ **7.** $a = 24$
9. $n = 63$ **11.** $x = 24$ **13.** $y = 16$

page 313 **1.** $37.50 **2.** $82.38 **3.** $57.12 **4.** 6.21% **5.** $3090.25
6. $3132.25 **7.** $132.25 profit **8.** 4.69% **9.** $297 **10.** $1.80

page 317 **1.** $4.50 **3.** $4.90 **5.** $6 **7.** $10.80 **9.** $7.50 **11.** $12
13. $21 **15.** 38¢ **17.** 60¢ **19.** $2.75 **21.** $3.13 **23.** $3.60

page 319 **1.** FEDERAL WITHHOLDING TAX 14.98 **3.** FEDERAL WITHHOLDING TAX 62.03
5. FEDERAL WITHHOLDING TAX 52.67 **7.** FEDERAL WITHHOLDING TAX 96.48
9. FEDERAL WITHHOLDING TAX 111.81

11. NUMBER OF PAY PERIODS PER YEAR 26
GROSS PAY FOR THIS PERIOD 478.93
NUMBER OF EXEMPTIONS 1
FILING STATUS 1
FEDERAL WITHHOLDING TAX 58.46

13. NUMBER OF PAY PERIODS PER YEAR 52
GROSS PAY FOR THIS PERIOD 392.61
NUMBER OF EXEMPTIONS 1
FILING STATUS 0
FEDERAL WITHHOLDING TAX 83.06
STATE WITHHOLDING TAX 9.33

page 323 **1.** 535 calories **3.** 480 calories **5.** 530 calories **7.** 1605 calories

page 325 **1.** 1180 calories **3.** 135 calories **5.** 662 calories **7.** 418 calories
9. 383 calories **11.** 331 calories **13.** 2697 calories

pages 326–328 **1.** $1.85 **3.** $3.03 **5.** $1.34 **7.** $1.24 **9.** $1.43
11. 0.19¢ per gram **13.** 0.12¢ per gram **15.** 0.09¢ per milliliter **17.** 0.08¢ per milliliter
19. 0.16¢ per gram **21.** $0.50/L; $0.47/L; $1.89 **23.** $1.46/kg; $1.28/kg; $12.75
25. $0.59/kg; $0.53/kg; $2.65 **27.** $1.78/kg; $1.58/kg; $0.95 **29.** $35.38

page 329 **1.** $3.71 **3.** $1.39 **5.** $1.81 **7.** $0.56 **9.** $2.85 **11.** $1.90
13. $2.09 **15.** $1.31

pages 330–331 **1.** 30%; $4.70 **3.** 24%; $4.38 **5.** 25%; $4.25 **7.** $86.26
9. $62.53 **11.** $41.23 **13.** $21.58 **15.** $5.67 **17.** $535.61

page 333 **1.** $6.12 **3.** $11.90 **5.** $4.54 **7.** $11.52

page 334

Multiplying decimals **1.** 0.3 **3.** 0.009 **5.** 0.0035 **7.** 0.00004 **9.** 120 **11.** 18 **13.** 1.2 **15.** 0.00004 **17.** 6.6 **19.** 41.71 **21.** 20.234 **23.** 16.8714 **25.** 152,668.8 **27.** 0.0030328

Dividing fractions and mixed numbers **1.** $\frac{4}{5}$ **3.** $\frac{2}{3}$ **5.** $2\frac{3}{16}$ **7.** 8 **9.** $\frac{4}{15}$ **11.** $2\frac{1}{2}$ **13.** $2\frac{15}{16}$ **15.** $1\frac{1}{5}$ **17.** $1\frac{3}{5}$ **19.** 5 **21.** $\frac{27}{28}$

Percent problems **1.** 1.25 **3.** 15 **5.** 0.6 **7.** 8.4 **9.** 75% **11.** 25% **13.** 75% **15.** 67.5% **17.** 56 **19.** 200 **21.** 150

page 335 **1.** 490 calories **2.** 585 calories **3.** $2.23 **4.** $0.66 **5.** 0.13¢ per gram **6.** 3.5 kilograms for $2.19 **7.** 26% **8.** $4.31 **9.** $64.15 **10.** $5.55

pages 339–340 **1.** $46.28 **3.** 3 lb. 12 oz. **5.** $50.76 **7.** $2.45 **9.** $2.43 **11.** $47.46 **13.** 3 lb. 8 oz. **15.** $52.99

page 341 **1.** $63.00; 15 boxes; 18 lb. 12 oz. **3.** $28.80; 6 boxes; 10 lb. 8 oz. **5.** $65.24; 7 boxes; 26 lb. 11 oz. **7.** $32.40; 24 boxes; 10 lb. 8 oz. **9.** $608.71; 141 lb. 0 oz. **11.** $15.51

page 343 **1.** 20 yards **3.** $8\frac{1}{2}$ yards **5.** $11\frac{1}{4}$ yards **7.** $87\frac{7}{8}$ yards **9.** $38.80 **11.** $4.50 **13.** 11 packages **15.** 105 buttons **17.** $24.30 **19.** $536.89

page 345 **1.** Jan., April, July, Dec.; $5.55; $31.45 **3.** November; $89.99; $269.96 **5.** February; $179.20; $716.79 **7.** May; $2.63; $14.87 **9.** July; $9.21; $17.09

page 347 **1.** $37.50 **3.** $19.62

page 349 **1.** $1.80 **3.** $0.55; $5.45 **5.** $7.90 **7.** $474.60 **9.** $12.40 **11.** $3.40; $5.44; $8.33 **13.** $858.06

page 351 **1.** $20 **3.** $6 **5.** $17 **7.** $20 **9.** $6 **11.** 9 years **13.** Car polisher

page 352

Dividing whole numbers   **1.** 2188   **3.** 888 R1   **5.** 194   **7.** 42 R19   **9.** 699
   11. 114 R15   **13.** 69 R20   **15.** 28 R54   **17.** 74 R13   **19.** 3192 R26
   21. 11,908 R5   **23.** 12,277 R65   **25.** 225 R48   **27.** 913 R396

Adding fractions and mixed numbers   **1.** $\frac{14}{15}$ **3.** $\frac{17}{24}$ **5.** $\frac{5}{6}$ **7.** $1\frac{1}{4}$ **9.** $1\frac{1}{18}$ **11.** $7\frac{4}{5}$
   13. $8\frac{1}{6}$ **15.** $20\frac{5}{6}$ **17.** $6\frac{17}{24}$ **19.** $18\frac{7}{20}$

Subtracting fractions and mixed numbers   **1.** $\frac{1}{3}$ **3.** $\frac{17}{24}$ **5.** $\frac{1}{24}$ **7.** $\frac{2}{21}$ **9.** $14\frac{1}{7}$
   11. $3\frac{1}{2}$ **13.** $9\frac{2}{5}$ **15.** $\frac{5}{24}$ **17.** $7\frac{5}{12}$ **19.** $16\frac{5}{6}$

page 353   **1.** $77.90   **2.** $3.90   **3.** $2.84   **4.** $84.64   **5.** $11\frac{1}{4}$ yards
   6. $318.75   **7.** $54.50   **8.** $76.75   **9.** $3.24   **10.** $7

pages 357–359   **1.** $5.00; $5.00; $6.29; $0.90 + $1.50; $19   **3.** $5.00; $2.50; $2.75; $10
   5. $1.80; $1.75 + $0.89; $1.25; $1.00; $7
   7. Week 1: $45.50, $15.50, $10.20, $20.17; Week 2: $57.25, $12.50, $9.00;
Week 3: $58.88, $12.57, $8.47; Week 4: $60.04, $13.75, $14.00; Total: $338
   9. Week 1: $15.00; Week 2: $17.50; Week 3: $18.00; Week 4: $17.25, $1.25; Total: $69
   11. Week 1: $10.00; Week 3: $13.00; Total: $23   **13.** Week 1: $9.85;
Week 2: $8.50; Week 3: $1.42, $6.00; Week 4: $13.00; Total: $39

page 361   **1.** $21   **3.** $9   **5.** $6   **7.** $352   **9.** $75   **11.** $24   **13.** $50

pages 363–364   **1.** $112   **3.** $480   **5.** $504   **7.** $835   **9.** $358   **11.** $835
   13. $2040   **15.** $2142   **17.** No

page 365   **1.** $150; 0.13; 13%   **3.** $245; 0.88; 88%   **5.** $51; 0.09; 9%

pages 366–367   **1.** $10   **3.** $20   **5.** $110   **7.** $70   **9.** $1188   **11.** $177
   13. $99   **15.** $27   **17.** No   **19.** Yes

page 369   **1.** $4830; $8050   **3.** $1560; $2310; $2800   **5.** $1200; $2730; $6300
   7. Food   **9.** Housing   **11.** $1050

page 370

Adding whole numbers and decimals   **1.** 72   **3.** 161   **5.** 199   **7.** 202   **9.** 233
11. 1649   **13.** 778   **15.** 18.07   **17.** 98.61   **19.** 17.85   **21.** 20.07   **23.** 1.25
25. 10.499   **27.** 21.23

Comparing and renaming fractions and mixed numbers   **1.** >   **3.** <   **5.** <   **7.** <
9. =   **11.** >   **13.** >   **15.** <   **17.** <   **19.** $4\frac{1}{2}$ **21.** $3\frac{1}{2}$ **23.** $1\frac{1}{2}$ **25.** $6\frac{1}{2}$
27. $2\frac{1}{2}$ **29.** $3\frac{7}{8}$ **31.** $4\frac{4}{11}$ **33.** $1\frac{1}{3}$ **35.** $6\frac{1}{2}$

Dividing fractions and mixed numbers   **1.** $\frac{3}{4}$ **3.** $\frac{3}{5}$ **5.** $\frac{3}{20}$ **7.** 8   **9.** $9\frac{1}{3}$ **11.** 7
13. $\frac{3}{25}$ **15.** $\frac{3}{5}$ **17.** $\frac{6}{7}$ **19.** $\frac{16}{49}$

page 371   **1.** $41   **2.** $22   **3.** $52   **4.** $87   **5.** $43   **6.** $77
7. $1440; $72; $1512   **8.** No   **9.** $39   **10.** $5130

page 375   **1.** 800   **3.** 273   **5.** 648   **7.** 910   **9.** 2170   **11.** 1872   **13.** 672
15. 560   **17.** 1148   **19.** 3504   **21.** 7735

page 377   Program modifications may vary. Samples are given.

1.
TENS	1
FIVES	1
ONES	1
NICKELS	1
CHANGE	$ 16.05

3.
ONES	2
QUARTERS	3
PENNIES	2
CHANGE	$ 2.77

5.
ONES	3
QUARTERS	1
DIMES	1
PENNIES	3
CHANGE	$ 3.38

7.
FIVES	1
ONES	1
DIMES	2
PENNIES	2
CHANGE	$ 6.22

9.
TENS	1
FIVES	1
ONES	2
QUARTERS	1
DIMES	1
NICKELS	1
PENNIES	4
CHANGE	$ 17.44

11.
ONES	4
PENNIES	3
CHANGE	$ 4.03

13.
FIVES	1
ONES	3
NICKELS	1
PENNIES	1
CHANGE	$ 8.06

15.
```
85 IF S>=0 THEN 90
86 PRINT "NOT ENOUGH MONEY"
87 GO TO 50
```

17.
```
30 PRINT "AMOUNT OF MERCHANDISE";
40 INPUT M
45 LET X=M*.05
46 LET X=INT(X*100+.5)/100
47 LET T=M+X
182 PRINT
183 PRINT "COST OF MERCHANDISE      $";M
184 PRINT "SALES TAX";TAB(22);"$";X
185 PRINT "TOTAL";TAB (22); "$";T
186 PRINT "AMOUNT GIVEN";TAB(22);"$";A
190 PRINT "CHANGE";TAB(22);"$";C
```

page 377 continued

19.
```
27 LET M = 0
28 PRINT "NO. OF ITEMS    COST/ITEM    COST"
30 PRINT "NUMBER OF ITEMS";
31 INPUT Q
32 IF Q = 0 THEN 45
33 PRINT "COST PER ITEM";
34 INPUT P
35 LET E = Q*P
36 LET E = INT(E*100+.5)/100
37 PRINT TAB(6);Q;TAB(17);P;TAB(25);E
38 LET M = M + E
39 GO TO 30
65 PRINT
```

Line 40 was deleted.

page 379   **1.** 1000; 710   **3.** 1000; 680   **5.** 1000; 850   **7.** 1000; 1390
9. 8000; 8390   **11.** 2000; 2420   **13.** 5000; 5230   **15.** 7000; 7080
17. 10,000; 9540   **19.** 9000; 8700   **21.** 5000; 4970   **23.** 7000; 6500
25. 7000; 6730   **27.** 3000; 2780   **29.** 9000; 8670   **31.** 8000; 7560
33. 10,000; 9670   **35.** 5000; 5000   **37.** 97,000; 96,930   **39.** 85,000; 84,850
41. 61,000; 61,470   **43.** 12,000; 11,710   **45.** 44,000; 43,670   **47.** 75,000; 74,910
49. 35,000; 35,030   **51.** 47,000; 46,960   **53.** 98,000; 97,500   **55.** 25,000; 25,010
57. 59,000; 58,690   **59.** 80,000; 79,620   **61.** 4; 4.17   **63.** 8; 7.86   **65.** 6; 6.29
67. 3; 2.94   **69.** 10; 9.73   **71.** 3; 3.47   **73.** 37; 37.11   **75.** 50; 49.66
77. 68; 68.26   **79.** 31; 31.49   **81.** 72; 71.55   **83.** 90; 90.23   **85.** 80; 79.53
87. 26; 26.38   **89.** 86; 86.05   **91.** 12; 11.94   **93.** 100; 99.83   **95.** 65; 65.07
97. 269; 268.87   **99.** 912; 912.05   **101.** 403; 403.19   **103.** 101; 100.89
105. 353; 352.88   **107.** 735; 735.04   **109.** 647; 646.72   **111.** 574; 574.19
113. 822; 821.64   **115.** 248; 248.34   **117.** 546; 545.57   **119.** 500; 499.83

page 380   **1.** 83   **3.** 146   **5.** 100   **7.** 171   **9.** 146   **11.** 119   **13.** 97
15. 232   **17.** 236   **19.** 261   **21.** 1181   **23.** 1035   **25.** 639   **27.** 1925
29. 2098   **31.** 10.28   **33.** 5.56   **35.** 86.61   **37.** 1.7   **39.** 16.83   **41.** 19.77
43. 11.63   **45.** 12.888   **47.** 23.8   **49.** 22.44   **51.** 16.51   **53.** 21.47
55. 18.39   **57.** 15.529   **59.** 23.066

page 381   **1.** 43   **3.** 25   **5.** 49   **7.** 25   **9.** 46   **11.** 43   **13.** 3   **15.** 92
17. 627   **19.** 327   **21.** 569   **23.** 1408   **25.** 1256   **27.** 7809   **29.** 34.7
31. 10.6   **33.** 55.12   **35.** 31.43   **37.** 47.41   **39.** 13.408   **41.** 20.905
43. 27.46   **45.** 93.96   **47.** 42.45   **49.** 55.051   **51.** 42.437   **53.** 33.314
55. 75.661   **57.** 13.4   **59.** 36.2   **61.** 25.7   **63.** 9.53   **65.** 23.14   **67.** 20.7
69. 33.7   **71.** 13.19   **73.** 47.61   **75.** 12.078   **77.** 1.886   **79.** 75.385
81. 78.075   **83.** 14.082

page 382 **1.** 2100 **3.** 1600 **5.** 2800 **7.** 8000 **9.** 54,000 **11.** 20,000
13. 300 **15.** 2800 **17.** 1500 **19.** 9000 **21.** 36,000 **23.** 30,000
25. 12,000 **27.** 12,000 **29.** 27,000 **31.** 420,000 **33.** 450,000 **35.** 350,000
37. 400,000 **39.** 2,800,000 **41.** 3,000,000 **43.** 1742 **45.** 748 **47.** 6560
49. 4015 **51.** 17,460 **53.** 20,196 **55.** 36,045 **57.** 28,925 **59.** 19,760
61. 78,642 **63.** 461,674 **65.** 132,664 **67.** 345,744 **69.** 521,136
71. 724,240 **73.** 242,305 **75.** 438,354 **77.** 599,828 **79.** 1,768,026
81. 991,676 **83.** 1,346,115

page 383 **1.** 0.24 **3.** 0.56 **5.** 0.014 **7.** 0.02 **9.** 0.0028 **11.** 0.0048
13. 0.0007 **15.** 0.002 **17.** 0.08 **19.** 0.06 **21.** 0.036 **23.** 0.016
25. 0.21 **27.** 1800 **29.** 5400 **31.** 0.00024 **33.** 0.00014 **35.** 18 **37.** 28
39. 120 **41.** 60 **43.** 523.6 **45.** 94.07 **47.** 21.36 **49.** 10.88 **51.** 11.7972
53. 547.8 **55.** 4738.89 **57.** 1.0122 **59.** 2.6676 **61.** 0.12978 **63.** 2.36684
65. 203.814 **67.** 335.818 **69.** 159.79 **71.** 259.25 **73.** 0.575757
75. 296.2768 **77.** 256.0642 **79.** 2.21008 **81.** 39.88194 **83.** 27.940826

page 384 **1.** 231 R1 **3.** 94 **5.** 590 R6 **7.** 318 R1 **9.** 1184 R4 **11.** 845 R5
13. 751 R3 **15.** 1108 R3 **17.** 2189 **19.** 7233 R2 **21.** 10,294 R2 **23.** 25 R9
25. 4 R8 **27.** 6 R71 **29.** 8 R20 **31.** 10 R56 **33.** 5 R17 **35.** 12 R13
37. 2 R46 **39.** 9 R37 **41.** 9 R17 **43.** 139 R24 **45.** 28 R86 **47.** 208 R2
49. 63 R1 **51.** 309 R3 **53.** 134 R23 **55.** 121 R13 **57.** 285 **59.** 50 R8
61. 102 R30 **63.** 95 R37 **65.** 764 **67.** 916 R37 **69.** 942 R14 **71.** 825 R30
73. 3379 R1 **75.** 7464 R18 **77.** 11,341 R1 **79.** 10,518 R2 **81.** 20,009
83. 3039 R25 **85.** 201 R386 **87.** 271 R24 **89.** 12 R213 **91.** 645 R71
93. 35 R249 **95.** 750 R49 **97.** 1049 **99.** 759 R120 **101.** 2940 R149
103. 1536 R317 **105.** 682 R289

page 385 **1.** 3.84 **3.** 232.18 **5.** 53.77 **7.** 1112.63 **9.** 925.57 **11.** 0.36
13. 0.07 **15.** 0.78 **17.** 2.65 **19.** 1.58 **21.** 1.04 **23.** 2.06 **25.** 1.23
27. 0.85 **29.** 6.12 **31.** 12.59 **33.** 10.68 **35.** 31.39 **37.** 0.12 **39.** 0.23
41. 2.41 **43.** 1.64 **45.** 0.43 **47.** 0.47 **49.** 4.14 **51.** 5.67 **53.** 18.56
55. 0.22 **57.** 5.59 **59.** 0.56 **61.** 4.32 **63.** 0.48 **65.** 1.64 **67.** 0.88
69. 12.88 **71.** 10.68 **73.** 31.39 **75.** 12.91 **77.** 18.21 **79.** 48.19
81. 6.67 **83.** 7.59 **85.** 18.05 **87.** 21.55 **89.** 5.85 **91.** 5.98 **93.** 19.36
95. 3.78 **97.** 0.47 **99.** 0.86

page 386 **1.** $>$ **3.** $=$ **5.** $>$ **7.** $<$ **9.** $<$ **11.** $>$ **13.** $<$ **15.** $>$
17. $<$ **19.** $\frac{3}{5}$ **21.** $\frac{1}{3}$ **23.** $\frac{1}{7}$ **25.** $\frac{2}{3}$ **27.** $\frac{13}{14}$ **29.** $\frac{1}{2}$ **31.** $\frac{3}{5}$ **33.** $\frac{1}{6}$
35. $\frac{4}{5}$ **37.** $\frac{2}{9}$ **39.** $\frac{1}{5}$ **41.** $\frac{2}{9}$ **43.** $\frac{2}{9}$ **45.** $\frac{7}{8}$ **47.** $\frac{5}{4}$ **49.** $\frac{7}{1}$ **51.** $\frac{21}{8}$
53. $\frac{81}{10}$ **55.** $\frac{43}{5}$ **57.** $\frac{39}{8}$ **59.** $\frac{41}{6}$ **61.** $\frac{29}{9}$ **63.** $\frac{61}{12}$ **65.** $\frac{69}{8}$ **67.** $\frac{80}{11}$

page 386 continued

69. $\frac{92}{15}$ **71.** $\frac{131}{11}$ **73.** $2\frac{1}{2}$ **75.** $1\frac{2}{5}$ **77.** $6\frac{1}{3}$ **79.** 6 **81.** $8\frac{1}{9}$ **83.** $5\frac{1}{2}$

85. $3\frac{5}{8}$ **87.** $12\frac{1}{2}$ **89.** $7\frac{2}{7}$ **91.** $1\frac{2}{3}$ **93.** $2\frac{1}{3}$ **95.** $1\frac{2}{3}$ **97.** $12\frac{1}{10}$ **99.** $11\frac{11}{12}$

page 387 **1.** $\frac{4}{15}$ **3.** $\frac{5}{12}$ **5.** $\frac{5}{16}$ **7.** $\frac{3}{5}$ **9.** $\frac{2}{11}$ **11.** $\frac{1}{3}$ **13.** $\frac{2}{3}$ **15.** $\frac{2}{3}$

17. $\frac{35}{144}$ **19.** $\frac{1}{12}$ **21.** $\frac{10}{21}$ **23.** $4\frac{2}{3}$ **25.** 3 **27.** 2 **29.** $2\frac{2}{5}$ **31.** $9\frac{1}{3}$

33. $3\frac{3}{5}$ **35.** 28 **37.** 70 **39.** $2\frac{6}{11}$ **41.** $26\frac{2}{3}$ **43.** $\frac{4}{5}$ **45.** $1\frac{3}{4}$ **47.** $\frac{7}{8}$

49. 1 **51.** $1\frac{17}{18}$ **53.** 4 **55.** $2\frac{4}{7}$ **57.** 10 **59.** $13\frac{1}{2}$ **61.** $11\frac{1}{4}$ **63.** $20\frac{2}{3}$

65. 18 **67.** 104 **69.** $30\frac{2}{3}$ **71.** $8\frac{1}{3}$ **73.** $3\frac{1}{4}$ **75.** $8\frac{1}{6}$ **77.** $9\frac{1}{3}$ **79.** $8\frac{3}{4}$

81. $12\frac{1}{2}$ **83.** $18\frac{1}{3}$ **85.** $\frac{1}{15}$ **87.** $\frac{3}{40}$ **89.** $\frac{5}{16}$ **91.** 12 **93.** $1\frac{3}{4}$ **95.** $10\frac{1}{2}$

97. $4\frac{2}{5}$ **99.** $2\frac{1}{3}$ **101.** $10\frac{4}{5}$ **103.** $27\frac{1}{2}$ **105.** 105

page 388 **1.** $1\frac{1}{2}$ **3.** $\frac{24}{35}$ **5.** 4 **7.** $1\frac{5}{9}$ **9.** $1\frac{4}{5}$ **11.** $\frac{1}{15}$ **13.** $\frac{4}{15}$ **15.** $\frac{5}{16}$

17. $\frac{2}{27}$ **19.** $7\frac{1}{2}$ **21.** 8 **23.** $9\frac{1}{3}$ **25.** $1\frac{1}{3}$ **27.** $10\frac{1}{2}$ **29.** $\frac{1}{4}$ **31.** $\frac{3}{10}$

33. $\frac{1}{10}$ **35.** $\frac{3}{28}$ **37.** $6\frac{1}{4}$ **39.** 7 **41.** $1\frac{7}{20}$ **43.** 50 **45.** $7\frac{1}{2}$ **47.** $2\frac{15}{16}$

49. $2\frac{3}{4}$ **51.** $\frac{3}{4}$ **53.** $1\frac{1}{3}$ **55.** 6 **57.** $3\frac{1}{5}$ **59.** $5\frac{1}{3}$ **61.** $7\frac{1}{2}$ **63.** 25

65. $3\frac{4}{11}$ **67.** $\frac{3}{4}$ **69.** $2\frac{1}{3}$ **71.** $1\frac{3}{5}$ **73.** 5 **75.** $\frac{27}{28}$ **77.** $\frac{9}{16}$ **79.** $3\frac{1}{10}$

81. $1\frac{7}{8}$ **83.** $\frac{8}{9}$ **85.** $1\frac{3}{5}$ **87.** $1\frac{3}{5}$ **89.** $3\frac{3}{4}$ **91.** 6 **93.** $\frac{3}{7}$ **95.** $\frac{1}{6}$ **97.** 4

99. $3\frac{1}{3}$ **101.** $\frac{3}{4}$ **103.** $3\frac{3}{4}$ **105.** $7\frac{1}{3}$

page 389 **1.** $1\frac{1}{12}$ **3.** $1\frac{1}{3}$ **5.** $1\frac{3}{14}$ **7.** $1\frac{13}{36}$ **9.** $1\frac{1}{18}$ **11.** $1\frac{2}{5}$ **13.** $1\frac{1}{2}$

15. $1\frac{1}{24}$ **17.** $\frac{4}{15}$ **19.** $1\frac{11}{40}$ **21.** $1\frac{7}{24}$ **23.** $1\frac{4}{9}$ **25.** $6\frac{1}{24}$ **27.** $5\frac{1}{36}$ **29.** $4\frac{7}{24}$

31. $5\frac{5}{12}$ **33.** $4\frac{1}{15}$ **35.** $12\frac{9}{10}$ **37.** $8\frac{1}{3}$ **39.** $5\frac{11}{18}$ **41.** $9\frac{9}{40}$ **43.** $8\frac{19}{24}$

45. $12\frac{13}{15}$ **47.** $7\frac{2}{15}$ **49.** $20\frac{5}{6}$ **51.** $9\frac{13}{15}$ **53.** $14\frac{7}{15}$ **55.** $14\frac{11}{30}$ **57.** $10\frac{1}{6}$

59. $18\frac{1}{2}$ **61.** $1\frac{5}{12}$ **63.** $4\frac{19}{30}$ **65.** $6\frac{1}{3}$ **67.** $4\frac{13}{24}$

page 390 **1.** $\frac{1}{2}$ **3.** $\frac{5}{8}$ **5.** $\frac{17}{24}$ **7.** $\frac{3}{14}$ **9.** $\frac{1}{2}$ **11.** $\frac{1}{6}$ **13.** $\frac{2}{15}$ **15.** $\frac{1}{15}$

17. $\frac{2}{15}$ **19.** $\frac{3}{14}$ **21.** $\frac{17}{30}$ **23.** $\frac{2}{15}$ **25.** $1\frac{3}{8}$ **27.** $8\frac{2}{3}$ **29.** $2\frac{1}{8}$ **31.** $9\frac{1}{7}$

33. $5\frac{1}{3}$ **35.** $9\frac{2}{5}$ **37.** $1\frac{2}{7}$ **39.** $6\frac{5}{8}$ **41.** $3\frac{1}{10}$ **43.** $4\frac{1}{2}$ **45.** $3\frac{1}{3}$ **47.** $4\frac{7}{8}$

49. $6\frac{1}{3}$ **51.** $5\frac{9}{16}$ **53.** $\frac{11}{24}$ **55.** $4\frac{1}{10}$ **57.** $2\frac{13}{20}$ **59.** $5\frac{11}{24}$ **61.** $2\frac{1}{2}$ **63.** $4\frac{11}{18}$

65. $6\frac{8}{15}$ **67.** $1\frac{19}{20}$ **69.** $4\frac{11}{12}$ **71.** $3\frac{23}{24}$

page 391   **1.** $120 = 120$ **3.** $140 \neq 144$ **5.** $1200 \neq 1280$ **7.** $90 \neq 99$
9. $120 = 120$ **11.** $64 \neq 60$ **13.** $60 \neq 52$ **15.** $798 = 798$ **17.** $360 \neq 390$
19. $4.2 = 4.2$ **21.** $117.6 \neq 144$ **23.** $183.6 \neq 180$ **25.** $17.94 \neq 19.9$
27. $25.6 \neq 28.8$ **29.** $12.6 = 12.6$ **31.** $67.94 \neq 64.4$ **33.** $7.65 = 7.65$
35. $0.45 \neq 0.525$ **37.** $n = 100$ **39.** $a = 15$ **41.** $b = 30$ **43.** $d = 2$
45. $c = 7$ **47.** $y = 4.5$ **49.** $s = 21.6$ **51.** $h = 1.5$ **53.** $k = 3.75$ **55.** $d = 1.2$
57. $b = 1$ **59.** $d = 0.9$ **61.** $n = 7$ **63.** $g = 10.8$ **65.** $v = 81$ **67.** $a = 2.6$
69. $m = 4.8$

page 392   **1.** 39%   **3.** 4%   **5.** 70%   **7.** 72.7%   **9.** 80.2%   **11.** 6.1%
13. 29.46%   **15.** 77.08%   **17.** 10.08%   **19.** 362%   **21.** 901%   **23.** 768.1%
25. 50%   **27.** 40%   **29.** 8%   **31.** 42%   **33.** 70%   **35.** 5%   **37.** 72%
39. 46.875%   **41.** 93.75%   **43.** 15.625%   **45.** 37.5%   **47.** 87.5%   **49.** 325%
51. 135%   **53.** 0.82   **55.** 0.9   **57.** 0.46   **59.** 0.08   **61.** 0.207   **63.** 0.0742
65. 0.0591   **67.** 0.045   **69.** 0.2325   **71.** 0.47375   **73.** 2.06   **75.** 1.59

77. $\frac{4}{5}$ **79.** $\frac{9}{10}$ **81.** $\frac{3}{4}$ **83.** $\frac{19}{20}$ **85.** $\frac{2}{25}$ **87.** $\frac{1}{100}$ **89.** $\frac{6}{25}$ **91.** $\frac{79}{100}$ **93.** $\frac{13}{100}$

95. $\frac{17}{50}$ **97.** $1\frac{18}{25}$ **99.** $2\frac{1}{2}$

page 393   **1.** 15   **3.** 5.74   **5.** 4.982   **7.** 1.125   **9.** 6.97   **11.** 3.8
13. 3.465   **15.** 86.4   **17.** 5.67   **19.** 46.8   **21.** 5.184   **23.** 26.325   **25.** 8%
27. 25%   **29.** 3%   **31.** 14%   **33.** 35%   **35.** 89%   **37.** 15%   **39.** 62.5%
41. 87.5%   **43.** 80%   **45.** 75   **47.** 150   **49.** 28   **51.** 7.2   **53.** 200
55. 48   **57.** 30   **59.** 85   **61.** 15   **63.** 3.5   **65.** 32

page 394   **1.**
```
THIS IS
A BASIC
PROGRAM.
```
3.
```
2+4=  6
9−7=  2
32  =8*4
1.8  =9/5
```
5. Answers will vary. A sample is given.
```
10 PRINT "MARY FRASER"
20 PRINT "AGE 16 YEARS"
30 PRINT "AUBURNDALE HIGH SCHOOL"
40 END
```

page 395   **1.**
```
? 7
? 15
   41
```
3. Answers will vary. A sample is given.
```
? DON WEE
? 88,95,90
DON WEE
TEST AVERAGE=  91
```
5.
```
? 7
? 8
   56
```

page 396

1. ? 20
60
?34
102
? 56
168
? 128
384
?

3. ? 66,75
A+B= 141
? NO
DONE

5. Answers will vary. A sample is given.

? J. KELLY
? 7
35
? 25
89
? 130
THAT'S ALL J. KELLY

---

page 397

1. PERIMETER = 13
PERIMETER = 58
PERIMETER = 34
PERIMETER = 18
PERIMETER = 5
PERIMETER = 74
OUT OF DATA AT LINE 10

3. R = 5   C = 31.4
R = 10   C = 62.8
R = 17   C = 106.76
OUT OF DATA AT LINE 10

5. ANDERSON   PAY = 367.5
JENSEN   PAY = 505.25
RIEDELL   PAY = 570
BRETZLAUF   PAY = 408.5
OUT OF DATA AT LINE 20

---

page 398

1. 3
4
5
6
7
8

3. NUMBER: 1 COST: 19.95
NUMBER: 2 COST: 39.9
NUMBER: 3 COST: 59.85
NUMBER: 4 COST: 79.8
NUMBER: 5 COST: 99.75
NUMBER: 6 COST: 119.7

5. Answers may vary. A sample is given.

10 FOR H=1 TO 8
20 LET P=4.5*H
30 PRINT "HOURS:";H;"PAY: $";P
40 NEXT H
50 END

---

page 399

1. 5
10
15
20
25
30
35
40
45
50
55
60

3.

PRICE	5% TAX	TOTAL
1.2	.06	1.26
6.8	.34	7.14
12.6	.63	13.23

OUT OF DATA AT LINE 20

5. Answers may vary. A sample is given.

10 INPUT N
20 IF N=0 THEN 80
30 IF INT(N/3)=N/3 THEN 60
40 PRINT N;"IS NOT DIVISIBLE BY 3"
50 GO TO 10
60 PRINT N;"IS DIVISIBLE BY 3"
70 GO TO 10
80 END

Index

Addition
of decimals, 6–7, 168, 296, 370, 380
of fractions, 18–19, 184, 248, 352, 389
of mixed numbers, 18–19, 184, 248, 352, 389
of whole numbers, 6–7, 168, 296, 380
Air travel, 178–179
Amortization table, 218–219, 223, 254-255
Annual percentage rates, 143
Annual yield, 304, 309
Area
metric units of, 44–45
of a rectangle, 44–45
of a triangle, 44–45
Assessed valuation, 226–227
Automobile
alternatives to owning, 166–167
cost of operating, 150–153, 164–165
deferred-payment price, 140–142
depreciation of, 152–154
equipment, options, 132–133
fees and taxes, 136–137
financing of, 140–143, 190–191
fuel economy rate, 150–151, 155
insurance on, 160–163
leasing of, 167
making an offer for, 134
net price of, 138–139
purchase of, 132–134, 136–142
rental of, 180–181
selling price of, 154
shopping for, 138–139
sticker price of, 132–134
total cost of, 136–137
total sale price of, 140–142
trade-in allowance, 138–139
trade-in value, 152–153
travel by, 172–177, 180–181
Automobile Mechanic, 156–159
Automobile Salesperson, 144–145
Average, 58
Average daily balance, 112, 114

Balance, charge account, 110–115
Balance, checking account, 91–97
Balance due, income tax, 264–269
Banking
check, *illus.*, 90
checking accounts, 88–97
check register, *illus.*, 92–93, 96–97
check stub, *illus.*, 91
deposit slips, *illus.*, 88–89
loans, 108–109, 116–117

savings accounts, 98–101
statement, reconciling of, 94–97
Bar graphs, 54–55
BASIC language. *See* Computer Literacy
Bearings, surveying, 238–239
Beneficiaries, 280–281
Board foot, 348–349
Bodily injury insurance, 160-161
Bonds, U.S. Savings, 300–301
face value, 300
maturity, 300
redemption value, 300–301
Bonus earnings, 144–145
Bookkeeper, 74–75
Borrowing money, 108–109, 218–221
Break Times, 15, 37, 45, 71, 99, 103, 111, 135, 159, 177, 201, 233, 242, 262, 289, 309, 333, 345, 359
Break Times/Mental Math, 65, 127, 189, 253, 317, 375
Bricklayer, 246–247
Broker, 306
Budgets
adjusting of, 366–367
annual expenses, 362–364
fixed monthly expenses, 362–364
planning of, 362–364
variable monthly expenses, 356–359, 360–361
Building materials, 348–349

Calculator Applications
amortization table, 223
annual percentage rates, 143
building costs, 243
car-rental costs, 181
charge accounts, 114
checking accounts, 97
completing an order form, 341
compound interest, 305
electricity costs, 200
finding the mean, 60
food costs, 329
fractions as decimals, 20
fuel economy rate, 155
insurance premiums, 288
percent and discounts, 38
percent of increase, 365
selling-cost percent, 77
tax penalty charges, 271
Calorie, 322–323
usage, 324–325

Canceled checks, 94
Capacity, metric units of, 46–47
Car. *See* Automobile
Careers, by career cluster
arts, 202–203
business contact, 98–99, 144–145, 182–183, 230–233, 286–287, 350–351
business detail, 74–75, 198–199
health, 322–323
science, 368–369
social service, 112–113, 268–270, 310–311
technology, 238–239
trades, 156–159, 246–247
Cash registers, 376–377
Cash value, insurance policy, 282, 284–285, 290
Catalog buying, 338–340
Celsius scale, 50–51
Centimeter, 42–43, 48–49
Central angle, 56
Certificates of deposit (CDs), *illus.*, 302–305
Chapter reviews, 21, 39, 61, 85, 105, 123, 147, 169, 185, 213, 235, 249, 275, 297, 313, 335, 353, 371
Chapter tests, 22, 40, 62, 86, 106, 124, 148, 170, 186, 214, 236, 250, 276, 298, 314, 336, 354, 372
Charge accounts, 110–115, 128–129
finance charges, 110–114
minimum payment, 115
Check, *illus.*, 90
Checking accounts, 88–97
balance, 91–97
canceled checks, 94
check, *illus.*, 90
check register, *illus.*, 92–93, 96–97
check stub, *illus.*, 91
outstanding checks, 94
outstanding deposits, 94
service charge, 94
Check register, *illus.*, 92–93, 96–97
Check stub, *illus.*, 91
Circle graphs, 56–57
Classified ads, 82–83, 196–197
Closing Costs, 228–229
Clothing
ordering from catalog, 338–340
sewing, 342–343
Collision insurance, 162–163

Commission
   graduated, 76–77
   on real estate sales, 230
   on stock sales, 306
   straight, 72–73, 77, 144–145
Common denominator, 18
Common multiple, 14
Common stocks
   annual yield on, 309
   broker of, 306
   commission on, 306
   dividends on, 306–307, 309
   prices of, 20, 307
   profit or loss on, 308
   shares of, 306–307
Compound interest, 100–103,
      300, 302–303, 305
   table, 102
Comprehensive insurance,
      162–163
Computer Applications
   amortization tables, 254–255
   auto financing, 190–191
   cash registers, 376–377
   charge accounts, 128–129
   payroll deductions, 318–319
Computer Literacy
   BASIC language, 394–399
   DATA statement, 397
   DEF function, 254
   END statement, 394
   FN function, 254
   FOR statement, 398
   GO TO statement, 396
   IF . . . THEN statement, 396
   input, 394
   INPUT statement, 395
   INT function, 399
   LET statement, 395
   loop, 398
   memory locations, 395
   NEXT statement, 398
   output, 394
   PRINT statement, 394
   program, 394
   READ statement, 397
   REM statement, 397
   RESTORE statement, 318
   STEP instruction, 398
   string variable, 395
   symbols of comparison, 396
   symbols of operation, 190, 394
   TAB function, 399
Craft supplies, 346–347
Credit. *See also* Loans; Mortgages
   automobile financing, 140–143
   average daily balance, 112–114
   charge accounts, 110–115

   comparing plans of, 120–121
   finance charges, 110–114, 118–121
   installment buying, 118–119
   level-payment loans, 116–117
   minimum payment, 115
   promissory notes, 108–109
Credit cards, 110–115
Credit Counselor, 112–113
Cross-products, 30–31, 104, 212,
      312

DATA statement, 397
Decimals
   adding, 6–7, 168, 296, 370, 380
   dividing, 12–13, 122, 184, 312, 385
   and fractions, 32
   multiplying, 10–11, 104, 168, 334,
      383
   and percents, 32–33, 104, 146, 392
   rounding, 4–5, 12–13, 84, 274, 312,
      379
   subtracting, 7, 84, 146, 274, 381
Deductions
   itemized, 268–269
   payroll, 81, 318–319
DEF function, 254
Denominator, 14
Deposit, 88
Deposit slip, *illus.*, 88–89
Depreciation
   of car, 152–154
   of personal property, 210–211
Differences. *See also* Subtraction
   estimating, 7, 18
Discount, 37–38, 134, 344–345
Distance chart, 172–173
Dividend, 12, 16–17. *See also*
      Division
Dividends, stock, 306–307, 309
Division
   of decimals, 12–13, 122, 184, 312,
      385
   of fractions, 17, 234, 334, 370, 388
   of mixed numbers, 17, 234, 334,
      370, 388
   of whole numbers, 12–13, 122, 212,
      352, 384
Divisor, 12, 16–17. *See also* Division
Down payment, 118, 140–141,
      218–219, 232–233

Economist, 368–369
Electric costs, 200
Electric meter, 198–199
Endowment insurance, 282–285
END statement, 394
Equal ratios, 30–31. *See also*
      Proportions

Equations
   addition, 24–25
   checking, 24, 26, 28–29, 31
   combining like terms in, 26–27
   division, 26–27
   multiplication, 26–27
   subtraction, 24–25
   two-step, 28–29
Estimation
   in division, 12–13, 17
   of differences, 7, 18–19
   of measurements, 43, 47, 51
   of products, 8–11, 16–17
   of sums, 6–7, 18–19
Exemptions, tax, 78, 263

Face value
   of bond, 300–301
   of insurance policy, 280
Factor, 8, 10, 14
Federal income tax, 78–79, 81,
      258–271. *See also* Income taxes
FICA (Federal Insurance
      Contributions Act), 80–81.
      See also Social security
Finance charges, 110–114,
      118–121, 140–141
FN function, 254
Food
   calories in, 322–323
   grocery and meat prices, 326–333
   unit prices of, 327–328
Form 1040, 260, 268–270
Form 1040A, *illus.*, 260–264,
      266–267
Formulas
   area, 44
   simple interest, 98, 100–101, 108
   volume, 44
Form W-2, *illus.*, 258
FOR statement, 398
Fractions
   adding, 18–19, 184, 248, 352, 389
   comparing, 14–15, 370, 386
   and decimals, 20, 32–33
   dividing, 17, 234, 334, 370, 388
   lowest terms, 14–15, 234, 386
   multiplying, 16–17, 122, 212, 248,
      387
   and percents, 32–33, 274, 392
   renaming, 14–15, 18, 168, 234, 370,
      386
   subtracting, 18–19, 184, 248, 352,
      390
Fuel economy rate, 150–151, 155

Gasoline costs, 150–151

GO TO statement, 396
Graduated commission, 76–77
Gram, 46–49
Graphs
　bar, 54–55
　circle, 56–57
　line, 54–55
Gross pay, 68–71, 74–76, 144–145

Health insurance, 278–279
Homeowner's insurance, 224–225
Housing
　building a house, 240–243, 246–247
　buying a home, 216–222, 228–229, 232–233
　closing costs, 228–229
　decorating a home, 202–209
　homeowner's insurance, 224–225
　installing a driveway, 244–245
　market value of, 226–227
　mortgages, 218–222
　personal property insurance, 210–211
　real estate taxes, 226–227
　renting a home, 194–197
　selling a home, 230–231

IF . . . THEN statement, 396
Income
　commission, graduated, 76
　commission, straight, 72–73, 144–145
　deductions, 81, 318–319
　gross pay, 68–71, 74–76, 144–145
　hourly rate, 68–69
　job hunting, 82–83
　net pay, 81
　overtime pay, 68–69
　tips, 70–71
Income taxes, 78–79, 81, 258–273
　adjusted gross income, 260–262, 266–267
　balance due, 264–269
　dividend exclusion, 261
　federal, 78–79, 81, 258–271
　filing status, 258
　Form 1040, 260, 268–270
　Form 1040A, illus., 260–264, 266–267
　Form W-2, illus., 258
　gross income, 258–259
　itemized deductions, 268–269
　refund, 264–269
　schedules X and Y, 270, 409
　state, 272–273
　tables A, B, and C, 263, 406–408
　taxable income, 270
　tax credit, 260–262, 264, 266–267
　tax liability, 263, 264, 266–270
　tax penalty charges, 271

tax returns, 258–259
zero bracket amount, 268–269
INPUT statement, 395
Installing floor tiles, 204–205
Installment buying, 118–119
Insurance. See also Life insurance
　automobile, 160–163
　deductible feature, 162, 210–211, 278
　health, 278–279
　homeowner's, 224–225
　life, 280–288
　personal property, 210–211
　premiums, 160–163, 224–225, 280–288, 290–291
Insurance Agent, 286–287
Insurance policy, 211, 278, 280, 282. See also Insurance; Life insurance
Interest. See also Finance charges
　on certificates of deposit, 302–305
　compound, 100–103, 300, 302–303, 305
　on loans, 108–109, 117
　on mortgage loans, 218–223
　on savings bonds, 300
　simple, 98–99, 108–109
Interior Designer, 202–203
Internal Revenue Service (IRS), 78, 258
INT function, 399
Investment Counselor, 310–311
Investments
　annual yield on, 304, 309
　certificates of deposit, 302–305
　mutual funds, 310–311
　stocks, 306–309
　U.S. Savings Bonds, 300–301

Job hunting, 82–83

Kilogram, 46–49
Kilometer, 42–43, 48–49
Kilowatt-hour, 198–200

Length
　estimating, 43
　metric units of, 42–43
LET statement, 395
Level-payment loans, 116–117
Liability insurance
　bodily injury, 160–161
　property damage, 160–161
Life insurance
　beneficiaries, 280–281
　cash value of, 282, 284–285, 290
　endowment, 282–283
　face value of, 280
　limited payment, 282–283

and savings plans, 290–291
straight, 282–285, 290
term, 280–281
Limited payment life insurance, 282–283
Linear foot, 348–349
Line graphs, 54–55
List price, real estate, 230–231
Liter, 46–49
Loans
　amortization table, 218–219, 223, 254–255
　automobile, 140–142
　home, 216–222
　interest on, 108–109, 116–117, 218–222
　level-payment, 116–117
　monthly payments, 116–117
　mortgages, 218–222
　principal of, 108, 222
　promissory notes, 108–109
Lowest terms, fractions, 14–15, 234

Market value, 226
Markup, 34, 36–37
Mass, metric units of, 46–49
Mean, 58–60
Measures, 42–53. See also Area; Metric system; Scale drawing
Median, 58–59
Meter, 42–43, 48–49
Meter Reader, 198–199
Metric system of measures
　area, units of, 44–45
　capacity, units of, 46–49
　length, units of, 42–43, 48–49
　mass, units of, 46–49
　renaming units, 48–49
　temperature, unit of, 50–51
　volume, units of, 44–45
Milligram, 46–49
Milliliter, 46–49
Millimeter, 42–43, 48–49
Minimum payment, charge account, 115
Mixed numbers
　adding, 18–19, 184, 248, 352, 389
　comparing, 14–15, 370, 386
　dividing, 17, 234, 334, 370, 388
　multiplying, 16–17, 122, 212, 248, 387
　renaming, 14–15, 18, 168, 234, 370, 386
　subtracting, 18–19, 184, 248, 352, 390
Mode, 58–59

Money. *See* Banking; Budgets; Income; Investments
Mortgages, 218–223
    down payment, 218–219
    interest on, 218–223
    monthly payment, 218–219, 222
    principal, 222–223
Multiple, 14
Multiplication
    of decimals, 10–11, 104, 168, 334, 383
    of fractions, 16–17, 122, 212, 248, 387
    of mixed numbers, 16–17, 122, 212, 248, 387
    of whole numbers, 8–9, 84, 234, 296, 382
Mutual funds, 310–311

Net deposit, 88–89
Net pay, 81
NEXT statement, 398
No-load mutual funds, 310
Numerator, 14
Nutritionist, 322–323

Order forms, 338–341
Ordering wallpaper, 208–209
Outstanding checks, 94
Outstanding deposits, 94

Painting an apartment, 206–207
Pay. *See* Income
Percent
    and decimals, 32–33, 104, 146, 392
    finding a base number, given a percent, 35–37, 146, 296, 334, 393
    finding a percent, 34–37, 146, 296, 334, 393
    finding a percent of a number, 34–37, 146, 296, 334, 393
    and fractions, 32–33, 104, 146, 274, 392
    of increase, 365
    selling-cost, 77
Percentage rates, annual, 143
Personal Banking Representative, 98–99
Personal property insurance, 210–211
Policy, insurance, 211, 278, 280
Premium, insurance, 160–163, 224–225, 280–288, 290–291
Principal, 98
    of loan, 108, 222–223
    in savings account, 98, 100–101
PRINT statement, 394

Problem solving, career applications
    auto-repair costs, 156–159
    building materials, 246–247
    calorie counting, 322–323
    cost of credit, 112–113
    equipment rental, 350–351
    gross pay, 74–75, 144–145
    income taxes, 268–270
    interest on savings, 98–99
    life insurance, 286–287
    mutual funds, 310–311
    reading an electric meter, 198–199
    real estate transactions, 230–233
    scale drawing, 202–203, 238–239
    spending patterns, 368–369
    straight commission, 144–145
    travel expenses, 182–183
Problem solving, consumer topics
    automobile, owning and operating of, 132–134, 136–142, 150–154, 164–165
    borrowing money, 108–109, 218–221
    budgets, 356–364, 366–367
    calories and exercise, 324–325
    catalog buying, 338–340
    checking accounts, 88–96
    clothing, 342–343
    commission, 72–73, 76
    credit plans, 110–111, 115–121
    discount, 134, 344–345
    grocery and meat prices, 326–328, 330–333
    home building costs, 240–242, 244–245
    housing, 194–197, 204–209, 216–222, 228–229, 240–242, 244–245
    income, 68–73, 76, 78–81
    insurance, 160–163, 210–211, 224–225, 278–285, 290–291
    investments, 300–304, 306–309
    job hunting, 82–83
    mortgages, 218–222
    projects, 342–343, 346–349
    public transportation, 166–167
    sale buying, 344–345
    sales tax, 136–137, 332–333, 338–340
    savings accounts, 100–103
    social security, 292–295
    tax, federal income, 78–81, 258–267
    tax, real estate, 226–227
    tax, state income, 272–273

    travel, 172–180
Problem solving, mathematical skills
    addition
        of decimals, 6–7
        of fractions and mixed numbers, 18–19
        of whole numbers, 6–7
    area, 44–45
    comparing fractions, 14–15
    division
        of decimals, 12–13
        of fractions and mixed numbers, 17
        of whole numbers, 12–13
    equations, 24–31
    estimation, 6–13, 16–19, 43, 47, 51
    graphs, 54–57
    mean, median, and mode, 58–59
    measurement, 42–53
    multiplication
        of decimals, 10–11
        of fractions and mixed numbers, 16–17
        of whole numbers, 8–9
    percent, 32–37
    proportions, 30–31
    ratios, 30–31
    rounding numbers, 4–5, 12–13
    subtraction
        of decimals, 7
        of fractions and mixed numbers, 18–19
        of whole numbers, 7
    volume, 44–45
Products. *See also* Multiplication
    estimating, 8, 10, 14
Programming. *See* Computer Applications; Computer Literacy
Promissory note, *illus.*, 108–109
Property damage insurance, 160–161
Proportions, 30–31, 104, 212, 312, 391
Public transportation, 166–167

Quotients, 12–13, 17. *See also* Division

Ratios, 30–31, 104, 212, 312, 391
READ statement, 397
Real Estate Agent, 230–233
Real estate taxes, 226–227
Reciprocals, 16–17
Rectangle, area of, 44–45
Rectangular prism, volume of, 44–45
Redemption value, 300–301
Refund, income tax, 264–269

REM statement, 397
Rental Clerk, 350–351
RESTORE statement, 318
Retirement benefits, 80–81,
    292–295
Reviews, chapter, 21, 39, 61, 85,
    105, 123, 147, 169, 185, 213,
    235, 249, 275, 297, 313, 335,
    353, 371
Road maps, 174–175
Rounding numbers
    decimals, 4–5, 12–13, 84, 274, 312,
    379
    quotients, 12–13, 122, 184, 312, 385
    whole numbers, 4–5, 84, 274, 312,
    379

Sale buying, 344–345
Sales tax, 136–137, 332–333,
    338–340
Savings accounts, 98–101, 302–305
Scale drawing, 202–203, 238–239
Selling-cost percent, 77
Selling price, auto, 154
Series EE Savings Bonds, 300–301
Service charge, 94
Sewing costs, 342–343
Shares of stocks, 306–307
Shipping charges, 338–341
Simple interest, 98–99, 108–109
Skills File
    adding fractions and mixed numbers,
    389
    adding whole numbers and decimals,
    380
    comparing and renaming fractions
    and mixed numbers, 386
    dividing decimals, 385
    dividing fractions and mixed
    numbers, 388
    dividing whole numbers, 384
    multiplying decimals, 383
    multiplying fractions and mixed
    numbers, 387
    multiplying whole numbers, 382
    ratio and proportion, 391
    rounding whole numbers and
    decimals, 379
    subtracting fractions and mixed
    numbers, 390
    subtracting whole numbers and
    decimals, 381
    using percent, 393
    writing percents, decimals, and
    fractions, 392
Skills Tune-Ups
    adding fractions and mixed
    numbers, 184, 248, 352

adding whole numbers and
    decimals, 168, 296, 370
comparing fractions and mixed
    numbers, 370
dividing decimals, 122, 184, 312
dividing fractions and mixed
    numbers, 234, 334, 370
dividing whole numbers, 122,
    212, 352
multiplying decimals, 104, 168,
    334
multiplying fractions and mixed
    numbers, 122, 212, 248
multiplying whole numbers, 84,
    234, 296
percent problems, 146, 296, 334
ratio and proportion, 104, 212,
    312
renaming fractions and mixed
    numbers, 168, 234, 370
rounding whole numbers and
    decimals, 84, 274, 312
subtracting fractions and mixed
    numbers, 184, 248, 352
subtracting whole numbers and
    decimals, 84, 146, 274
writing percents, decimals, and
    fractions, 104, 146, 274
Social security, 80–81, 292–295
Statement, bank, illus., 94–97
Statistics
    mean, 58–60
    median, 58–59
    mode, 58–59
Sticker price, 132–134
Stocks. See Common stocks
Straight commission, 72–73,
    77, 144–145
Straight life insurance,
    282–285, 290
Subtraction
    of decimals, 7, 84, 146, 274, 381
    of fractions, 18–19, 184, 248,
    352, 390
    of mixed numbers, 18–19, 184,
    248, 352, 390
    of whole numbers, 7, 84, 146,
    274, 381
Sums. See also Addition
    estimating, 6, 18
Surveyor, 238–239

TAB function, 399
Tables
    amortization, 218–219, 223,
    254–255
    compound interest, 102

income tax, 81, 263, 270, 272,
    402–409
insurance, 280, 282, 284
of measures, 400
of repayments on loans, 116, 401
retirement benefits, 293
Take-home pay, 81
Tax Consultant, 268–270
Taxes. See also Income taxes
    assessed valuation, 226–227
    exemptions, 78, 263
    income, federal, 78–79, 81, 258–271
    income, state, 272–273
    real estate, 226–227
    sales, 136–137, 332–333, 338–340
    tables, 402–409
    withholding of, 78–79, 81, 258–271
Temperature, Celsius, 50–51
Term life insurance, 280–281
Tests
    chapter, 22, 40, 62, 86, 106, 124,
    148, 170, 186, 214, 236, 250,
    276, 298, 314, 336, 354, 372
    unit, 63–64, 125–126, 187–188,
    251–252, 315–316, 373–374
Time, 52–53
Time and a half, 68–69
Tips, 70–71, 332–333
Trade-in allowance, 138–139
Trade-in value, 152–153
Travel
    air, 178–179
    automobile, 172–177, 180–181
    distance chart, 172–173
    expenses of, 176–183
    road maps, 174–175
Travel Agent, 182–183
Triangle, area of, 44–45

Unit price, 327–328
Unit tests, 63–64, 125–126,
    187–188, 251–252, 315–316,
    373–374

Volume
    metric units of, 44–45
    of a rectangular prism, 44–45

Wages. See Income
Weighted balance, 112–114
Whole numbers
    adding, 6–7, 168, 296, 370, 380
    dividing, 12–13, 122, 212, 352, 384
    multiplying, 8–9, 84, 234, 296, 383
    rounding, 4–5, 84, 274, 312, 379
    subtracting, 7, 84, 146, 274, 390
Wind-chill index, 51